KARST HYDROLOGY
AND
WATER RESOURCES

Proceedings of the U.S.-Yugoslavian
Symposium, Dubrovnik, June 2-7, 1975

Volume 1

KARST HYDROLOGY

Editor of English Language Edition
Vujica Yevjevich

Water Resources Publications
Fort Collins, Colorado 80522, USA
1976

English language edition of this two-volume publication can be
purchased through:

WRP, P.O. Box 303, Fort Collins, Colorado 80522, USA.

Titles of the English language edition:
KARST HYDROLOGY AND WATER RESOURCES
Volume 1:   KARST HYDROLOGY
Volume 2:   KARST WATER RESOURCES

Title of Serbocroation language edition:
HIDROLOGIJA AND VODNO BOGATSTVO KRŠA
Edited by the Editorial Board Composed of
Stjepan Mikulec, Avdo Sarić, Jakov Šunjić
and Aleksander Trumić, and published
by the Institute of Water Resources Engineering
(Hidrotehnički Zavod) of the University of
Sarajevo, Sarajevo, Yugoslavia, 1976

KARST HYDROLOGY AND WATER RESOURCES
Volume 1
KARST HYDROLOGY

Library of Congress Catalog Card Number 76-012972

This publication is printed and bound by LithoCrafters,
Ann Arbor, Michigan, U.S.A.

Last names of Symposium participants present in this photo (for full names and affiliations, see page 871-873, Volume 2): 1. Radeljković, 2. Habič, 3. Simpson, 4. Bahun, 5. Komatina, 6. Žibret, 7. Thrailkill, 8. Ramljak, 9. Boreli, 10. Bergman, 11. Borić, 12. Huzbašić, 13. Dragović, 14. Jamaković, 15. Bagarić, 16. Blagojević, 17. Andričević, 18. Miličević, 19. Avdagić, 20. Barbalić, 21. Knežević, 22. Sarić, 23. Breznik, 24. Šimunić, 25. Sarini, 26. Selimović, 27. Ivanković, 28. Šoše, 29. Lipold-Preka, 30. Janežić, 31. Pavlović, 32. Hajdin, 33. Torbarov, 34. Faulkner, 35. Teftedarija, 36. Parizek, 37. Arandjelović, 38. Herak, 39. Petrik, 40. Le Grand, 41. Preka, 42. Mladenović, 43. Milanović, 45. Stojić, 46. Šunjić, 47. Mikulec, 48. Carmithcel, 49. Yevjevich, 50. Trumić, 51. Pehar, 52. Miličević, 53. Oziš, 54. Duckstein.

THE LATIN ALPHABET AND PRONUNCIATION OF SERBOCROATIAN LETTERS

Many papers and discussions of this book contain the names of persons and the geographical names in latin alphabet of the Serbocroatian language. It was considered useful by the Editor to reproduce here both the latin alphabet, which is an alternative with the cyrillic alphabet, and the pronunciation of the Serbocroatian letters of latin alphabet (by comparison with the pronunciation of English words). The pronunciation examples are those given in English-Serbocroatian DICTIONARY, I (Enciklopediski Englesko-Srpskohrvatski Rečnik, I), by Svetomir Ristić, Zivojin Simić, and Vladeta Popović, Prosveta-Beograd, and Cambridge University Press-London, 1963. The alphabet is strictly phonetic; the pronunciation of each letter or the same combination of two letters (dj, lj, nj, dž) is always the same.

The alphabetical order of the latin alphabet is the following:

a, b, c, č, ć, d, dž, đ, e, f, g, h, i, j, k, l, lj, m, n, nj, o, p, r, s, š, t, u, v, z, ž.

Printed	Pronunciation	Printed	Pronunciation
a A	English *a* in *father*	n N	English *n*
b B	English *b*	nj Nj	English *ni* in *onion* / French *gn* in *Boulogne*
v V	English *v*	o O	English *o* in *hot*, sometimes as *or* in *lord*
g G	English *g* in *go*	p P	English *p*
d D	English *d*	r R	Scottish *r* in *merry*
đ (dj), Đ Dj	A sound like *j* in *Jew*, but slightly softer	s S	English *ss* in *glass*
e E	English *e* in *pet*	t T	English *t*
ž Ž	English *s* in *pleasure* / French *j* in *jour*	ć Ć	A sound between the English *t* in *tune* and *ch* 'n *chalk*
z Z	English *z*	u U	English *u* in *rule*
i I	English *i* in *machine*	f F	English *f*
j J	English *y* in *yet*	h H	Scottish *ch* in *loch*, English *h*
k K	English *k*	c C	English *ts* in *lots*
l L	English *l*	č Č	English *ch* in *chalk*
lj Lj	English *lli* in *million* / Italian *gl* in *egli*	dž, ǵ, Dž	English *j* in *John*
m M	English *m*	š Š	English *sh* in *she*

PREFACE

The United States-Yugoslavian Symposium on karst
hydrology and water resources was held in Dubrovnik, Yugoslavia, June 2-7, 1975. Its results in the form of papers submitted and discussions presented are the subject of this
two-volume proceedings book. The incentive for holding the
symposium was the bilateral U.S. - Yugoslavian cooperative
research project on analytical and field studies of the
hydrology, water resources, pollution, and economic development
of karst (limestone) regions, which started in 1972, and still
operate at the time of publication of this book.

Problems of development, control and conservation of
karst water resources have become of great importance in many
regional developments around the world. Under such conditions,
the prevailing approach of the past, namely the study of the
karst mainly as a natural phenomenon related to soluble carbonate rocks, required a substantial extension in the direction
of studying the processes directly related to utilization of
karst water resources. In many karst regions of the world,
their water resources are either the only or the most important
natural resource for economical development.

The idea of a U.S. - Yugoslavian cooperation in the field
of hydrology and karst water resources originated when a group
of U.S. specialists, as a team of the U.S. National Science
Foundation, visited Yugoslavia in 1971 in order to organize an
international scientific and technologic assistance to the
Bosanska Krajina region after the Banja Luka earthquake of
1969. After the intensive consultations, a program of bilateral cooperative research in karst water resources was
established, and the administrative and financial modes of
operation worked out, with the research activities initiated
and carried out successfully since 1972. The research activities and all the coordinating work in Yugoslavia centered in
the Institute of Water Resources Engineering of the University
of Sarajevo, Sarajevo, Yugoslavia, while on the U.S. side the
research and coordination were undertaken by the Hydrology and
Water Resources Program of the Civil Engineering Department of
Colorado State University, Fort Collins, Colorado, USA. The
Yugoslav coordinator of the bilateral karst research project is
Aleksander Trumić, and the U.S. coordinator is Vujica Yevjevich,
professors of the above two cooperating universities.

The cooperative research project developed on a simple
idea, namely, for each side to contribute its best share for
the benefit not only of both countries but for any other

country with karst water problems as well. The Yugoslav
scientists and engineers made available a rich experience in
water resources development in karst regions, which transcends
the national significance. The US scientists and engineers
cooperated in a joint effort to develop the advanced, karst
water resources oriented, scientific methods and planning technology. Several by-products of the project, such as the
education of high level specialists and the transfer of water
resources knowledge, resulted from this cooperative research
program.

The financial support for the bilateral karst research
project is as follows: (i) On the Yugoslavian side of the
project, the support is through the U.S. National Science
Foundation grants to the Institute of Water Resources Engineering of the University of Sarajevo from the U.S. PL-480
counterpart funds available in Yugoslavia, matched approximately in equal amounts by the national funds, raised through
the Association of Yugoslav Organizations for Promotion and
Support of Research in Karst Hydrology and Water Resources
(Sarajevo, Yugoslavia). For the first two years of the project
the PL-480 funds were granted to the Institute by the U.S.
National Science Foundation, while for the second two years
both the PL-480 and the matching funds were allocated by the
American-Yugoslav Joint Board for Scientific and Technological
Cooperation. (ii) On the U.S. side of the project, the
support is provided by the U.S. National Science Foundation
through grants to Colorado State University. In a limited
amount, the organization of the Dubrovnik Symposium was supported by the bilateral research project, while its major cost
was financed by several Yugoslav water resources and general
scientific and professional organizations.

The objectives of the Symposium, apart from presenting
and evaluating the results of the bilateral research project,
were: (i) To encourage the advanced research for a better
understanding of phenomena related to karst hydrology and karst
water resources; (ii) To stimulate an exchange of ideas and
experience; and (iii) To single out new areas in karst water
resources, which deserve systematic investigations by using
the advanced research methods.

For helping both the bilateral karst research project and
the Dubrovnik Symposium, the acknowledgements and thanks are
expressed to the following organizations: (i) The American-
Yugoslav Joint Board for Scientific and Technological Cooperation; (ii) The U.S. National Science Foundation; (iii) The
Yugoslav Committee for Science and Technology; (iv) The
Yugoslav and U.S. Committees of the UNESCO International Hydrology Program; and (v) The Association of Yugoslav Organizations for Promotion and Support of Research in Karst
Hydrology and Water Resources (Sarajevo, Yugoslavia).

The holding of the Dubrovnik Symposium on karst hydrology and water resources, and the publication of this proceedings book, in both the U.S. and Yugoslav versions, are contributions by hydrologists, hydrogeologists, hydraulic engineers and water resources specialists of Yugoslavia and United States to the International Hydrology Program of UNESCO.

Though many individuals contributed to the bilateral research project and the Dubrovnik Symposium, both within and without the project activities, the particular acknowledgement and thanks go to the following individuals from the two countries, for their help and encouragements, namely to: Dr. Sida Marjanović, Chairman of the Yugoslav Commission for UNESCO, and former Chairman of the Yugoslav Council for Scientific and Technological Cooperation, Dr. Zvonko Knežević, Vice Chairman of the Committee for Science and Technology of the Yugoslav Federal Government, Mr. Salko Ajanović, former director of the Institute of the International Technological Cooperation of Bosnia and Herzegovina, Dr. Michael Gaus, Head, Engineering Mechanics Section, Engineering Division, U.S. National Science Foundation, Dr. Charles Zalar, Program Director in the Office of International Programs, U.S. National Science Foundation, and Dr. Arthur A. Ezra, Program Director, Water Resources, Urban and Environmental Program, Engineering Division, U.S. National Science Foundation.

This two-volume proceedings book contains thirty-eight papers, specific discussion on most of the presented papers, as well as a general discussion on research needs. The material is organized in six parts: (1) Karst hydrogeology, (2) Karst hydrology, (3) Technology for development of karst water resources, (4) Quality of karst waters, and protection of karst water environments from contamination, (5) Karst water resources, and (6) Research needs in karst hydrology and water resources. To approximately equal the number of pages in the two volumes, Volume 1 is composed of the first two parts, while Volume 2 contains the remaining four parts. The grouping of the papers was made by the editors of the two versions, English and Serbocroatian, with the intention that the parts represented the most homogeneous unities, and that the sequence of papers inside each part treat first the more general subjects, followed by those investigating the more specific topics.

The original material of the sixth part of the book, on research needs in karst hydrology and water resources, consisted of the discussion by symposium participants. The sequence of the presentation of this material has been changed in such a way that instead of its chronological sorting by the authors of discussions, the material is grouped by the ideas presented and suggestions given. In this grouping the divisions of ideas and suggestions are made basically by the titles of the first five parts of the book. The editors of the two versions of the book

expect that this type of presentation will be more attractive
to readers.

The printing of the English language edition of this book
is financially supported by UNESCO through an advanced order
of one hundred copies of the two-volume book, to be distributed
to the national committees of the UNESCO International Hydrology Program. This support is duly acknowledged.

The publishing of this proceedings book of the bilateral
Symposium results from the conclusion by the editors that the
book contents have a general significance, transcending the
needs of scientists and engineers of the two countries only.

Editor of the English version

Fort Collins,
Colorado, USA
April 1976.

Vujica Yevjevich
Professor of Civil Engineering,
and Professor-in-Charge of
Hydrology and Water Resources
Program, Civil Engineering
Department, Colorado State
University, Fort Collins,
Colorado, USA

TABLE OF CONTENTS

Volume 1

TABLE OF CONTENTS - (Continued)

TABLE OF CONTENTS - (Continued)

Page

TABLE OF CONTENTS - (Continued)

Page

TABLE OF CONTENTS - (Continued)

TABLE OF CONTENTS - (Continued)

PART I
KARST HYDROGEOLOGY

PART I
KARST HYDROGEOLOGY

THE YUGOSLAV CONTRIBUTION TO THE KNOWLEDGE OF KARST HYDROLOGY AND GEOMORPHOLOGY

by

Milan Herak, Professor
Faculty of Sciences and Mathematics of the University of Zagreb;
Member Yugoslav Academy of Sciences and Arts,
Zagreb, Yugoslavia

Synopsis. J. W. Valvasor clearly recognized the role of water in formation of karst phenomena in 1689, though partly influenced by the mystical interpretation of the underground world. Next Th. Gruber (1781) and B. Hacquet (1778-1789) opened the discussion on the role of subsidence and weathering in the formation of closed surface depressions in karst. The scientific exploration of the Dinaric Karst grew in scope during the 19th century. J. Wessely (1876) wrote on karst with special emphasis on forestry. The need for water led to a special interest in karst springs, underground connections, and improving water supply. The second half of the 19th century is characterized by a growing interest of geologists in karst problems (Staché, 1864; Tietze, 1874; Pilar, 1874; etc.). The end of individual efforts to explain karst phenomena came with Cvijić's work *Das Karstphänomen* (1893). The turn of the century was marked by the application of cyclic theory on the formation and disappearance of karst forms (Cvijić, 1901; Grund, 1903; etc.). The first important resistance to the application of cyclic theory to karst came from Katzer (1909). The criticism increased between 1932 and 1956. The cooperation of karst experts was stimulated in 1957. The progress was achieved in speleology, hydrogeology and methodology. Many methodological innovations are made recently by increasing karst investigations. Theoretical, but sometimes unrealistic, interpretations of karst have been replaced by advanced geologic methods with a considerable re-evaluation of geomorphologic, hydrologic and hydrogeologic concepts of the past.

1. Introduction.

The Dinaric mountainous and adjacent coastal landscapes with their peculiar features and modest living conditions have for millenia inspired both the native and the newcomer to exploratory ventures. They were at first aimed at preserving the life and satisfying the curiosity, but later at gaining broad scientific knowledge. The latter objective is the source of an ever-growing body of information about the phenomenon called karst (synonyms: krš, kras, carso).

Prehistoric inhabitants of the Dinaric Region sought shelter in subterranean karst caves and looked for water. The

same was true of succeeding populations. Regardless of the
degree of civilization, this practice continued down to present days.

The first written information on Dinaric regions, including the karst area, can be found in works of Greek, Roman,
Egyptian and other writers, who in their travel accounts recorded interesting details, without attempting their explanation, such writers as Herodotus, Strabo, Pliny the Elder and
Ptolemy. The karst landscape and its accessible underground,
its interesting and in places bizarre features continuously
led to speculations, projecting concepts of a peculiar area
with a wealth of strange forms and water scarcity.

Caves, swallow holes (ponors), and large springs inspired
the first concepts of a subterranean world in which the
mystical and the natural intertwine. Surface forms point out
to a broad activity of streams in the past, in spite of present water scarcity in karst areas. The meagre remains of
arable terra rossa and vegetation call for an explanation of
the former natural environment under karst conditions.

When natural sciences began to develop, foreign explorers,
followed by their native colleagues, found in karst the prototype of a new geomorphologic and hydrogeologic phenomenon,
which only gradually and very reluctantly revealed the
secrets of its genesis and more recent conditions. Even present-day scientific knowledge about karst is only partial.
Concepts of karren, dolines, uvalas, poljes, plains and caves
were cropping up. Scientists tried to explain the scarcity
of surface waters and the distribution of groundwater, the
mechanism of their movement, as well as the practical consequences of specific relations in karst. The generic and areal
links between the various karst phenomena gradually brought
about a complex approach to their solving, accompanied by a
broadening of the field of the problems involved. I will
try to present the chronology of that process, dividing it
into several stages, mainly on the basis of works published
on the subject (see: Herak, Magaš, and Sarić, 1973).

2. Speleologic Exploration and First Knowledge on Karst.

Serious endeavors to give a scientific interpretation to
karst started in the 17th century. One of the first works
was the speleologic treatise by J. Gaffarel published in 1654
under the title *Le Monde Souterrain* (Underground World). Since
the work was destroyed we know little about it from a fragment
kept in the National Library in Paris. However, judging by
the influence the work had on other authors (especially A.
Kirshner), his classification of the subterranean karst world
must have contained a great deal of mystical ideas (by
distinguishing between divine, human, animal, artificial and

natural caves), though he also mentions the geographic, geologic, and mining discoveries of his time.

The next step was made by the Yugoslav explorer J. W. Valvasor (1689), who describing his native land, Kranjska, and the neighbouring Croatian regions, laid special stress on karst phenomena, especially on caves, underground links between sinkholes and springs, and on periodic lakes. Though partly influenced by the mystical interpretation of the underground world, he clearly recognized the role of water in its formation. Some observations on karst are also found in I. Lovrić's review of Fortis's description of the Dinaric regions (1776).

The beginnings of a consistent analysis of karst phenomena in Yugoslavia and in the world date back to the 18th century. Th. Gruber (1781) and B. Hacquet (1778-1789) opened the discussion. Gruber emphasized the role of the groundwater, which causes the weathering of rocks, the enlargement of subterranean cavities and subsidences reflected on the surface. He ascribed the formation of vertical jamas (pits) and dolines to this activity. Hacquet, however, was more impressed by the surface weathering of limestone and the role of that process in the genesis of closed depressions on the karst surface.

It was only at the middle of the 19th century that the interest in the Dinaric Karst was revived. This was for the most part due to road construction (when new caves were discovered) or to water supply. Thus, it can be said that the literature on karst grew more or less fragmentarily, without a clear concept of karst as a whole in the generic or areal sense.

Speleologic explorations attracted lasting attention, first of foreign investigators and later of an ever increasing number of Yugoslav explorers, ranging from amateurs to experts in various specialized fields. It would be impossible to present this activity in its entirety. Only some of the explorers, in the order in which they first published their works, will be given: A. Schmidl, D. Hirc, S. Robič, R. Gasperini, H. Mihajlović, W. Putick, J. Cvijić, F. Fiala, J. Vavrović, J. Marinitsch, R. Vasović, W. Knebel, J. Poljak, B. Ž. Milojević, U. Girometta, L. V. Bertarelli, S. M. Milojević, V. Bohinec, M. S. Radovanović, A. Lazić, I. Michler, A. Šerko, D. Kuščer, M. Malez, D. Novak, B. P. Jovanović, F. Habe, V. Kostovsky, S. Božićević, I. Gams, F. Jenko, D. Petrović, J. B. Petrović, D. Manaković, V. Ržehak, J. Trifunovski, I. Baučić, O. Zubčević, D. Gavrilović, R. Gospodarić, P. Habič, P. Kunaver, Z. Pepeonik and others.

Their works are mainly descriptive. However, in recent times the problems of speleogenesis within the general framework of karst genesis are coming more and more to the foreground.

3. Sporadic Attempts at Studying Karst as a Whole.

In the course of the 19th century the scientific exploration of karst grew in scope. A number of regional studies of karst were published by Cvijić (1896, 1900, 1901), Gorjanović (1882), Hirc (1889), Majnarić (1891), Mihajlović (1887), Radovanović (1894), etc. A general study of karst with special emphasis on forestry was written by J. Wessely (1876). Surface karst forms are the subject of studies by A. Boué and J. Cvijić. Boué (1864) analysed primarily funnel-shaped topography, and Cvijić (1898) karren.

The need for water led to a special interest in springs, underground connections between sinkholes and springs, for improving the water supply. These problems preoccupied both speleologists and geologists.

Problems concerning waters in Kras Region of Slovenia and Istria were treated by A. Schmidl (1851), T. Taramelli (1877 and 1878), and F. Müller (1891). The latter performed the dye test of Škocijanska Reka. Also mentioned should be J. Lorenz (1858) and G. Staché (1864, 1880, 1889). L.R.J. Liburnau wrote about Rečina near Rijeka (1860). A short study of the Plitvice Lakes was written by Lj. Vukotinović (1859). The possibility of water flowing from the mainland into the Vrana Lake on the island of Cres was discussed by J. Lorenz (1859), L.R.J. Liburnau (1859), E. Mayer (1873) and A. Gavazzi (1889).

The second half of the 19th century is characterized by a growing interest of geologists in karst problems. The Dinaric Karst terrain induced them to offer their versions on the genesis of karst in general and of dolines and jamas in particular. That was the subject of studies by G. Staché, E. Titze, E. Mojsisovics and Gj. Pilar. Staché (1864) and Mojsisovics (1880) considered tectonics the most important factor in the formation of karst. Titze (1873, 1874, 1880) opposed this view and drew attention to the importance of rock composition, erosion, chemical solution, subsidence, etc., thus emphasizing the complexity of karst processes.

For our purposes, however, the role of Gj. Pilar in solving general and particular karst problems is of the greatest interest. Together with Bayer and Titze he published a work on the scarcity of water in the Croatian karst areas (Bayer, Titze and Pilar 1874), the first study dealing in more detail both with the theoretical and practical problems

concerning karst in general and the possibilities of a better
water supply in particular. Since this is the first Yugoslav
investigator to have studied exhaustively the karst aspects
from the geological point of view, some of his observations
(Pilar, 1874) are presented. Speaking about the general
characteristics of karst, Pilar mentions bare ridgy rocks
with dolines and *sinkholes*, ridges and *faulted elongated
valleys*. He remarks that precipitation quickly disappears
underground through *tunnels*, connected with the lower parts
of the crust by subterranean *grooves*. In his observations on
rocks he points out to limestones and dolomitic limestones
and gives their stratigraphic sequence in the Mesozoic. In
places where such rocks abound, water levels (or water-nets)
are created, with water percolating further underground.
However, if recharge from the surface exceeds the possibility
of runoff, the water will ooze out in many places, thus
sometimes causing floods in areas which otherwise lack water.
Apart from rocks and water, karst is also influenced by movements upsetting the balance, by mountain pressure and the like.
Pilar furthermore mentioned the former frequent occurrence of
lakes in karst regions. Though allowing that their disappearance may be due to a gradual decrease in precipitation, he is
in favor of ascribing it to fissures leading underground. This
could be prevented by natural sealing, which can lead to a
change in karst conditions. Solving the actual problems of
Močila in Mala Kapela and the connections of the lost river
Jasenica with the spring of Slunjčica, Pilar goes into some
aspects of hydraulics and suggests practical measures.

The complexity and breadth of his observations and his
attempt at a geologic documentation of conclusions gives Pilar
an important place in creating the hydrogeology of karst. It
should be particularly noted that he was the first to oppose
quite plainly the then current one-sided view that waters in
karst flow only along more or less isolated routes. According
to him, at least in the area he studied, there exists groundwater adapted to the specific conditions of the karst underground.

All the above mentioned works on karst, however, are
fragmentary studies. The general subjects, most often discussed, include the role of water in the genesis of karst
forms in connection with surface weathering, subsidence or
the like. In dealing with practical problems special stress
is laid on water supply and afforestation. They remain outside
the influence of a well rounded geomorphological system and
even outside the cyclic system, applied to non-karst terrain
since 1884, when it was inaugurated by W. M. Davis.

Though such a situation persisted until the turn of the
century, the real end of individual efforts to define karst
as broadly as possible came with J. Cvijić's work *Das*

Karstphänomen (1883), which as the author himself says, represents an attempt at a morphological monograph. In accordance with this, Cvijić tries to give clear definitions of all phenomena.

He considers karren a general karst phenomenon, occurring in the karst of all regions, at all altitudes and in different climates. Their formation requires pure, dipping limestone, without any cover. He disagrees with Mojsisovics' opinion that karren might be a substitute for dolines. Supporting the theory of chemical erosion as the generic factor, he counterbalances Staché, who ascribes an important role in that process to marine abrasion.

In order to defend his theory about the formation of dolines due to surface water activity, he distinguishes between real dolines (dish-like, funnel-shaped and well-shaped), furthermore jamas (aven), connected with blind caves, pit-like forms called *light holes* leading directly into horizontal caves and river courses, and finally *Trebić-type* depressions, which in deeper underground continue into fissures. He accepts the formation due to subsidence only in alluvial dolines and stresses the irregular distribution of dolines, admitting that some are connected with fractures. He also mentions the difference between dolines and *geological organs*. According to him, *organs* are non-karst forms occurring in covered terrain, while dolines are characteristic of bare limestone rocks, which developed in their most typical form as a consequence of climatic change and chemical weathering.

Cvijić distinguishes between three kinds of caves. The first group includes large, highly ramified cave corridors which are either active or abandoned bed of karst rivers. They are connected with surface forms of the type *light holes* and *Trebić*. The second group includes dry, short, blind caves located near the surface. Their formation is entirely due to the solution of limestone and erosion caused by percolating water. They may contain subterranean dolines. The third group of caves is located on the border between limestones and the underlying impermeable rocks. The deepest of all caves are formed by groundwater activity. Like the first group, they too are linked with surface forms of the type *light holes* and *Trebić*.

In karst streams Cvijić makes a distinction between smaller streams (mainly lost streams) and permanent rivers, whose valleys most often reach as far as the impermeable base or the groundwater.

The valleys of present or former karst water courses may
be bag-like, blind, half-blind and dry. Some blind and dry
valleys are of primary and some of secondary formation.

Poljes in the Dinaric Karst are large, flattened
karst depressions with a large bottom, abrupt flanks and are
elongated parallel with the strike of beds. They occur only
in tectonically dislocated areas. They may be dry, periodically flooded or contain lakes. They have springs, estavelles,
rivers, brooks and sinkholes. Their formation is connected
with folds (anticlinal additionally eroded or synclinal), or
faults which lead to the formation of closed depressions by
intersecting river courses and elevating the downstream part
of the terrain. If faults are present on flanks as well, one
is dealing with a rift-polje.

As we can see, in this work Cvijić tried to give a
comprehensive study of karst and elaborate a classification
of its forms. His classification is partly descriptive and
partly generic. Tectonics is taken into account, but not
fully, which reflects the state of geologic studies at his
time. The process of karstification is considered to be
autonomous to a large degree, fluvial erosion where it exists
being only complementary.

4. Dominance of Cyclic Concept in Karstology.

The turn of the 19th century was marked by the application
of cyclic theory (Davis, 1884) to the explanation of formation
and disappearance of certain geomorphologic units (*young,
mature, old*) in karst, analogous to the application of the
same concept to non-karst terrains. The initiators were W. M.
Davis, A. Penck and J. Cvijić.

In this paper we are primarily interested in the extent
to which Cvijić changed his approach to karst. Under Davis's
and Penck's influences he first of all adopted the priority
of fluvial erosion in the formation of karst features (Cvijić,
1901), which is followed by *karstification*. He set up for
the first time the succession: doline-uvala-polje.

It is interesting to note that in the same year (1901)
H. Hranilović, analyzing some geomorphologic problems in the
Croatian karst, gives priority to subterranean erosion in the
formation of valleys of some karst rivers and to subaerial
erosion in the formation of plains.

The complex conditions of the Dinaric Region and the wish
to apply the cyclic concept to karst, induced A. Grund (1903,
1910, 1914) to make an attempt at discovering the laws of
karst hydrography. He tried to find out whether it was
possible to explain a *puzzling multitude* of individual

phenomena by a simple comprehensive law, representing the framework within which each phenomenon would occupy its proper place. His studies include the karst of Lika, Unac, Bosansko Grahovo, Livanjsko Polje, Glamočko Polje, Duvanjsko Polje and others. He came to the conclusion that the observed relations confirmed the existence of groundwater in karst. In this he emphasized Pilar's observation of 1874 and, partly, those of Cvijić of 1893. However, he went a step further in concluding that karst groundwater consists of two levels, the lower, *stagnant level*, and the upper, *karst level*. The lower one moves only under exceptional circumstances (e.g., discharge of some water into the sea), and the upper one is fluctuating entirely. He accepted Cvijić's idea about the existence of a generic succession in the development of karst forms (in the sense of cyclic theory), but added that the final member could not be a polje (since every polje is the consequence of tectonics), but *cockpit country*.

Cvijić realized in 1909 the need for a closer link with tectonics when the genesis of karst forms is being considered. In spite of that, however, in explaining plains in karst he resorts to specific *karst erosion*, which consists of two components, the first being surface erosion with washing out of materials and the second one with the enlarging of underground fissures.

The first important resistance to the application of cyclic theory to karst came from E. Katzer (1909, 1921). He distinguished between shallow and deep karst. In shallow karst rocks suitable for karstification constitute a relatively thin cover. In deep karst, on the contrary, the base is located in unknown depths. In what has become the classical schematic profile he presents the conditions of various hydrographic and hydrogeologic phenomena (intermittent springs, permanent karst springs, dry cave systems, sinkholes, estavelles, brackish springs, submarine springs). A specific feature of karst hydrography is that waters are located and flow along underground fissure systems *(Karstgerinne)*, which permeate the karst terrain differently at different depths. This is why there is no continuous water table with a constant gradient in deep karst fissures; therefore, all conclusions based on table assumption are false and can only result in disappointment, according to Katzer.

Investigating the Gacko Polje in Lika in 1913, K. Terzaghi returned to the autonomy of the karst process and emphasized *marginal denudation*, using the term to denote corrosion due to biofactors, which in his opinion is especially marked in afforested karst.

Though Cvijić criticized in 1918 the opponents of the cyclic theory, he admitted that Davis's erosion cycle was

hardly applicable to karst, its erosion not being subject to
the same laws as erosion in non-karst terrain. However, he
persisted in his opinion that the karst underground contains
groundwater, opposing at the same time the differentiation
between stagnant and karst water (Grund, 1903). Cvijić points
out that there exist valleys in karst which were formed before
the onset of the karst process (karstification). At that
time, primary fissures were neither enlarged nor transformed
into caves. Thus, surface water could penetrate the ground
only shallowly and erode it only on the surface.

However, even the deeper located fissures are gradually
enlarged; caves are formed, the surface part of the terrain
dries out and the valley is disorganized by the formation of
karst features at its bottom. The valley is shortened from
the river mouth towards the spring by the formation of sinkholes. Old sinkholes turn into caves and new ones form in
the direction of the spring. In this way the water course of
a pre-karst river practically disappears. There are cases in
which the disorganization occurs first in the upper part of
the valley. As some water courses disappear, others are
formed due to the denudation of the karst surface. The process
can penetrate deep because of the superposition of several
systems of undergound channels. In this connection Cvijić
describes the succession in time and space of the often
mentioned hydrographic zones (the dry zone, the transition
zone and the zone with permanently flowing water). The
essential characteristic of this succession is that the
three hydrographic zones change their characteristics in
accordance with hydrographic evolution.

In Cvijić's opinion, the different lithologic properties
of the terrain, dislocations and the climate are reflected
in the different types of karst. Thus, Europe has northern
and Mediterranean types of karst. In northern karst limestones are even less pure than the chalk and are not as
cracked. The humid climate favors the formation of a thick
layer of residual clay. The aforementioned three hydrographic
zones can rarely be observed. There is no significant disorganization due to karstification. This type of karst can
be found in Belgium, England, etc.

The typical representative of Mediterranean karst is
the Dinaric Karst. It may be shallow as the northern type,
but also very deep. Limestones are purer. The climate is
not humid so that there is not much residual material. Karst
forms develop for the most part independently one from another,
but sometimes one form will develop into another. Dolines
may develop into elongated karren, which in turn may coalesce
into uvalas, to be followed in the next stage by poljes. Being
aware of the fact that this kind of genesis of the polje
causes most confusion, he emphasizes that it applies only to

one among several types of polje, while the genesis of the
others is connected with tectonics (rifts, faults, folds),
and the *karst erosion* that followed later gave the poljes
their final shape.

Apart from the two types described above, Cvijić distinguishes a transition type (Moravia, Slovakia, Podolia, the
northern zones of the Alps, Germany, the Jura Mountains, etc.).
Unlike in the northern type, in this type karstification
leads to disorganization; karst and glacial phenomena are
found side by side. However, by the number and dimensions
of its forms this type of karst is less developed than the
Mediterranean one.

Cvijić tried to define more clearly the morphological
types of karst. Thus, in 1924 he differentiated two basic
types of karst. He called them *holokarst* and *merokarst* (which
more or less coincides with Grund's *Halbkarst*).

Holokarst is fully developed karst with all the forms
and sub-surface hydrography. The thick carbonate rocks contain some impervious layers but these are negligible in
comparison with the huge masses of limestone and cannot stop
the sub-surface circulation of water, which either bypasses
them or flows beneath them. The evolution of the forms and
hydrography is of a purely karst character, without the
intervention of the normal erosion, which is to be found in
all other types of karst. Another specific feature of this
type of karst are poljes. It is found in the Dinaric Mountains,
on Peloponnesus, in Asia Minor, in Jamaica and elsewhere.

Merokarst is incomplete because the rocks are for the
most part impure and are not eroded easily or completely.
However, the influence of fluvial erosion is all the stronger.
Sub-surface waters are less dispersed. It occurs in middle
and northern Europe.

Cvijić also mentions two transition types. One of them,
the *Causses*, has more in common with holokarst than with
merokarst in that it develops far below land surface. In
some valleys the impervious layers are located on the surface
and sub-surface waters can be reconstructed more easily than
in holokarst, where they are located in unknown depths. The
dominating feature are limestone plains, separated by river
valleys or ravines. It occurs in the Massif Central in
France, the Alps, Slovakia, Rumania, on the Balkan Peninsula.
Cvijić called the other transition type *Jurassic;* it is
characterized by alternating limestone and marl. The terrain
is often folded and dissected by valleys following impervious
layers and frequently also by limestone zones, which are
usually thin. It occurs in the Jura Mountains in Eastern
Italy, Albania, in the Tara Region in Yugoslavia, etc.

In his works published in 1925, 1926, and 1960 Cvijić
tried to outline the basic concepts of his previous works,
showing, however, an obvious uncertainty as to the primary
or secondary importance of the karst processes. This, as well
as some hesitation in the matter of generic succession, is a
clear indication of the dilemmas Cvijić was facing, constricted
by the rather schematized, almost dogmatic cyclic theory he
was trying to follow, sometimes at the expense of his vast
experience and his remarkable observations of the specific
features, which did not fit easily into the general system.
We are left with the impression that Cvijić's great scientific
contribution might have been even more important had he
broken the chains of the cyclic theory earlier and given an
unprejudiced scientific formulation to his extremely rich
and discerning observations.

In the shadow of Cvijić, Katzer and Grund, a teeming
exploratory activity was going on in Yugoslavia, bringing in
new data and putting old conceptions to a test.

A number of explorers made regional contributions, e.g.,
D. Hirc, F. Katzer, J. Poljak, P. S. Jovanović, B. Ž. Milojević,
A. Melik, etc. Comparatively little attention was paid to
conceptual problems. Geomorphologists mainly adhered to the
cyclic theory, while geologists tried to dispute it whenever
they came upon discrepancies in the field, aware of the insufficient consideration of geologic basis in all its variability. In this situation, a controversy arose about explaining the genesis of the Plitvice Lakes between H.
Hranilović (1901) and D. Gorjanović (1903), and between
Gavazzi (1904) and F. Koch (1925, 1926). F. Simonović went
back to the *subsidence* concept, emphasizing underground
ancient holes (1925, 1926). At that time also the now
generally accepted theory of the biodynamic genesis of
travertine barriers was formulated (Pevalek, 1925, 1926).

5. The Period of Criticism, Hydraulic Supplementation and
    Increasing Experimentation.

In the period between 1932 and 1956, in spite of the
persistence of general concepts of the previous era, particularly of the cyclic theory, more and more of the exceptions
were cropping up that interfered with practical work based on
the existing theory. This led to an increase of criticism,
and contributed hydraulic additions, with the application of
hydraulic experimentation. Research work was still carried
out individually, but with a significantly larger role of
Yugoslav investigators.

Among surface forms, poljes in particular attracted
further attention. A. Lazić (1933) wrote on Dabarsko Polje
and Fatničko Polje, A. Lönnberg (1934) and M. Pleničar (1953)

on Cerkničko Polje, S. M. Milojević (1934, 1936) on Cetinsko
Polje, A. Malicki (1937) on Gatačko Polje, J. Roglić (1938)
on Imotsko Polje. The same author wrote on Kupreško Polje
and Vukovsko Polje (1939). M. Margetić (1947) wrote on poljes
in Dalmatia and R. Lazarević (1949) on Grahovsko Polje. In
1948 A. Šerko wrote a comprehensive study of the polje within
the framework of a general presentation of karst phenomena in
Yugoslavia. J. Cvijić's study of Popovo Polje was published
in 1950. B. Radoičić (1953) and V. Vlahović (1956) wrote on
Nikšićko Polje and J. Stini (1953) on Buško Blato, etc. Other
regional-morphological problems were treated by a number of
authors.

While some investigators supported the cyclic theory,
others started deviating from it. In a number of works J.
Roglić, adopting a geomorphologic approach, pointed out the
autonomy of karst processes, which is not in full agreement
with the application of the cyclic theory of karst; J. Poljak
(1952) presented geologic arguments against the generic
succession doline-uvala-karst polje.

Hydrographic and hydrogeologic phenomena are treated by
S. M. Milojević (1939), I. Rubić (1939), M. Luković (1940,
1951), F. Jenko (1953, 1955), M. Herak (1954), A. Lazić (1954),
I. Gams (1955), R. Meissner (1956) and others. Mentioned also
should be the increasing practice of dyeing the water at
sinkholes in order to determine groundwater connections
(Šerko, 1946; Čadež, 1952; Michler, 1952; etc.).

The absence of the hydraulic component in observing
groundwater in karst, and particularly the problem of the
mingling of sea and fresh waters and the occurrence of
brackish and submarine springs led to a heated discussion
initiated by K. Gjurašin (1942, 1943) and taken up by A.
Franković (1943) and later by I. Kuščer (1950). Basing his
observations on the difference in the specific gravity between
sea and fresh water, K. Gjurašin demonstrated how sea water
can encroach into the land, mix with fresh water and how this
can result in brackish springs. He also explained the reverse
process, i.e., the conditions under which fresh water over-
comes the pressure of sea water and appears as a spring at
the sea bottom. This principle was further elaborated by I.
Kuščer, who illustrated it with examples from the field, taking
partially into account the sucking-in phenomenon under certain
conditions. Though the principles thus put are clear and
applicable, their general drawback is that they are insufficiently connected with the real tectonics, with a connection
that would make it possible to select structures in which this
mechanism may or even must be expected. The reasons for this
are to be found in unsatisfactory cooperation between
specialists in various relevant fields.

6. Beginnings of a Complex Approach to Research on Karst.

The growing need for a practical evaluation of karst
soon led to the realization that there could be no progress
in the exploration and application of the data available
without team work and cooperation of experts in various fields.
The first step in that direction was made in 1957 when a
Federal Conference on Karst was organized in Split, Yugoslavia.
On this occasion a review was made of the state of Yugoslav
research into the various aspects of karst and numerous
problems requiring a solution were brought up. Since the
conference, the agenda of scientific meetings of geographers,
speleologists, geologists, water resources specialists, and
other experts has included the problems of karst. The same
is true of the work of international associations, in which
Yugoslav experts have also taken part. This approach has also
been furthered by the UN agencies--FAO and UNESCO. As a
result, a fast progress in the knowledge about karst both as
a whole and in many details has occurred. A common characteristic of these efforts has been the emphasis on collecting
comprehensive and precise data, while too many generalized
speculations, which tended to dominate in previous periods
have been placed into the background. However, one should
not jump to the conclusion that theoretical issues have been
neglected. On the contrary, they remain the ultimate aim
that should be reached by respecting physical relationships
and observable regularities.

Progress has been achieved in speleology, surface morphology, hydrology and hydrogeology and in methodological
innovations. In speleology the number of investigators has
been increasing and with it the precision and complexity of
research. The possibility of applying the results to practical
purposes, particularly in evaluating the possibility of
surface and underground water storage in karst terrains,
has resulted in increased investments into equipment and research.

Comprehensive regional studies of karst areas were
published by numerous authors. Sub-surface karst forms were
treated by I. Baučić (1961), J. Roglić (1961) and I. Gams
(1971). Gypsum formations were the subject of a work by D.
Rodić (1957). Dolomite formations attracted the attention of
J. Poljak (1958), J. Roglić and I. Baučić (1958). Roglić also
wrote on the problems of plains in karst (1957) and on the
relationship between fluvial erosion and the karst processes
(1959, 1960), emphasizing the importance of corrosion in the
genesis of karst forms. C. Milić wrote on climatic morphology
(1960) and I. Gams (1962) on blind valleys. He differentiates
two types of such valleys in Slovenia. One is formed mainly
by corrosion and the other is the consequence of erosion-
denudation. A geological view of the genesis of dolines was

presented by S. Bahun (1969), who pointed out the great
potential importance of developments that took place before
the terrain came to the surface. The notion of primary importance of fluvial erosion is still occasionally encountered;
however, experts increasingly point out the autonomy of the
karst processes dominated by corrosion, and the influence of
other geologic factors. I. Gams (1963, 1969) even tried to
give a classification of waters with respect to the intensity
of corrosion.

Hydrography too has been the subject of numerous studies.
Hydraulic problems have continuously attracted the attention
of Yugoslav research workers, primarily in connection with
hydrotechnical construction work in karst. At the speleologic
congress in Split in 1958 J. Baturić expressed the opinion
that subterranean fissure reservoirs exist, separated by
compact rocks. The thesis, however, was not substantiated by
concrete geologic structures. I. Kuščer (1961), and later with
D. Kuščer (I. Kuščer and D. Kuščer, 1964) returns to the
earlier discussed problems. M. Jevremović (1962) wrote on
the disturbance in the fresh and salt water balance and on
the hydraulic characteristics and classification of brackish
springs. B. Knežević (1962) described, among other things,
the role of diffusion in the mixing of salt and fresh water.
Together with M. Vojnović, he tried to determine by laboratory
tests the system of sub-surface water courses in karst (B.
Knežević and M. Vojnović, 1962). B. Petrović (1962) analysed
the hydraulic gradient in karst channels. D. Ristić (1962),
D. Srebrenović (1964, 1965) and S. Mikulec and I. Bagarić
(1966) dealt with the problem of capacity of sinkholes. B.
Mijatović (1964) gave a comprehensive study of the mixing of
salt and fresh water and tried to determine via experiments
to the conditions of natural salification and the influence
of salt water on fresh water in pumping. He, too, considers
the hydraulic factor basic in the dynamic balance in salt
and fresh water. He later wrote on the exploration of the
hydrodynamic regime of groundwater in karst by means of
analysis of the discharge and fluctuation curve of the water
table under recession conditions (Mijatović, 1968). I. Avdagić
(1970) wrote on the problem of determining the runoff in the
natural karst estavelle system accumulation.

A number of works deal with local problems and do not
enter into an analysis of general problems. Generally speaking,
all the problems mentioned so far lack a clear presentation of
the geologic framework that could serve as the basis in explaining the hydraulic mechanism. The authors most frequently
resort to their own constructions of possible relations. This
indicates that satisfactory links with geology have not yet
been established. Only such a link can provide the necessary
structural framework for hydraulic relationships. A prerequisite for a fuller cooperation between experts in hydraulics

and geology is a high requirement of hydrogeologic investigations, based on a more consistent application of fundamental
knowledge, a more critical analysis of geophysic data, a more
accurate information on subterranean connections, etc.

An important step towards this objective is a restudy of
the numerous hydrogeologic works showing differences in
approach to hydrologic problems, adapted mainly to regional
conditions. More precise data on submarine springs can be
found in S. Alfirević (1966), who in one of a number of works
gave a comprehensive study of the morphology and geologic
conditions in the occurrence of submarine springs in Kaštela
Bay. Many authors have written on regional hydrogeologic
problems of the main karst areas.

Hydrogeologic explorations have covered all the essential
regions in solving their hydrogeologic problems, thus
adding valuable information to hydrogeology in general.
Nevertheless, we are still waiting for a definite explanation
of these complex phenomena. We shall, therefore, proceed to
present in more detail the works which led to the consideration of problems that had hitherto been neglected.

The Federal Conference on Karst in Split and the Geologic
Congress in Sarajevo in 1957 offered the opportunity for presentation of new views on hydrogeologic phenomena in Dinaric
Karst (Herak, 1957). The role of tectonics in the genesis of
karst was again pointed out. In this connection it was
established that tectonic movements had localized all the
more important karst phenomena both horizontally and vertically.
After an analysis of hydrogeologic function of rocks, it was
emphasized that it is fully dependent not only on the characteristics of rocks, but also on their tectonic position, a fact
that was substantiated by a number of actual examples from the
Dinaric Karst.

J. Poljak (1952) called attention to the presence of
Triassic karst forms in Velebit. D. Petrović (1963) analyzed
the paleorelief of Timočka Krajina and K. Sakač (1966) the
paleorelief and pseudo-paleorelief of bauxite containing karst.
R. Kajmaković and B. Petrović (1961) wrote about the depth and
intensity of karstification depending on geologic and particularly tectonic conditions and the hydraulic gradient. B.
Stepanović (1956) wrote on the porosity of rocks in karst.
B. Milovanović (1965) tried to link the epeirogenetic and orogenetic dynamics with karstification problems in past geologic
periods and with the geologic evolution of holokarst. M. Herak
(1965) again analyzed the importance of geologic processes in
the genesis of karst and of the lithostratigraphic and tectonic
relationships in determining hydrogeologic conditions.

Alongside the broadening and deepening of problems, the methodologic approach to karst has been improved also. Underground tracing of water movement has been carried out with a more critical approach. The application of geophysic methods (Z. Krulc, B. Milanović, D. Arandjelović, M. Mladenović, B. Miličević, S. Slimak, R. Drecun and others) has been elaborated in a number of works, with a marked improvement in the applicability of the conclusions to field problems, in which they can be correlated with reliably established data in fixed locations.

In geologic mapping, photogeologic data and microtectonic elements have found an ever increasing application. Rock complexes have been standardized by permeability, a distinction between surface and underground watersheds has been established, the depth of karstification determined and the grading of rock complexes by permeability carried out (high permeability, fair permeability, poor permeability and imperviousness). The Zagreb geologic school has shown in practical work on mapmaking that the relations in the terrain depend not only on the permeability of rocks, but also on their tectonic position, so that categories by function are graphically singled out, such as complete topographic barriers, and permeable areas, all of which are the result of hydrogeologic characteristics of rocks and structures in which they are located. Thus, impervious rocks of the stratigraphic footwall (e.g., Paleozoic clastics in the Dinaric Karst) represent complete barriers in autochthonous position. The same rocks in allochthonous position, if located on permeable rocks, represent relative (hanging) barriers. Impervious rocks of the stratigraphic hanging wall (e.g., Paleogene flysch in the Dinaric Karst) in a hypsometrically low position, as the thrust base of permeable karst terrain, may play the role of incomplete (and sometimes even complete) barrier.

Many methodologic innovations were made possible by increasing research on karst, primarily within the framework of the design and carrying out construction of reservoirs in karst for hydroelectric power, and to a lesser extent, for water supply. The advantage of such cooperation is not only the availability of more funds, but also the possibility of testing ideas and concepts in direct application acting as a safe and complex experiment. We shall mention only some of the more important examples.

A detailed geologic analysis has shown under what conditions the water of Cerknica Lake in Slovenia could be used more economically. Thorough geologic research preceded the design of the Zoretići Reservoir at Rijeka in the region of *hanging* flysch. The Cretaceous dolomite core of the left side of the Peruča Dam on the Cetina River played an important role in determining the dimensions of the grouting curtain.

The Triassic anticline in the Rama Region was decisive in
choosing the site and designing where the dam will be built.
The folds on the margin of Buško Blato were the basis for
step-by-step sealing of the reservoir rim. The Triassic
anticline at Lastva in Hercegovina influenced the location of
the Grančarevo Dam on the Trebišnjica River. The evaluation
of autochthonous and allochthonous elements led to the decision on constructing the Mratinje Dam and Reservoir on the
Piva River. The imbricate structure of Nikšićko Polje and
the antiform of Stara Crna Gora brought about the complex
problems in constructing the reservoirs there. In all these
ventures the methodologic approach adopted was very complex
in order to obtain as unquestionable results as feasible.

In this way the theoretical and at times rather unrealistic interpretations of karst have been replaced by a geological
approach with considerable possibilities of comparing it with
other types of terrain and in re-evaluating the geomorphologic,
hydrologic, and hydrogeologic concepts of the past.

The first fact to emerge from this was that there exist
far more paleokarst phenomena than had been assumed and that
neokarst phenomena did not start developing all at the same
time, some of them developing continuously since the Paleozoic,
others since the Mesozoic and yet others (again in a different
way) since a younger period. The link with the orogenetic
and epeirogenetic development as the initiator of the karst
processes should not be bypassed in the description of the
development of karst in any area.

The possibility of the same lithological type to be
found within different lithogenetic complexes (first of all
geosynclinal and epicontinental ones) which presuppose an
essentially different structural framework of the rocks, has
led to a re-examination of karst typology. It has become
evident that the term *karst* covers a large variety of
different karst units, differing from each other both morphologically (including structural elements) and hydrogeologically. Some of these, in spite of their specific karst
properties, have more in common with non-karst terrains than
with others, more pronounced karst types. This has shown
beyond any doubt that the term karst, in all but the most
general cases, should be preceded by one or more modifiers,
thus placing the type in question into a definite morphologic
and hydrogeologic framework, which allows further theoretical
and practical conclusions. This also applies to the broader
terminology.

Let us take Cvijić's *holokarst* as an example. Concep-
tually speaking it is beyond reproach. However, in applying
it to a particular terrain difficulties crop up because that
type of karst may be situated in an orogenic structural

complex, such as the Dinaric Karst, or in an epiorogenic
(epicontinental) one, such as the karst of Jamaica. The
deeper base of the former is completely undefined, while
in the latter it is rather clear.

Even greater variability is found in *merokarst*. It may
occur in the fold lenses of orogenes, it may be intercalated
in the folds of epicontinental layers, it is also found in
the form of epiorogenetic platforms, basins, etc. It goes
without saying that in each of these cases not only the
genesis but also the morphologic and hydrogeologic (and even
hydrologic) consequences are different. Similar problems
arise with the terms *fluviokarst, deep karst, shallow karst,*
etc.

At the Symposium on General Water Resources Economy in
Karst, held in Split in 1966, attempts were made at breaking
down even the Dinaric Karst in connection with hydrogeology,
although it belongs to Cvijić's category of holokarst. Thus,
on the territory of Croatia (Herak, Bahun and Magdalenić,
1969) three belts are distinguished: the Adriatic, the Middle
and the Inner belt. Coastal springs, submarine springs and
submarine estavelles are the main hydrogeologic characteristics
of the Adriatic belt, which is geotectonically connected with
the foothills and the para-autochthone of the Dinaric Mountains.
Estavelles and lost rivers dominate the Middle belt, which
covers the main part of the Outer (miogeosynclinal) Dinaric
Mountains. Shallow karst with numerous fluviokarst areas and
water courses that often cut as deep as the groundwater,
characterize the Inner belt, which occurs mainly in the Inner
(eugosynclinal) Dinaric Mountains. P. Habič (1969) made the
same classification for Slovenia, while J. Papeš and R. Srdić
(1969) called the equivalents of the Inner and Middle belt
in Bosna and Hercegovina the northeastern and southwestern
belts, accompanying it with approximately the same description.

The above mentioned tripartite classification has been
preserved in later works; only the term *middle belt* has been
changed into *Highkarst belt* (Herak, 1972a). It has also
been recommended to differentiate between *geosynclinal* and
epicontinental karst regions (Herak, 1972b).

As we can see, in all these classifications efforts have
been made at linking the hydrogeologic (and geomorphologic)
characteristics of the belts with the conditions offered by
geotectonic belts for the formation of rocks suitable for
karstification and the tectonic structures which directed,
simulated or slowed down the processes. The terminology,
however, is not uniform.

M. Komatina (1972) differentiates between the karst of
platforms and geosynclinal regions. In the classification

of the karst of the Dinaric Mountains he differentiates between littoral and inner karst (Komatina, 1967, 1972), on the basis of *regions of tectonic compression and regions of tension of the Earth's crust*. The former covers the territory to the southwest of the line Muč, Aržano and Rakitno Polje, and the latter is the rest of the karst terrain reaching as far as impervious layers. It can be argued, however, that both belts were subject to compression and tension at one time in their history. There is only the question of the succession in time of these processes. In *region of tension*, for instance, the tension was preceded by strong folding and overthrusting. In the littoral belt there are certainly elements of younger tension.

Neither of the attempts at a classification made so far has succeeded in considering all the relevant elements that would reflect both the genesis and indicate recent morphologic and hydrologic relations. Even the choice of terms has not always been fortunate. For instance, we should discard the term *geosynclinal karst,* because during the stage of the geosyncline there was no karstification--it occurred later, when the geosyncline had turned into a structurally more or less formed orogen. It is equally inadequate to apply the term *platform karst* to tabular and basin karst, because the term platform has a broader meaning and includes the orogenic base and epicontinental cover. It would be more adequate to use the term *orogenic* instead of *geosyncline* and *epiorogenic* instead of *platform*. Each of them reflects the characteristics of the sedimental environment and the type of structural deformations, thus offering a clear starting point for a further morphologic and hydrogeologic classification (shallow, deep, basin, confined, complex, etc.).

Taking into consideration that there were several periods of orogenesis in the past (Pre-Cambrian, Caledonian, Hercynian and Alpine) and that each of them was preceded by geosynclinal and followed by epicontinental sedimentation, it becomes evident that a generic classification that could be used as the foundation of a more practical classification based on recent relations requires accurately determined temporal and areal relations in which a karst region developed. Once this has been established, it should be possible to set up a number of characteristics of sub-surface morphology and water distribution even in a region which has not been fully explored. In this way, theoretical geologic observations can be applied directly in geomorphology and hydrogeology both in theory and practice. Solutions can be reached only through joint efforts of experts from all the relevant fields.

In concluding, we say that the Dinaric Karst has been used to create the prototype of the concept of karst, that it stimulated scientists to formulate theories on its genesis,

that its complex problems have attracted the attention of
leading experts in the world, thus serving as the model on
which knowledge about the very phenomenon of karst was accumulated. From the very beginning Yugoslav experts have kept pace
with the development of karstology, applying their experience
to regions outside Yugoslavia, thus furthering the science of
karst.

A further step in such a practice is the cooperation in
research projects such as the one carried out jointly by
Yugoslavia and the United States, in which experience gained
in different methodologic approaches to theoretical and practical problems is being exchanged. These problems may sometimes
be identical, they may also differ, but never to such an
extent as to prevent the reaching of applicable conclusions.

7. Selected References*

ALFIREVIĆ, S. (1966): Hydrogeological investigations of submarine springs in the
Adriatic. Assoc. intern. hydrogéol. (Belgrade 1963), 6, 255-264, Beograd.
AVDAGIĆ, I. (1970): Određivanje proticaja u prirodnoj kraškoj akumulaciji esta-
velnog sistema metodom analogije. Građevinar, 22/6, 203-208, Zagreb.
BABIĆ, Ž., CUKOR, V., FRITZ, F. and RALJEVIĆ, B. (1968): Prilog poznavanju hi-
drogeoloških odnosa južne i srednje Istre. (Contribution to the study of hy-
drogeologic relations in the South and Middle Istria.). Geol. vjesnik, 21,
295-302, Zagreb.
BAHUN, S. (1968): Geološka osnova hidrogeoloških odnosa krškog područja izmedu
Slunja i Vrbovskog. (Geologic basis of hydrogeologic relations of the karst
area between Slunj and Vrbovsko in Croatia.). Geol. vjesnik, 21, 19-81,
Zagreb.
BAHUN, S. (1969): On the formation of karst dolinas. Geol. vjesnik, 22, 25-32,
Zagreb.
BAHUN, S. (1970): Geološka osnova krške zavale Ogulin-Plaški. (Geological basis
of the Ogulin-Plaški karst depression.). Krš Jugosl. Jugosl. akad. znan.
umjet., 7/1, 1-20, Zagreb.
BAHUN, S. and FRITZ, F. (1971): Hidrogeologija Ličkog polja. (Donje Pazarište-
Gospić-Gornja ploča.). (Hydrogeology of the Ličko polje, Croatia.). Zbornik
radova I. jugosl. simp. hidrogeol. inž. geol., Hercegnovi (1971), 1, 7-13,
Beograd.
BATURIĆ, J. (1961): Neki rezultati ispitivanja cirkulacije vode u obalnom
području. II jugosl. speleol. kongr. Split (1958), 35-37, Zagreb.
BAUCIĆ, I. (1961): The importance of impermeable sediments in origin, evolution
and form of underground cavities in Dinaric karst region. Symp. intern.
speleol. Varenna. (1960), Mem. 5, 1-5, Rass. speleol. Ital., Como.
BEHLILOVIĆ, S. (1958): Geološka grada područja rijeke Trebišnjice. (Die geolo-
gische Beschaffenheit des Flussgebietes der Trebišnjica.). Geol. glasnik,
2, 21-34, Sarajevo.
BEŠIĆ, Z. (1959): Geološki vodič kroz Narodnu Republiku Crnu Goru. (Geologischer
Führer durch die Volksrepublik Crna Gora.). Geol. društvo Crne Gore, pp. 559.
Titograd.
BEŠIĆ, Z. (1965): Hydrologic characteristics of the karst regions in the Social-
istic Republic of Montenegro with special reference to subterranean connex-
ions. Naše jame, 7/1-2, 97-106, Ljubljana.
BEŠIĆ, Z. (1969): Karst jugoslovenskog dinarskog prostora. U: Bešić, Z.: Geologija Crne Gore II. Karst Crne Gore. Zavod za geol. istraž. Crne Gore,
65-97, Titograd.
BEYER, A., TIETZE, E. and PILAR, Gj. (1874): Die Wassernoth im Karste der
kroatischen Militärgrenze. Albrecht and Fiedler, 160 s., Zagreb.

*Editor's Note: This reference list departs from the general
pattern of references in this book by using the original
author's approach.

BOJANIĆ, L. and FRITZ, F. (1970): Geološki i hidrogeološki odnosi u području Grnog Luga. (Geological and hydrogeological relations in the area of Crni Lug.). I kol. geol. Dinaridov.

BOUÉ, A. (1861): Über die Karst-und Trichterplastik. Sitzungsber. Akad. Wiss. Matem.-naturwiss. Kl., 43, Wien.

BREZNIK, M. (1961): Akumulacija na Cerkniškem in Planinskem polju. (Water accumulation in the Cerknica and Planina Poljen.). Geologija, 7, 119-149, Ljubljana.

BREZNIK, M. and ŽLEBNIK, Lj. (1961): Geološke razmere v okolici Kolašina v zvezi s projektiranimi hidroenergetskimi objekti na Tari in Morači. Geologija, 6, 146-163, Ljubljana.

BUŠATLIJA, I. (1962): Novo shvatanje o porijeklu reljefa Pljevljanske kotline. (The new apprehension of the origin of the landscape of Pljevlje basin-valley.). Geogr. pregled, 6, 39-52, Sarajevo.

BUŠATLIJA, I. (1963): Neki problemi hidrografije i morfologije Nevesinjskog polja i njegovog oboda. (Certains problèmes de l'hydrographie et de la morphologie de la plaine de Nevesinjsko polje et dans ses bords.). III jugosl. speleol. kongr. Sarajevo. (1962), 57-63, Sarajevo.

ČADEŽ, N. (1952): Barvanje ponikalnice Logaščice v letu 1951. (The subterranean course of the Logaščica.). Geogr. vestnik, 24, 177-189, Ljubljana.

CVIJIĆ, J. (1893): Das Karstphänomen. Versuch einer morphologischen Monographie. Geogr. Abhandl. (Penck), (B), 5/3, 1-114, Stuttgart.

CVIJIĆ, J. (1896): Izvori, tresave i vodopadi u istočnoj Srbiji. Glas Srp. akad. nauka, 51, 1-122, Beograd.

CVIJIĆ, J. (1898): Über die Entstehung der Karre. Mitt. geogr. Ges., 41, Wien.

CVIJIĆ, J. (1899): Glacijalne i morfološke studije o planinama Bosne, Hercegovine i Crne Gore. Glas Srp. akad. nauka, 57, 1-196, Beograd.

CVIJIĆ, J. (1900): Morphologische und glaciale Studien aus Bosnien, der Herzegowina und Montenegro I Teil: Das Hochgebirge und die Kantontaeler. Abhandl. geogr. Ges., 2, 1-94, Wien.

CVIJIĆ, J. (1901): Morphologische und glaziale Studien aus Bosnien, der Hercegowina und Montenegro II Teil: Die Karstpoljen. Abhandl. geogr. Ges., 3/2, 1-85, Wien.

CVIJIĆ, J. (1909): Bildung und Dislozierung der Dinarischen Rumpffläche. Peter-mans geogr. Mitt., 6, 121-127; H 7, 156-163; H 8, 177-181, Gotha.

CVIJIĆ, J. (1918): Hydrographie souterraine et évolution morphologique du karst. Recueil Trav. Inst. géogr. alpine, 6/4, 1-56, Grenoble.

CVIJIĆ, J. (1924): Types morphologiques des terrains calcaires. Glasnik geogr. društva, 10, 1-7, Beograd.

CVIJIĆ, J. (1925, 1926): Circulation des eaux et érosion karstique. Xenia Gorjanović-Kramberger. Glasnik Hrv. prir. društva, 38-39, 43-62, Zagreb.

CVIJIĆ, J. (1926): Cirkulacija vode i erozija u karstu. Glasnik geogr. društva, 12, 1-16, Beograd.

CVIJIĆ, J. (1950): Stare otoke Popova polja i hidrografske zone u karstu. (The ancient effluents of Popovo poje and the position of hydrographic zones in karst.). Glasnik Srp. geogr. društva, 30/1, 3-9, Beograd.

CVIJIĆ, J., Čadež, N. (1960): La géographie des terrains calcaires. Acad. Serbe sci. arts. Monographies I, 341/26, 1-212, Beograd.

DAVIS, W.M. (1884): Geographic classification by a study of plains, plateaux and their derivatives, Proc. Amer. Assoc., 33, 428-432.

DIMIĆ, J. (1958): Lelićki krš. (Le karst de Lelić.). Geogr. pregled, 2, 43-54, Sarajevo.

FRANKOVIĆ, A. (1942): Prilog hidrografiji primorskog krša. Tehnički vjesnik, 10-12, 360-361, Zagreb.

FRITZ, F. (1965): Hydrogeological relations in the western part of Ravni Kotari, Dalmatia. Bull. sci. cons. Acad. Yougosl., 10.2, 37-38, Zagreb.

FRITZ, F. and BOJANIĆ, L. (1967): Prikaz geoloških kartiranja izvršenih za potrebe hidroenergetike na području izmedu Rječine, Kupe i Zrmanje. (An outline of geological mapping work carried out for the needs of hydroelectric projects in the region between the Rječina, Kupa and Zrmanja rivers-Croatia.). Geol. vjesnik, 20, 337-345, Zagreb.

FRITZ, F. (1970): Hidrogeološki odnosi u zapadnom dijelu Ravnih Kotara, Dalmacija. (Hydrogeological relations in the area of the Western part of Ravni Kotari, Dalmatia.). I kol. geol. Dinaridov, 2, 160-162, Ljubljana.

GAMS, I. (1955): Morfološki problemi jame in potoka Mitoščice. (The morphological problems round the cave and brook Mitoščica.). Acta carsologica Slov. akad. znan. umet., 1, 159-166, Ljubljana.

GAMS, I. (1962): Slepe doline v Sloveniji. (Blind valleys in Slovenia.). Geogr. zbornik Slov. akad. znan. umet., 7, 265-305, Ljubljana.

GAMS, I. (1963): Klasifikacija kraških voda Slovenije v pogledu morfogenetskih sposobnosti. (Klassifikation der Karstgewässer Sloweniens in Hinblick auf ihre morphogenetische Aktivitat.). III jugosl. speleol. kongr. Sarajevo (1962), 67-75, Sarajevo.

GAMS, I. (1969): Ergebnisse der neueren Forschungen der Korrosion in Slowenien. (NW-Jugoslawien). Studia Geographica Ceskosl. akad. věd, 5, 9-20, Brno.

GAMS, I. (1971): Podtalne kraške oblike. (Subsoil karst forms.). Geogr. vestnik, 43, 27-45, Ljubljana.

GAŠEVSKI, M. (1962): Karsniot reljef na planinata Bistra. Geogr. razgledi, 1, 59-67, Skopje.

GAVAZZI, A. (1889): Vranjsko jezero u Dalmaciji. Rad Jugosl. akad. znan. umjet., 95, 217-225, Zagreb.

GAVAZZI, A. (1904): Die Seen des Karstes, Teil Il Morphologisches Material. Abhandl. Geogr. Ges., 5/2, 1-136, Wien.

GAVRILOVIĆ, D. (1965): Ein Beitrag zur Kenntnis des Karstes in Serbien. Naše jame, 7/1-2, 107-117, Ljubljana.

GJURAŠIN, K. (1942): Prilog hidrografiji primorskog krša. Tehnički vjesnik, 4-6, 107-112, Zagreb.

GJURAŠIN, K. (1942): Prilog hidrografiji primorskog krša. Tehnički vjesnik, 10-12, 36-362, Zagreb.

GJURAŠIN, K. (1943): Prilog hidrografiji krša. Tehnički vjesnik, 1-2, 1-17, Zagreb.

GORJANOVIĆ, D. (1882): Die Karsterscheinungen im westlichen Theile des Agramer Gebirges. Kroatische Revue, 1, 22-32, Agram (Zagreb).

GORJANOVIĆ-KRAMBERGER, D. (1903): Geomorfološki problemi iz hrvatskog krasa. Glasnik Hrv. naravosl. društva, 13/4-6, 193-206, Zagreb.

GOSPODARIĆ, R. (1963): Sledovi tektonskih premikav iz ledene dobe v Postojnski jami. (Traces of the tectonic movements in the glacial period in the Postojna cave.). Naše jame, 5, 5-11, Ljubljana.

GOSPODARIĆ, R.; HABE, F. and HABIĆ, P. (1970): Orehovški kras in izvir Korentana. Acta carsologica Slov. akad. znan. umet., 5/2, 97-108, Ljubljana.

GROLLER, M. (1889): Das PopovoPolje in der Hercegovina. (Ein Beitrag zur Kenntniss des Karstterains.). Mitt. geogr. Ges., 32, 80-89, Wien.

GRUBER, Th. (1781): Briefe hydrographischen und physicalischen Inhalts aus Krain J.P. Krauss, 162 str., Wien.

GRUND, A. (1903): Die Karsthydrographie. Studien aus Westbosnien. Geogr. Abhandl. (Pencks), 7/3, 103-300, Wien.

GRUND, A. (1910): Zur Frage des Grundwasser im Karst. Mitt. geogr. Ges., 53, 606-617, Wien.

GRUND, A. (1914): Der geographische Ziklus im Karst. Zeitschr. Ges. Erdkunde, 621-640, Berlin.

HABE, F. (1961): Pivška kotlina, hidrografska streha Slovenskega. Geogr. obzornik, 8, 7-12, Ljubljana.

HABE, F. (1966): Die Tektonik des nördlichen Randes des Pivkabeckens unter besonderer Berücksichtigung des Höhlen-Systems von Predjama. III intern. Kongr. Speläol., 5, 93-97, Wien.

HABIĆ, P. (1968): Geomorphological evolution of the mountainous karst in West Slowenia. Actes IV congr. intern. spéléol. Yougosl., Postojna-Ljubljana-Dubrovnik (1965), 3, 469-476, Ljubljana.

HABIĆ, P. (1969): Hidrografska rajonizacija krasa v Sloveniji. (Hydrographic regionalisation of the Slovene karst.). Krš Jugosl. Jugosl. akad. znan. umjet., 6, 79-88, Zagreb.

HACQUET, B. (1778-1789): Oryctographia Carniolica oder physikalische Beschreibung des Herzogthums Krain, Istrien und zum Theil der benachbarten Länder. Vol. I-IV, Leipzig.

HASSERT, K. (1894): Die Landschaften von Montenegro. Peterm. geogr. Mitt., 40, Gotha.

HASSERT, K. (1895): Beiträge zur physischen Geographie von Montenegro. Peterm. geogr. Mitt., 115, 174, Gotha.

HERAK, M. (1954): O geološkim prilikama područja Korane uzvodno od Slunja. (Über die geologischen Verhältnisse des Korana Gebietes SO von Slunj in Kroatien.). Geol. vjesnik, 5-7, 7-24, Zagreb.

HERAK, M. (1957): Geološka osnova nekih hidrogeoloških pojava u Dinarskom kršu. (Geologische Grundlagen einiger hydrogeologischen Erscheinungen im Dinarischen Karst.). II kongr. geol. Jugosl., 523-539, Sarajevo.

HERAK, M.   (1959):   Prilog geologiji i hidrogeologiji otoka Hvara.   (Zur
    Geologie und Hydrogeologie der Insel Hvar.).   Geol. vjesnik, 12, 135-148,
    Zagreb.
HERAK, M.   (1960):   Geologija Gračačkog polja u Lici.   (Geologie des Karstpolje
    von Gračac in der Lika, Kroatien.).   Geol. vjesnik, 13, 31-56, Zagreb.
HERAK, M.   (1962):   Tektonska osnova hidrogeoloških odnosa u izvorišnim područjima
    Kupe i Korane.   (s Plitvickim jezerima)   (Tektonische Grundlage der hydro-
    geologischen Verhältnisse in den Quellengebieten von Kupa und Korana mit
    Plitwitzer Seen.).   Referati V. sav. geol. Jugosl., 3, 17-25, Beograd.
HERAK, M.   (1965):   Geologische Übersicht des Dinarischen Karstes.   Naše jame,
    7/1-2, 5-11, Ljubljana.
HERAK, M., BAHUN, S. and MAGDALENIĆ, A.   (1969):   Pozitivni i negativni utjecaji
    na razvoj krša u Hrvatskoj.   (Positive and negative influences on the
    development of the karst in Croatia.).   Krš Jugosl. Jugosl. akad. znan.
    umjet., 6, 45-78, Zagreb.
HERAK, M.   (1971):   Tektonska osnova hidroloških pojava u okolini Skrada.   (Gorski
    kotar).   Ljetopis Jugosl. akad. znan. umjet., 75, 425-426, Zagreb.
HERAK, M.   (1972a):   Karst of Yugoslavia.   In: Karst.   Important Karst Regions of
    the Northern Hemisphere.   Edit.:   M. Herak and V.T. Stringfield.   Elsevier
    Publ. Comp.   25-83, Amsterdam.
HERAK, M.   (1972b):   Terminology, Genesis and Classification.   In: Karst Important
    Karst Regions of the Northern Hemisphere. Edit.:   M. Herak and V.T.
    Stringfield.   Elsevier Publ. Comp., 504-515, Amsterdam.
HERAK, M. and STRINGFIELD, V.T.   (1972):   Historical review of hydrogeologic con-
    cepts.   In: Karst.   Important Karst Regions of the Northern Hemisphere.
    Edit.:   M. Herak and V.T. Stringfield. Elsevier Publ. Comp., 19-24, Amsterdam.
HERAK, M., MAGAS, B. and SARIC, A.   (1973):   Hidrogeološka, geološka, geomorfolo-
    ška i hidrotehnička bibliografija krša Jugoslavije.   (1689-1972).   Vodopriv-
    redni problemi krša.   Bilten Poslovne zajed. izuč. vodopr. probl. krša, 4,
    209 str., Sarajevo.
HIRC, D.   (1889):   Jugozapadna visočina hrvatska u oro- i hidrografskom pogledu.
    Rad Jugosl. akad. znan. umjet., 98, 154-235, Zagreb.
HRANILOVIĆ, H.   (1901):   Geomorfološki problemi iz hrvatskog krasa.   Geneza
    Plitvičkih jezera.   Glasnik Hrv. naravosl. društva, 13/1-3, 93-133, Zagreb.
JENKO, F.   (1953):   Hidrologija in vodno gospodarstvo krasa.   Gradbeni vestnik,
    21-22, 1-7, Ljubljana.
JENKO, F.   (1955):   Kraška hidrogeologija in geomorfologija v luči novih raziskav
    na Dinarskem krasu.   Geologija, 3, 266-268, Ljubljana.
JEVREMOVIĆ, M.   (1959):   Hidrogeološke veze Fatničkog i Dabarskog polja i njihov
    uticaj na kotu akumulacije "Miruše" Vodoprivreda, 4-5, 77-85, Beograd.
JEVREMOVIĆ, M.   (1962):   Narušavanje hidrostatičke   ravnoteže slatke i slane vode
    probnim crpljenjem slatke vode iz bušotina u Marini kod Trogira.   (Störungen
    des hydrostatischen Gleichgewichtes von Süss-und Salzwasser als Folge der
    Bohrungen in Marina bei Trogir.).   III kongr. geol. Jugosl. Budva (1959), 2,
    139-153, Titograd.
JEVREMOVIĆ, M. and MLADENOVIĆ, M.   (1962):   Kratak prikaz kompleksnih hidrogeo-
    loških istraživanja u dolini Marina-Stupin kod Trogira.   (Kurze Darstellung
    der komplexen hydrogeologischen Untersuchungen in Marina-Stupin bei Trogir.).
    III kongr. geol. Jugosl. Budva (1959), 2, 123-138, Titograd.
JEVREMOVIĆ, M.   (1966):   Hydraulic characteristics and classification of brackish
    springs in the Adriatic zone of the Dinaric karst.   Assoc. intern.   hydrogéol.
    Belgrade (1963), 6, 293-297, Belgrade.
KAJMAKOVIĆ, R. and PETROVIĆ, B.   (1961):   Dubina i intenzitet karstifikacije u
    zavisnosti od geološko-tektonskih uslova i hidrauličkog gradijenta pada.
    (Depth and intensity of karstification in dependence of geological tectonic
    conditions and of hydraulic gradient of head.).   II jugosl. speleol. kongr.
    Split (1958), 67-70, Zagreb.
KATZER, F.   (1909):   Karst und Karsthydrographie.   Zur Kunde der Balkanhalbinsel,
    8, 1-88, Sarajevo.
KATZER, F.   (1921):   Die Hydrographie des Lušci Polje in Westbosnien als Beweis
    gegen die Karstwasserhypothese.   Glasnik Geogr. društva, 7, 102-119, Beograd.
KNEZEVIĆ, B.   (1962):   Hidraulički problemi karsta.   Saopštenja Inst. vodopr.
    "Jaroslav Cerni," 25, 1-14, Beograd.
KNEŽEVIĆ, B. and VOJNOVIĆ, M.   (1962):   Laboratorijsko ispitivanje podzemnih
    tokova u kršu.   III savj. jugosl. stručnjaka za hidraulička istraživanja,
    48-53, Opatija.

KOCH, F. (1925, 1926): Tektonika i hidrografija u kršu. (Zur Tektonik und Hydrographie des Karstes.). Xenia Gorjanović-Kramberger. Glasnik Hrv. prir. društva, 38/39, 71-87, Zagreb.

KOMATINA, M. (1964, 1965): Prilog rešavanju problema određivanja hidrogeoloških razvoda i pravaca cirkulacije podzemnih voda u karstu. (Contribution à la solution du problème de la détermination des lignes de partage hydrogéologique et des directions de la circulation des eaux souterraines dans le karst.). Vesnik Zav. geol. geofiz. istraž. (B), 4/5, 63-79, Beograd.

KOMATINA, M. (1966): Prilog proučavanju hidrogeoloških odnosa centralnodinarskog karsta. (Contribution à l'étude des rapports hydrogéologique dans le karst des Dinarides centrales.). Vesnik Zav. geol. geofiz. istraž. (B), 6, 113-129, Beograd.

KOMATINA, M. (1967): Sur le problème de la détermination des bassins versants et des directions de la circulation des eaux souterraines dans le karst Dinarique. Hydrol. of fractured rocks. Proceed. Dubrovnik symp. (1965), 1, 190-199, Paris.

KOMATINA, M. (1967): Hidrogeološke specifičnosti terena Jugoslavije i problematika bilansiranja podzemnih voda. (Propriétés characteristiques hydrogéologique des terrains yougoslaves et problème du calcul du bilan des eaux souterraines.). Vesnik Zav. geol. geofiz. istraž. (B), 7, 115-162, Beograd.

KOMATINA, M. (1968): Karst i hidrogeološke mogućnosti racionalnijeg zahvatanja podzemnih voda. (Karst et possibilites hydrogéologique d'un captage plus rationnel des eaux souterraines.). Vesnik Zav. geol. geofiz. istraž. (B), 8, 83-121, Beograd.

KOMATINA, M. (1972): Hidrogeološki odnosi u centralnodinarskom karstu i mogućnost korišćenja podzemnih voda. VII kongr. geol. SFRJ, Zagreb (1970), 3, 435-447, Zagreb.

KUNAVER, J. (1961): Visokogorski kras v zahodnih Julijskih in Kamniških Alp. (High Mountain karst in the eastern part of the Julian Alps and in the Kamnik Alps, Northwestern Slovenia.). Geogr. vestnik, 33, 95-135, Ljubljana.

KUŠCER, I. (1950): Kraški izviri ob morski obali. Razprave Slov. akad. nauka umet., 1, 97-147, Ljubljana.

KUŠCER, I. (1961): Metode raziskovanja ob morskih kraških izvirov. (Rapport entre la circulation de l'eau dans le karst et le niveau de la mer.). II jugosl. speleol. kongr. Split (1958), 39-43, Zagreb.

KUŠCER, I. and KUŠCER, D. (1964): Observations on brakish karst sources and sea swallow-holes on the Yugoslav coast. Assoc. intern. hydrogéol. Athènes (1962), 5, 344-353, Athènes.

LAZAREVIĆ, R. (1949): Grahovsko polje. Glasnik Srp. geogr. društva, 29/2, 143-146, Beograd.

LAZIĆ, A. (1933): La régime de la Trebišnjica rivière karstique. Mém. Soc. géogr., 5, 1-23, Beograd.

LAZIĆ, A. (1954): Buna-hidrološka razmatranja. Glasnik Srp. geogr. društva, 34/2, 111-117, Beograd.

LIBURNAU, L.R.J. (1859): Die Quellen des liburnischen Karstes und der vorliegenden Inseln. Mitt. geogr. Ges., 3, 103-108, Wien.

LIBURNAU, L.R.J. (1859): Der Vrana See. (Krähen-See) auf Cherso. Peterm. geogr. Mitt., 5, 89-93, Gotha.

LIBURNAU, L.R.J. (1860): Die Rečina. Hydrographische Skizze. Programm k.k. Obergymnasiums, 17 S., Agram (Zagreb).

LIBURNAU, L.R.J. (1860): Bericht über die Bedingungen und Kultivierung des kroatischen Karstgebirges. Mitt geogr. Ges., 4, 97-140, Wien.

LORENZ, J. (1858): Die Quellen des liburnischen Karstes und der vorliegenden Inseln. Mitt. geogr. Ges., 2, 103, Wien.

LORENZ, J. (1859): Notizen über den kroatischen Karst. Verh. zool. bot. Ges., 13 S., Wien.

LÖNNBERG, A. (1934): Zur Hydrographie des Zirknitzer Beckens. Mém. soc. géogr., 3, 1-114, Beograd.

LOVRICH, G. (1948): Osservazioni di Giovaninni Lovrich sopra diversi pezzi del viaggio in Dalmazia del signor abate Alberto Fortis coll'aggiunta della vita di Socivizca. Venezia, Presso Francesco Sansoni, 1776. Prijevod: Mihovil Kombol. Ivan Lovrić. Bilješke o putu po Dalmaciji opata Alberta Fortisa i život Stanislava Sočivice. Izd. zavod Jugosl. akad. znan. umjet., 229 str., Zagreb.

LUKOVIĆ, M. (1940): Izvor Oplovi u Orebiću na Pelješcu prema Korčuli kao nov tip bogatih izvora. Zapisnici Srp. geol. društva za 1939, 5, Beograd.

LUKOVIĆ, M. (1951): O izvorima i podzemnim vodama Gorskog kotara i Hrvatskog primorja. Prilog hidrogeologiji ovih oblasti. (On springs and underground waters of Gorski Kotar SW Croatia and Croatian Littoral.). Geol. anali Balk. poluostr., 19, 155-176, Beograd.

MAGAŠ, N. (1965): O depresiji Vranskog jezera na otoku Cresu i geološkim odnosima njegovog užeg područja. (About the lake Vrana depression on the island of Cres and the geological relations of its narrower area.). Geol. vjesnik, 18/2, 255-261, Zagreb.

MAGDALENIĆ, A. (1965): Hidrogeološka interpretacija bazena Prančevići na Cetini. (Hydrogeological interpretation of the Prančevići basin on the Cetina river.). Geol. vjesnik, 18/2, 385-404, Zagreb.

MAGDALENIĆ, A. (1971): Hidrogeologija sliva Cetine. (The hydrogeology of the river Cetina.). Krš Jugosl. Jugosl. akad. znan. umjet., 7/4, 89-169, Zagreb.

MAJNARIĆ, J. (1891): Osvrt na krš Grobnika. Šumarski list, 307-324, Zagreb.

MALICKI, A. (1937): Gatačko polje. Szkic z morfologii krasu dynarskiego. Kosmos (A), Rozprawy Rocz. 57/1-2, 51-72, Zwow.

MANAKOVIĆ, D. (1965): Le karst de la Macédonie. Naše jame, 7/1-2, 119-120, Ljubljana.

MANAKOVIĆ, D. (1970): Peštera Ubavica-Golema peštera Špela Moze. (La grotte Ubavica). V jugosl. speleol. kongr. Skopje (1968), 35-40, Skopje.

MARGETIĆ, M. (1947): Tektonski poremećaji kao temelj postanka krških polja srednje Dalmacije. (Tectonic disturbances as the basis for the formation of the karst plains in middle Dalmatia.). Geol. vjesnik, 1, 68-110, Zagreb.

MARKOVIĆ, J. (1968): Pocerski merokras. (Mérokarst de Pocerina). Cvijićev zbornik Srp. akad. nauka umet., 103-116, Beograd.

MAYER, E. (1873): Der Vranasee. Mitt. geogr. Ges., 16, 241, Wien.

MEISSNER, R. (1956): Zum Problem der intermittierenden Quellen. (Karstgebiet). N. Jb. Geol. Paläont. (Mh), (B), 510-512, Stuttgart.

MICHLER, I. (1952): Barvanje ponikalnice Lokve pri Predjami. Proteus, 14, 338-342, Ljubljana.

MIHAJLOVIĆ, H. (1887): Popovo u Hercegovini. Glasnik Zemalj. muz. u Sarajevu, 1, 15, Sarajevo.

MIJATOVIĆ, B. (1967): Hidraulički mehanizam kraških izdani u niskim primorskim kolektorima. (Le mécanisme hydraulique des nappes karstiques dans les bas collecteurs littoraux.). Vesnik Zav. geol. geofiz. istraž., (B), 7, 5-114, Beograd.

MIJATOVIĆ, B. (1968): Metoda ispitivanja hidrodinamičkog režima kraških izdani pomoću analiza krive pražnjenja i fluktuacije nivoa izdani u recesionim uslovima. (Methode d'étude du régime hydrodynamique des nappes karstiques par analyse de la courbe de tarissement et de retardation du niveau de nappe dans conditions d'étiage.). Vesnik Zav. geol. geofiz. istraž., (B), 8, 45-81, Beograd.

MIKULEC, S. and BAGARIĆ, I. (1966): Izbor pajpogodnije metode mjerenja kapaciteta ponora. Radovi i saopštenja Zavoda za hidrotehniku, 7, 119-130, Sarajevo.

MILANOVIĆ, P. (1971): Savremene metode primenjene u toku istraživanja hidrogeoloških karakteristika Popovog polja. (The modern methods applied within exploration of hydrogeological characteristics of Popovo polje.). Zbornik radova I. jugosl. simp. hidrogeol. inž. geol. Hercegnovi (1971), 1, 151-156, Beograd.

MILIĆ, Č. (1960): Lužnička vrela. Prilog klimatskoj morfologiji krasa. (Une contribution à la morphologie climatique du karst.). Zbornik radova Srp. akad. nauka umet., Geogr. inst., 17, 23-68, Beograd.

MILIĆ, Č. (1962): Glavne odlike krasa Suve planine. (Principales caractéristiques du karst de la Suva planina.). Zbornik radova Srp. akad. nauka umet., Geogr. inst., 18, 93-153, Beograd.

MILOJEVIĆ, S.M. (1934): Hidrografska veza Cetinjskog polja sa rijekom Crnojevića. Glasnik Srp. geogr. drustva, 20, 106-108, Beograd.

MILOJEVIĆ, S.M. (1936): Vrelo Moravice u Sokobanjskoj kotlini. (Karstquellen der Moravica im Becken von Sokobanja.). Glasnik Srp. geogr. drustva, 22, 68-79, Beograd.

MILOJEVIĆ, S.M. (1939): L'abaissement et le déplassement des sources karstiques. Geogr. glasnik, 8-10, 156-159, Zagreb.

MILOVANOVIĆ, B. (1965): Epirogenetska i orogenetska dinamika u prostoru spoljašnjih Dinarida i problemi paleokarstifikacije i geološke evolucije holokarsta. (Le dynamique épirogénetique et orogénetique dans le domaine des Dinarides externes et les problémes de la paléokarstification·et l'évolution de l'holokarst.). Vesnik Zav. geol. geofiz. istraž. (B), 4/5, 5-44, Beograd.

MLADENOVIĆ, J. and UZUNOVIĆ, O. (1963): Prilog poznavanju hidrogeologije na području sliva Omble. (Compte rendu hydrogéologique sur la région de la source de l'Ombla.). III jugosl. speleol kongr. Sarajevo (1962), 111-120, Sarajevo.

MLADENOVIĆ, J. (1968): Contribution à la solution de certains problémes hydro-géologique dans le bassin de la Neretva. Actes IV congr. intern. spéléol. Yougosl., Postojna-Ljubljana-Dubrovnik (1965), 3, 341-344, Ljubljana.

MOJSISOVICS, E. (1880): Zur Geologie der Karsterscheinungen. Zeitschr. österr. Alpenver., 111-117, Wien.

MÜLLER, F. (1891): Resultate der Färbung des Höhlenflusses Reka mit Fluorescein. Mitt. österr. Alpenver., 230, Wien.

NOVAK, D. (1961): Raziskovanje podzemeljskih vodnih tokov, njegov pomen in metode. Nova proizvodnja, 12/2-3, 108-111, Ljubljana.

PAPEŠ, J. and SRDIĆ, R. (1969): Opće hidrogeološki odnosi na teritoriji B i H. (General hydrogeological characteristics of the area of Bosnia and Hercegovina, Yugoslavia.). Krš Jugosl. Jugosl. akad. znan. umjet., 6, 93-104, Zagreb.

PENCK, A. (1900): Geomorphologische Studien aus der Hercegovina. Zeitschr. deutsch. österr. Alpenver., 31, München.

PETROVIĆ, B. (1962): Analiza hidrauličkog gradijenta pada u kraškim kanalima pomoću natrijum fluoresceina. III savj. jugosl. stručnjaka za hidrauličko istraživanje, 61-64, Opatija.

PETROVIĆ, D. (1963): Paleoreljef Timočke Krajine. (Le paléorelief d'une partie de la Serbie orientale.). Zbornik radova Geogr. inst., 10, 5-15, Beograd.

PETROVIĆ, J.B. (1961): O postanku Dabarskog, Fatničkog i Planskog polja. (Sur la genèse des poljes Dabarsko, Fatničko et Plansko.). Glasnik Srp. geogr. društva, 41, 59-67, Beograd.

PEVALEK, I. (1925, 1926): Oblici fitogenih inkrustacija i sedre na Plitvičkim jezerima i njihovo geološko znamenovanje. (Die Formen der phytogenen Inkrustationen und des Travertins in den Plitvicer Seen und ihre geologische Bedeutung.). Xenia Gorjanović-Kramberger. Glasnik Hrv. prir. društva, 37/38, 101-110, Zagreb.

PILAR, Gj. (1874): Beitrag zur Lösung der Wassernothfrage im kroatischen Karst. Prinos riešenju pitanja o bezvodici u hrvatskom krasu) U: Beyer, A.; Tietze, E. and Pilar, Gj.: Die Wassernoth im Karste der kroatischen Militärgrenze. (Oskudica vode po krasu u hrvatskoj vojničkoj krajini.). Albrecht i Fiedler, 135-160, Zagreb.

PLENIČAR, M. (1953): Prispevek h geologiji Cerkniškega polja. (Contribution to the geology of Cerkniško polje.). Geologija, 1, 111-119, Ljubljana.

PLENIČAR, M. (1960): Prispevek h geologiji postojnskega jamskega sistema. (Beitrag zur Geologie des Höhlensystems von Postojna.). Naše jame, 2, 54-58, Ljubljana.

POLŠAK, A. (1960): Prilog poznavanju hidrogeoloških odnosa okolice Plitvičkih jezera. Ljetopis Jugosl. akad. znan. umjet., 64, 315-320, Zagreb.

POLŠAK, A. (1963): Hydrogeological relations of Plitvice Lakes. Assoc. intern. hydrogéol. Guide pour le voyage d'études, Belgrade.

POLJAK, J. (1952): Je li krška uvala prijelazan oblik izmedu ponikve i krškog polja? (Ist die Karstmulde eine Übergangsform die Verbindung zwischen Doline und Karstpolje herstellt?). Geogr. glasnik, 13, 25-48, Zagreb.

POLJAK, J. (1952): Pojava starih krških oblika i njihova veza sa rudnim ležištima područja Debeljaka na sjevernom Velebitu. (Über die Erscheinung von fossilen Karstformen und ihre Zusammenhang mit der Erzlagerstätte am Debeljak in nördlichen Velebit.). Geol. vjesnik, 2-4, 98-109, Zagreb.

POLJAK, J. (1958): Razvoj morfologije i hidrogeologije u dolomitima dinarskog krša. (Die Entwicklung der Morphologie und Hydrogeologie in den Dolomiten des Dinarischen Karstes.). Geol. vjesnik, 11, 1-20, Zagreb.

PUTICK, W. (1887): Zur Erforschung der hydrologischen Verhältnisse des Inner-krainer Karstes. Centr. gesamt. Forstw., 126-135,

PUTICK, W. (1888): Die Geschichte der Untersuchungen des Innerkrainer Karstes. Mitt krain kstl. Forstver., 10, 40-44,

PUTICK, W. (1889): Die unschädliche Abteilung der Hochwässer aus den Kessel-thalern in Innerkrain. Mitt. krain kstl. Forstver., 13, 132-142,

PUTICK, W. (1889): Uber hydrologische Forschungen in den Höhlenflüssen des Karstes. Centr. gesamt. Fortw., 15, 179-184; 16, 44-47,

PUTICK, W. (1887-1890): Die Ursache der Ueberschwemmungen in den Kesselthälern von Innerkrain. Wochenschrift des österr. Ing. und Arch. Vereines. (U nastavcima 1888-1889). Mitt. geogr. Ges., Wien.

PUTICK, W. (1890): Die unterirdischen Flussläufe von Innerkrain. Mitt. geogr. Ges., 246 S. Wien.

PUTICK, W. (1892): Zur Entwasserung der Kesselthäler von Reifnitz und Gottsche. Laibacher Zeitung, Laibach.

PUTICK, W. (1899): Die Katavatrons in Kesselthale von Planina in Krain. Wochenschrift des österr. Ing. und Arch. Vereines, 46 and 47.
RADIMSKY, W. (1890): Visoravan Rakitno u Hercegovini. Glasnik Zemalj. muz. Sarajevo, 3, 413, Sarajevo.
RADOJČIĆ, B. (1953): Nikšičko polje. Geomorfološka promatranja. (Le polje de Nikšić. É'tude morphologique.). Geogr. glasnik, 14-15, 71-86, Zagreb.
RADOVANOVIĆ, S. (1894): Les phénomenes du karst dans la Serbie orientale. Ann. géogr., 56-61, Paris.
RALJEVIĆ, B. (1967): Geološki i hidrogeološki odnosi šireg područja Buškog Blata. (Geological and hydrogeological relations of the wide area of Buško Blato.). Geol. vjesnik, 20, 273-283, Zagreb.
RIĐANOVIĆ, J. (1966): Orjen--trajnost krškog procesa i njegove modifikacije. (Orjen--a contribution to the knowledge of the relief of littoral karst mountains.). Radovi Geogr. inst. Sveuč. u Zagrebu, 5, 5-103, Zagreb.
RISTIĆ, D. (1962): Problemi odredivanja kapaciteta ponora, III savj. jugosl. struč. za hidraulička istraž., 65-72, Opatija.
RISTIĆ, D. (1963): Problemi odredivanja kapaciteta ponora. Gradevinar, 15/9, 326-333, Zagreb.
RODIĆ, D. (1957): Gipsni reljef Srpsko-suvajske kotline. (Le relief de gypse du bassin deffondement de Srb-Suvaja.). Glasnik Srp. geogr. društva, 37/1, 17-29, Beograd.
ROGLIĆ, J. (1938): Imotsko polje--fizičko geografske osobine. Posebna izd. Srp. geogr. društva, 21, 1-118, Beograd.
ROGLIĆ, J. (1939): Morphologie der Poljen von Kupres und Vukovsko. Zeitschr. Ges. Erdkunde, 7-8, 299-316, Berlin.
ROGLIĆ, J. (1940): Geomorphologische Studien über das Duvanjsko polje in Bosnien. Mitt. geogr. Ges., 83/5-8, 1-26, Wien.
ROGLIĆ, J. (1957): Zaravni na vapnencima. (Les surfaces d'aplanissement dans les calcaires.). Geogr. glasnik, 19, 103-134, Zagreb.
ROGLIĆ, J. and BAUČIĆ, I. (1958): Krš u dolomitima izmedu Konavoskog polja i morske obale. (Le karst dans les dolomies entre le polje de Konavle et la côte de l'Adriatique.). Geogr. glasnik, 20, 129-137, Zagreb.
ROGLIĆ, J. (1959): Odnos riječne erozije i krškog procesa. (Le rapport entre l'érosion fluviale et le processus karstique.). Zbornik radova V kongr. geogr. FNRJ, Cetinje (1958), 263-275, Cetinje.
ROGLIĆ, J. (1960): Das Verhältnis der Flusserosion zum Karstprozess. Zeitschr. Geomorph., 4/2, 116-128, Berlin.
ROGLIĆ, J. (1961): Prilog poznavanju Cvijićeve misli o kršu. (Contribution à la connaissance de l'évolution de la pensée de Cvijić sur le karst.). Geogr. glasnik, 23, 37-53, Zagreb.
ROGLIC, J. (1961): Oblici korozije u pokrivenom kršu. Glasnik Srp. geogr. društva, 41/1, 7-13, Beograd.
RUBIĆ, I. (1939): Podmorski mlinovi (Über unterseeische Mühlen.). Geogr. vestnik, 15, 43-58, Ljubljana.
SAKAČ, K. (1966): O paleoreljefu i pseudopaleoreljefu boksitonosnih područja krša. (O paleoreljefe i pseudopaleoreljefe boksitonosnyh rajonov karsta.). Geol. vjesnik, 19, 123-129, Zagreb.
SCHMIDL, A. (1851): Unterirdischer Lauf des Recca-Flusses. Jahrb. geol. Reichsanst., 2/2, 184, Wien.
SIMONOVIĆ, R. (1925): Tektonische Urhohlräume unter den Falten-Gebirgen. Neue Erklärung des Karstphaenomens. 1-141, Sombor.
SREBRENOVIĆ, D. (1964): Kraški ponori i njihova propusna moć. Gradevinar, 16/12, 425-436, Zagreb.
SREBRENOVIĆ, D. (1965): Hidrološke veličine i odnosi u jednom kraškom sistemu. Zavod za hidrolg. Geodetskog fak. u Zagrebu, 1-17, Zagreb.
STACHÉ, G. (1864): Die Wasserverhältnisse von Pirano und Dignano in Istrien. Verh. gool. Reichsanst., Wien.
STACHÉ, G. (1880): Über die Trinkwasserfrage von Pola in Istrien. Verh. Reichsanst., 19, 141-146, Wien.
STACHÉ, G. (1889): Die Wasserversorgung von Pola, Jahr. geol. Reichsanst., 39, 83-180, Wien.
STEPANOVIĆ, B. (1956): Struktura poroznosti stena i njen praktični značaj u hidrogeologiji. Zbornik radova Geol.-rud. fak., (1953, 1954), 141-155, Beograd.
STINI, J. (1953): Zur Frage der Aufspeicherung von Wasser in Karsttrichtern und Karstwannen. (Buschko Blato in Bosnien.). Mitt. Höhlenkomm., 36, Wien.
ŠERKO, A. (1946): Barvanje ponikalnic v Sloveniji. (Les colorations des rivieres karstique en Slovenie.). Geogr. vestnik, 18, 125-139, Ljubljana.

ŠERKO, A. (1948): Kraški pojavi v Jugoslaviji. Geogr. vestnik, 19, 43-70, Ljubljana.

TARAMMELI, T. (1878a): Descrizione geologica del bacino idrografico del Fiume Recca e del tratto dell'altipiano del Carso da traforasi per la condotta di esso fiume S. Canziano alla valle di Longera. Tipogr. G. Caprin, Trieste.

TARAMMELI, T. (1878b): Alcune osservazioni geologiche sul carso di Trieste e sulla valle del fiume Recca stabilite in occasione di un progetto di derivazione di questo fiume in citta mediante una galleria di 14 chilometri. Rediconti reale Ist. Lombardo sci. lett., 2, p. 289, Milano.

TERZAGHI, K. (1913): Beiträge zur Hydrographie und Morphologie des kroatischen Karstes. Mitt. aus d. Jahrb. Ungarn. Reichsanst., 20/6, 255-369, Budapest.

TIETZE, E. (1873): Geologische Darstellung der Gegend zwischen Karlstadt in Kroatien und dem nördlichen Teil des Canals der Morlacca. Jahrb. geol. Reichsanst., 23/1, 25-70, Wien.

TIETZE, E. (1874): Geologische Darstellung der Gegend zwischen Karlstadt in Kroatien und dem nördlichen Theils des Kanals Morlacca. Mit. besonderer Rücksicht auf die hydrographischen Verhältnisse jener Gegend und die Karst-bildung im Allgemeinen. (Zemljoslovni opis okolice medju Karlovcem u Hrvatskoj i sjevernim dielom sinjega mora uz osobiti obzir na hidrograficne odnošaje one okolice i na postojanje krasa uploške.). IN: Beyer, A.; Tietze, E. and Pilar, Gj.: Die Wassernoth im Karste der kroatischen Militärgrenze. (Oskudica vode po krasu u hrvatskoj vojničkoj krajini.). Albrecht and Fiedler, 71-131, Zagreb.

TIETZE, E. (1880): Zur Geologie der Karsterscheinungen. Jahr. geol. Reichsanst., 30, 729-756, Wien.

UZUNOVIĆ, O. (1962): Prilog poznavanju geomorfoloških i hidrografskih karak-teristika zaravni Zagorje-Bosna. (Beitrag zur Kenntniss der geomorpho-logischen und hydrologischen Kennzeichen der Hochebene Zagorje.). Geogr. pregled, 6, 53-63, Sarajevo.

VALVASOR, J.W. (1689): Die Ehre des Herzogsthums Krain. Endter, I Buch 696 pp; II Buch 835 pp:, III Buch 730 pp:, IV Buch 610 pp., Nürnberg.

VLAHOVIĆ, V. (1956): Geologija akumulacije Krupac u Nikšićkom polju i način obezbjedenja vododrživosti u njoj. (Géologie de l'accumulation Krupac et la facon d'y retenir l'eau. Geol. glasnik, 1, 271-277, Cetinje.

VLAHOVIĆ, V. (1958): Hidrogeologija Niksickog polja, Crna Gora. (La hydro-géologie de Nikšićko polje.). Geol. glasnik 2, 243-266, Titograd.

VLAHOVIĆ, V. (1972): Zavisnost proticanja rijeke Donje Zete od nivoa kraške izdani i poplava u Nikšićkom polju. (Sur la dépendance de la Donja Zeta du niveau des eaux souterraines et des inondations dans le Nikšićko polje.). Krš Jugosl. Jugosl. akad. znan. umjet., 8/2, 17-41, Zagreb.

VUKOTINOVIC, L. (1859): Die Plitvica-Seen in der oberen Militärgrenze in Kroatien. Sitzungsber. Mathem.-naturwiss. Akad., 33, 268-280, Wien.

WESSELY, J. (1876): Karstgebiet Militär-Kroatiens und seine Rettung dann die Karstfrage ueberhaupt. Herausgegeben k. Generalkommando in Agram aus Landes-Verwaltungs-berhörte der Croat.-Slavon. Militärgrenze, verfasst von Joseph Wessely. Prijevod I. Trnski: Kras Hrvatske Krajine i kako da se spasi zatiem kraško pitanje uploške. Commissions-Verlag der Universität Buchhandlung Albert and Fiedler, IX 357, Agram.

HYDROLOGIC FEATURES OF UNITED STATES KARST REGIONS

by

Harry LeGrand, Consulting Hydrogeologist,
Raleigh, North Carolina,
V. T. Stringfield,
U. S. Geological Survey, Reston, Virginia,
and P. E. LaMoreaux,
Alabama Geological Survey, Tuscaloosa, Alabama, U.S.A.

Synopsis. Karst regions are widespread in the United States where carbonate rocks are exposed to solutional and physical erosion. Prominent exposed regions include: (1) a belt of the Tertiary Coastal Plain in South Carolina, Georgia, Florida, and Alabama; (2) a folded Paleozoic belt extending from Pennsylvania into Alabama; (3) nearly flat lying Paleozoic areas of Alabama, Tennessee, Kentucky, Ohio, Indiana, Illinois, Wisconsin, and Missouri; (4) a nearly flat lying Cretaceous area of Texas; (5) a nearly flat lying Permian area of New Mexico; and (6) an arcuate Paleozoic belt in South Dakota and Wyoming. The extensive karst regions are on elevated plains or slight structural arches where circulation of sub-surface water is adequate to result in such characteristics as dolines, caverns and related solution openings in the rock, long dry valleys, scarcity of surface streams, and scarcity of soils. The tectonic structural features associated with considerable topographic relief, typically developed in Yugoslavia, are not common in the United States.

Carbonate rocks may have a hydrologic framework that appears to be somewhat self-engendering. Where other factors and constraints are not limiting, circulation of water leads to solution of the rock, which in turn, favors greater circulation.

Some practical problems of karst regions include: (1) scarcity and poor predictability of groundwater supplies; (2) scarcity of surface streams; (3) instability of the ground; (4) leakage of surface reservoirs; and (5) an unreliable waste-disposal environment. The environment is delicately sensitive where natural or man-influenced extremes of water-level fluctuations cause springs to dry up, lake levels to fluctuate, and dolines to develop almost suddenly. Specific local studies in conjunction with comparative hydrogeologic analyses of many karst regions are needed to manage the characteristic environmental problems.

1. Introduction.

Karst regions are widespread in the United States and also in many parts of the world. They are characterized by soluble

rocks at or near land surface. These rocks, chiefly limestone
and dolomites, may be etched in many ways on the land surface
and have solution openings, such as caverns, beneath the
ground where circulating water has been able to move into the
rocks and to discharge from them.

In this paper a review will be made of the major karst
regions of the United States. As a preface to a description
of the karst regions, a summary of some karst phenomena and
karst development is presented. Principles relating to karst
topography and karst hydrology have been progressively established through research and field work by geologists, engineers,
hydrologists, and speleologists from many countries. The
broad scope of international work in karst hydrology is indicated in the annotated bibliography by LaMoreaux and others
[1]. Recent books on karst also emphasize features and problems of karst hydrology, such as Herak and Stringfield [2],
Sweeting [3], Jennings [4], and Proc. Symp. Fractured Rocks,
Dubrovnik of 1965, [5].

Karst regions appear to be more sensitive to environmental
changes than do other rock terrains. This sensitivity is
related to karst dynamics - changes in hydrology with inter-
related change in karst land features. The practical and
ecological problems of karst regions are conspicuously dynamic
in nature. For example, localities where the natural rate of
stripping of soils exceeds the soil generation rate are un-
suitable for agriculture, which greatly restricts habitation.
Delicate imbalances in erosion at different places in some
karst regions lead to rugged topography that also restricts
habitation. The tendency of carbonate rocks to develop local
zones or places of high permeability causes many problems including: ready escape of groundwater that results in scarcity
and poor predictability of groundwater supplies, scarcity of
surface streams, instability of the ground for foundation
purposes, leakage of surface reservoirs and unsatisfactory
waste disposal environments. Unless the hydrology of karst
terranes is understood, methods of handling the many types of
karst environmental problems will not be properly directed.

The international exchange of information, as demonstrated
in this Dubrovnik symposium, is helpful in comparing karst
features. Much progress is being made, and evaluations of
problems relating to karst hydrology are coming into better
focus.

2. General Features of Karst Development.

Since the early part of the present century, investigators have made much progress in understanding karst hydrology.
Early emphasis was put on surface forms as Grund [6] produced
his geographical cycle in karst and as Cvijić [7] discussed

the evolution of karst landforms. These workers, considering
the classic Yugoslav karst as a type region, could see stages
in the development of karst. Some objections have arisen because each sequence of karst development does not lead to a
distinct set of karst features over the entire terrane, to be
followed by another set of features. Yet, progressive changes
in both surface and subsurface karst features are recognized
by all workers. These changes are caused by differential
circulation of water and solution of the rocks. Thus, it
is the dynamics of the system - both the water and the soluble
rocks - that causes the uniqueness of karst.

The presence of surface and subsurface karst features have
resulted from actions of the following factors: soluble rocks,
presence of carbonic acid, precipitation, openings in the
rocks, and topographic and structural setting of the rocks.

Carbonate-rock terranes are not entirely water bearing, as
some parts of the rock system either are impermeable or are
above the zone of saturation. In the development of a karst
system, some parts of the formations are not in the path of
water movement, and these parts may remain relatively impermeable. In those parts where an aquifer has developed and where
the permeability is high, the slope of the water table is
flattened, and a permeable unsaturated zone remains. Thus the
permeable zones commonly extend above and below the water table.

The great range in overall permeability of karst aquifers
and the relatively common uneven distribution of permeability
have been noted by many workers [5].

Three types of permeability development leading to three
types of karst aquifers or systems can generally be recognized.
These are the (1) fine textured system dominated by veins or
closely spaced openings, (2) coarse textured, dominated by
arteries or large openings not necessarily closely spaced, and
(3) reactivated system that shows a history of early karst
development followed by burial and later resurrection.

The fine textured karst system, as regards permeability,
may have either low or high permeability and is commonly an
immaturely developed karst of young geologic age. White [8]
applied the term *diffused flow* to this system.

Carbonate rocks that are generally characterized by mature
karst topography may be considered coarse textured as regards
development of permeability. This is White's *free flow* system
[8]. This system shows an appreciable range in permeability.
In such aquifers, large solution channels as arteries are inter-
spersed with large volumes of poorly permeable rock, and wells
penetrating solution channels yield many times more water
than those that do not penetrate the large openings. Where

circulation of water and solution of the carbonate rocks have progressed fully, there is a tendency for the aquifer to have some of the following characteristics:

(1) a channel or artery network type of permeability, especially near the water table;
(2) rapidly decreasing overall permeability with increasing depth below the water table;
(3) an exceptionally high zone of permeability in valleys;
(4) a very permeable and cavernous unsaturated zone;
(5) salty water in the lower and less permeable part of the aquifer;
(6) moderately low storage of freshwater in long periods of fair weather.

The reactivated karst aquifer is recognized by its geologic and hydrologic history. At an earlier geologic time it was part of a mature karst area that had a coarse textured permeability system. Since that earlier karst period it was submerged and covered with younger sediments and because of subsequent erosion is now again in a fresh-water circulation system. Most of the reactivated karst aquifers are artesian, having water confined beneath less permeable beds.

Even in humid regions, not all mature karst areas contain readily usable aquifers. If the fractures and solution openings are small and poorly developed, the rocks, in a sense, are nearly impermeable. Very permeable karst systems also may not be good aquifers because water can pass readily through large openings to a saturated zone and flow quickly, to discharge out of the ground; under this condition the water table is likely to be deep, perhaps near the base of the carbonate rocks. In highly permeable coastal karst regions the fresh water zone is commonly a thin lens overlying salty karst water; this fresh water may appear to be of large volume where it discharges as coastal springs, but it is difficult to capture the fresh water.

3.   Regions of Carbonate Rocks.

Limestones and dolomites are present throughout the world in the sedimentary rock sequence and occur over several million square miles near land surface on the continents. Considering the great thicknesses of sedimentary rocks in many regions, it is not surprising that many carbonate rocks are buried beneath other rocks and are almost hydrologically inert; these concealed rocks contain salty water that is not a part of the overall fresh-water circulation system that characterizes most carbonate rocks near land surface. Such deeply buried limestones and dolomites containing salty water are especially widespread beneath the Gulf Coastal Plain, the Appalachian Plateau, and the Mid-Continent Region. They are not considered further in this report and are not indicated on Fig. 1, which shows the general areas where carbonate rocks are near land surface in the United States and where many of these rocks have been karstified.

Puerto Rico. Tertiary limestones are widespread on the North Coast of Puerto Rico. The island was uplifted many hundreds of meters above sea level during Miocene time, and the limestones have been continuously karstified since then. Because the topographic relief is great and the climate is humid and tropical, solutional erosion and attendant land collapse have resulted in deep dolines and pronounced conical hills, which combine to make the terrane difficult to cross. Soils are thin, especially on upland slopes. The water table is deep below upland areas, and large caverns in the unsaturated zone transmit storm waters to openings, such as dolines, in the lowlands, where flooding may sometimes occur. Because the permeability of the carbonate rocks is unevenly distributed, the yields of wells range greatly. Some springs are polluted at times. Large amounts of fresh groundwater are discharged to the sea, while some inland areas are short of water because the runoff quickly infiltrates to the subsurface by way of the intricately dissected surface.

Atlantic Coastal Plain. Limestone formations of Tertiary age underlie all of Florida and parts of adjacent areas in Alabama and Georgia; they extend northward through Georgia and South Carolina and into North Carolina. They are at or near land surface through much of the Coastal Plain province in these states. Collectively they represent one of the most productive aquifer systems in the United States.

The Coastal Plain, beneath which the limestone formations have a widespread occurrence, ranges in altitude from sea level at the coast to as much as 200 meters along the inner margin. The formations also dip gently toward the coast, the dip being only slightly greater than the land surface; a general homoclinal artesian system results in which the limestone thickens to several hundreds of meters near the coast. Bare karst rocks are rare because the raised coastal plain has left a veneer of sandy surface deposits. Relatively flat interstream areas are characteristic of coastal regions, and the remnants of Pleistocene coastal terraces extending to an elevation of about 90 meters have been only slightly dissected in most places. Dolines and doline lakes are especially common in north-central Florida where a structural arch brings the limestone to the land surface; in much of this area drainage is underground except for a few perennial streams that are entrenched into the limestone and that draw water from it.

The climate is temperate and humid. Annual rainfall ranges from about 950 mm at the southern tip of Florida to

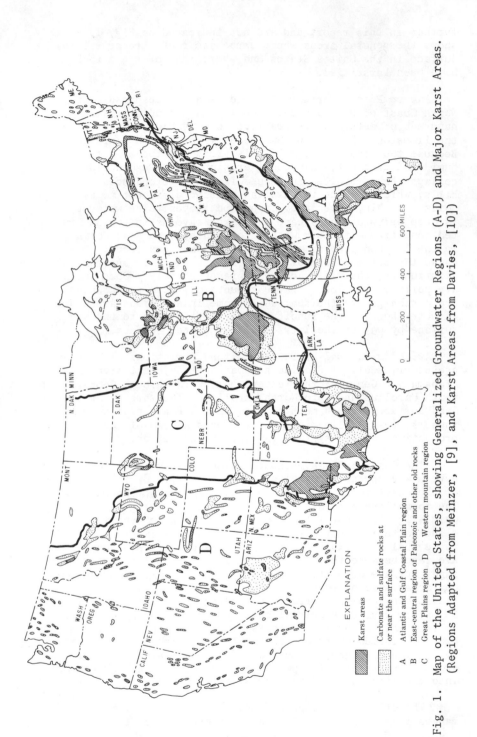

Fig. 1. Map of the United States, showing Generalized Groundwater Regions (A-D) and Major Karst Areas. (Regions Adapted from Meinzer, [9], and Karst Areas from Davies, [10])

EXPLANATION

Karst areas

Carbonate and sulfate rocks at or near the surface

A   Atlantic and Gulf Coastal Plain region
B   East-central region of Paleozoic and other old rocks
C   Great Plains region   D   Western mountain region

0   200   400   600 MILES

about 1500 mm in western Florida, and the rainfall has a
fairly even distribution during each year. The humid conditions, coupled with subdued topography and prevalent sandy
soils, result in high rates of recharge to the limestone and
in a relatively high water table where the limestone is at or
near the ground surface. Consequently, almost all the limestone, considered in aggregate volume, is below the water
table.

A map of the piezometric surface of water in the limestone
aquifer in Florida and Georgia (Fig. 2) indicates the general
direction of movement of water, as well as areas of recharge

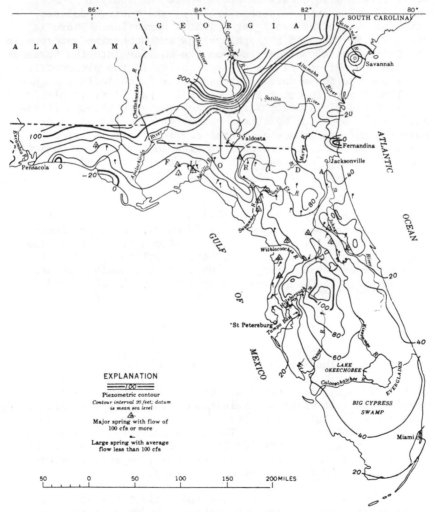

Fig. 2. Piezometric map of Water in the Principal Limestone
Artesian Aquifer, (Stringfield, [13]).

2-7

and discharge. The value of this regional piezometric map was demonstrated by Stringfield [11], who mapped the Florida part, and by Warren [12], who mapped the Georgia part. The current map is based on recent compilations by hydrologists of the U.S. Geological Survey.

In general, water enters the aquifer where the piezometric surface is relatively high and is discharged where the surface is low. The water moves from that general recharge area toward the south and the Atlantic Coast. Much natural discharge occurs offshore. In Florida west of the Suwannee River the general movement of the water is south, toward the Gulf of Mexico. Recharge occurs in areas where the aquifer is near the surface (except in stream valleys) and through dolines which penetrate the overlying Hawthorn Formation. There is discharge to the Gulf through springs and submarine outcrops in the Coastal belt. Discharge from the aquifer into the Suwannee and Santa Fe Rivers causes a large valley in the piezometric surface where these surface streams flow in channels cut into the limestone. In central and north-central Florida; high areas of the piezometric surface show recharge through filled dolines now occupied by lakes. Where the aquifer is at or near the surface in north-central Florida there is large recharge, but the large groundwater flow to the Gulf of Mexico and to the large springs, such as Silver Springs and Rainbow Springs, causes the piezometric surface to stand relatively low.

In the lake region of south-central Florida where the piezometric surface is as much as 30 meters above sea level, the water moves laterally in all directions from this recharge area. Part of the water on the north, northeast, and west is discharged through large springs. To the south, southeast, and southwest the water moves many miles to the coast and beyond.

The karst areas of the Coastal Plain have some assets and some liabilities. The favorable aquifer characteristics are due to high permeability of the limestone coupled with the sand covering near land surface that allows moderate and favorable infiltration of precipitation. It is one of the most productive karst aquifers known (Stringfield and LeGrand, [14]. Some problems of salt-water contamination exist in coastal areas. Problems of pollution near the land surface are less common than in many karst regions. The close interrelations of groundwater levels, river levels, and lake levels in central Florida cause some environmental problems, especially where groundwater levels are lowered by pumping.

Ridge and Valley. The Ridge and Valley province is composed of many tens of separate interior hydrologic systems. The province extends from New York to Alabama. Each system is

elongated northeastward and is characterized by a perennial
stream acting as a groundwater and surface-water drain. The
elongated systems result from structural conditions and the
erosional history of the region. The carbonate rocks are
chiefly of Cambrian and Ordovician age but also of Devonian
and Mississippian age; the entire sequence of carbonate and
clastic rocks have been folded and have been broken by over-
thrust faults. Subsequent erosion, which has removed many
hundreds of meters of rock in some places, has resulted in the
ridge and valley topography, as resistant sandstones form
ridges and carbonate rocks and shales commonly form valleys
of subdued upland slopes. The ridge and valley characteristic
is especially prominent in the northwest part of the province
but is less prominent to the southeast in low subdued topography, such as the Great Valley of Virginia. Some general
features of the province include:

1. There are anticlinal and monoclinal valleys where
carbonate rocks are prominent and synclinal ridges of sandstone.
2. Thin soils and bare rock are common, although thick
cherty soils occur on some formations.
3. Dolines and air-filled caverns are locally common.
4. Generally there is only one major stream in a valley.
Some small streams go into swallow holes and reappear as
resurgencies.
5. There is appreciable recharge from upland slopes of
clastic rocks into lower lying carbonate rocks through dolines
and diffuse seepage.
6. The permeability is of coarse texture as the most
permeable zones represent solution channels, commonly beneath
topographic sags or fracture traces.
7. Permeability decreases exponentially with increasing
depth.
8. The hydrologic system generally does not cross major
ridges and is confined to the drainage basin between two
ridges of clastic rocks. A large cone of depression resulting
from pumping of water from wells may be constricted laterally
between ridges but can spread up or down the valley.
9. Storm water goes underground quickly, and much of
this water discharges as turbid water at large springs in a
day or two.
10. There is a great range in yields of wells--from less
than 1 liter per second to more than 60 liters per second.
Open-end wells are predominant, most of which are deeper than
25 meters but shallower than 100 meters.
11. The hydrologic balance is easily disturbed, especially
in terms of pumping of wells and the decreasing of spring flow.
12. Pollution of spring water and well water is locally
common, as the thin soils and cavernous rocks through which
water moves quickly are not favorable for the removal and
attentuation of pollutants in water.

Central Arched Areas of Tennessee, Kentucky, Missouri. In Tennessee, Kentucky, and Missouri there are separate but somewhat similar karst settings. Each is characterized by a slight structural dome which has brought to the land surface Middle Paleozoic carbonate rocks, concentrically surrounded by younger Paleozoic noncarbonate rocks. The formations have broad outcrop areas before dipping gently beneath younger beds. Topographic relief locally or regionally is not as great as in many karst regions. Dolines abound and cuestas tend to define the boundaries between carbonate and noncarbonate rocks. The climate is temperate and humid. The permeability is unevenly distributed, most of the solution openings lying within 30 meters of the land surface. Streams are fairly scarce, most of the streams being fed by large springs. Soils are generally thin. Many wells are polluted, chiefly because of effluent from septic tanks. Locally, the collapse of land into subsurface caverns forms dolines, which in the more populated areas may create serious problems for houses, roads, and public utilities.

Special hydrologic characteristics of the region include:

(1) Salty water with depth.
(2) Decreasing permeability with depth.
(3) Low average yields of wells.
(4) Key master streams.
(5) Considerable solution at the base of soil zone.
(6) Cuesta topography which results in a water table as deep as 20 to 50 meters beneath uplands near escarpments; the water table in lowlands is rarely deeper than 10 to 15 meters below land surface.

Wisconsin. The dome-shaped Laurentian Shield in north-central Wisconsin is flanked on the southwest, south, and east by plateau-like Paleozoic carbonate rocks. The Niagara Dolomite of Silurian age, as well as the underlying Galena and Prairie du Chien carbonates, have broad surface and shallow subsurface positions and form significant escarpments.

Carbonate rocks form part or all of 2 of the 3 main aquifers in Wisconsin. Pollution is a major consideration in the Door Peninsula where soils on the Niagara Dolomite are quite thin.

Black Hills. Arching in the Black Hills region of western South Dakota has resulted in the elliptical exposure of limestone beds about 200 kilometers long. Slightly tipped and bevelled edges of limestone of the Madison Group of Mississipian Age form a concentric ring around the central crystalline rock core. Consequent streams flowing down dip tend to lose water in the limestone belt. The water is regained through springs where the limestone goes under cover of less soluble beds. Fractures in the limestone have enlarged to the extent that the water table is below the limestone out-crop area, and no streams originate in the limestone. The limestone belt is a good recharge area for the large springs and for the down basin artesian system.

Edwards Plateau and Balcones Fault Zone. Limestone beds of Cretaceous age crop out on the Edwards Plateau of west-central Texas. Both the land surface and the strata extend southward as a gently dipping monocline. Much of the plateau lies above an elevation of 830 meters, especially to the north and west. The Edwards Plateau is mostly semi-arid and covers an area of more than 78,000 square kilometers. Karst topo-graphy is not as fully developed as on many limestone regions of the world, but there are widely scattered shallow basins that are dolines; caverns are fairly common, but there is no extensive and profuse cavern development. The central part of the Edwards Plateau has little relief except along major stream valleys, but along these the limestone forms bold valleyside cliffs. Dissection increases toward the southeast margin of the plateau, and along with it the amount of relief. The ragged Balcones Escarpment, which forms the southeastern boundary of the plateau, is a prominent and striking feature. The Balcones Escarpment separates the Edwards Plateau from the lower-lying Gulf Coastal Plain on the south.

The Edwards limestone aquifer is one of the most important underground reservoirs in the southwestern part of the United States. The limestone aquifer system is especially prolific in the Balcones fault zone, which is a belt about 29 kilometers long and extends westward and eastward from an area several miles north of San Antonio. Several west-trending normal faults have lowered the limestone to the south against over-lying less permeable beds to the extent that coastward move-ment of water in the limestone south of the fault zone is obstructed. Along the fault zone the limestone is sufficiently permeable because of faulting and fracturing of the rock to allow downward leakage of streamflow; this leakage provides recharge that makes the aquifer especially productive. Move-ment of water along this fault zone tends to be eastward, and much discharge occurs at such springs as San Antonio, San Pedro, Hueco, Comal, and San Marcos. The large development of groundwater in the Balcones fault zone has caused concern about the relation of surface to underground water and has led to the formation of the Edwards Underground Water District, created in 1959, to conserve and manage the water for the best interest of the region (Green, [15]).

The Pecos Valley of New Mexico. The Pecos River drainage basin, extending southward through east-central New Mexico and into Texas, does not appear to be extensively karstified if

viewed from above the ground. Yet, the volume of soluble
material that has been removed by solution has been considerable. The Pecos River cuts into Triassic and Permian rocks
that have a gently eastward dip. Rocks of several formations
change laterally according to their depositional environment,
limestone, dolomite, and anhydrite being prevalent. Westward
from the Pecos River the land rises somewhat gradually until
peaks of the Guadalupe Mountains are reached, where reef
limestone is boldly exposed at elevations greater than 2,500
meters. The climate is semi-arid, and rocks denuded of soil
abound everywhere, although a broad belt of alluvium borders
the river and covers low reentrants into the canyoned upland
areas.

Much of the solution in the evaporite beds has been along
the bedding planes, especially west of the river where the land
surface crudely parallels both the dip slope and the gross movement of groundwater. Some of the evaporite beds west of the
river have been removed by sheet-like solution, but the extent
of lowering of land surface by this solution is not easy to
distinguish from lowering caused by physical erosion. Vertical
permeability does not appear to be well developed in the
evaporites.

Dolines are not common in the Guadalupe Mountains, and one
must look underground, as in Carlsbad Caverns, to see the
effects of solution in the limestone.

Groundwater tends to flow eastward from beneath the
Guadalupe Mountains toward the Pecos River, and the river is
a discharge area for much of the moving water. A combination
of factors, including good dipslope permeability and relatively
easy means for water to discharge into the Pecos River, has
resulted in good circulation of potable water in the upper part
of the zone of saturation west of the river. Wells tapping
the artesian aquifer of Permian limestones originally had
considerable head, and one had a natural flow in 1926 of 360
liters per second. The water levels have since declined,
chiefly because of withdrawal of water for irrigation.

Kaibab Plateau in Northern Arizona. Limestone of Permian
age occurs on a north-south trending arch near the Grand
Canyon. Overlying Triassic and Jurassic beds have been stripped off to expose the limestone on this north-trending arch.

On the Kaibab Plateau are north-trending interior valleys
called parks. These are believed by Strahler [16] and by
these writers to be former solution valleys developed when the
climate was more humid. The climate is now arid to sub-humid.

Nevada. Limestones are exposed in some of the mountains
in Nevada. These Paleozoic limestones also underlie some

basin-fill alluvium. The topography is of the basin and range type, in which fault-block structures are common. Fracturing of the limestone has been generally good, leading to fairly good permeability. Dolines are not common but fractures are enlarged by solution.

A few large springs occur. An unusual feature of the region is the movement of water in the carbonate rocks laterally beneath the mountain ranges.

Karst topographic features are in general not evident. The water table is very deep in most places, and streams are rare. The general problems are those of arid lands.

4. Problems Related to Hydrology.

In karst regions, the circulation of water and solution of the rock by circulating water tend to accentuate the cause and effect relations of the water and of the host rock. Practical problems having some relation to hydrology of karst are common and complex. One or more of the following problems are likely to exist.

Undesirable topography. Erosional degradation of carbonate formations carried to an advanced stage results in dolines and other locally depressed features and in many cases to residual positive elements such as mounds and hills. Such karst topography can be obstructive to many of man's land surface activities. In contrast with other karst regions of the world, the United States does not have rugged karst topography; a small area of Puerto Rico does have distinctive dolines and mogotes.

Instability of the ground. Removal of dissolved mineral matter by circulating groundwater results in underground cavities that weaken the structure of the rock. Dolines are minifestations of past subsidence of the ground, but land subsidence may not follow the development of solution cavities. Even though cavities exist in the underlying carbonates, it is impossible to predict the amount of related subsidence of the ground surface. Such activities of man as heavy structural loading and excessive pumpage of water from wells may cause subsidence of the ground. Problems of land subsidence are common where soil and other unconsolidated materials overlie cavities, such as in eastern United States.

Scarcity of perennial surface streams. In maturely developed karst terranes the development of cavities underground, resulting in an increase in permeability, causes the water table to recede--even below the level of some surface streams. Thus, some of the surface streams *go underground*.

The scarcity of surface streams may cause problems of water supply and waste disposal.

Insufficient soils. Many carbonate formations are relatively pure, resulting in almost no insoluble residue after the rocks near the land surface are removed by solution. Thus, little soil may form, and that which does form is removed easily by surface wash. Residual soils on many karst formations are thin or absent.

Mineralized water. A common feature of most karst regions is the zonation of low- and high-mineralized water, fresher water generally overlying saltier water. Also, in coastal regions less mineralized water may be in contact with sea water. In many cases the pumping of fresh water may cause salt-water contamination.

Undesirable permeability. Some carbonate rocks contain very few openings through which water can move and are essentially impermeable; at the other extreme are some karstified rocks that contain many openings capable of transmitting water with almost no resistance. The poorly permeable rocks, of course, are poor aquifers; those having extremely high permeability may have the disadvantage of having a water table so low (a) that storage of water underground is slight or (b) that water of poor quality underlies a thin freshwater zone.

Unreliable waste-disposal environment. Although in some places wastes may be disposed to the ground in karst terranes without fear of contamination of groundwater, karst terranes in general are not considered ideal places for disposal of wastes to the ground. Where soils are thin or absent the contaminants may reach the groundwater without attenuating sufficiently, and where permeability is great the contaminants may move readily through the rock with little attenuation. Moreover, the erratic movement of water in many places in karst formations prevents a satisfactory knowledge of the direction of movement of water and of contaminants that might be with it.

5. Conclusions.

A review of the karst regions of the United States indicates a broad range in topographic and hydrologic features. These features can be considered in terms of the following factors that caused them: climate, structure, topography, and permeability.

Karsts in the eastern half of the United States are exposed to a humid temperate climate; soils and also surface streams are more common here than in the less humid western karsts, and in fact somewhat more common than in many other humid karst regions of the world.

Most of the karst regions are on slight structural arches or represent homoclinal plains; exceptions are the folded Ridge and Valley Province of the east and the block faulted carbonate rocks of Nevada in the west.

In contrast to the rugged karst of the Mediterranean region and the steep-sloped mogote karst of some tropical regions, the topography of most U.S. karst regions is subdued. Dolines and solution valleys are common, but many are draped with soil and represent sags in the topography. In contrast to many karst regions also is the fact that the carbonate rocks are less resistant to erosion than the clastic rocks and tend to underlie valleys rather than ridges in the humid east; the plateau karsts that are widespread on the slight structural arches are characterized by escarpments above which are clastics and below which are the less resistant karst rocks.

Most of the karst areas are underlain by dense carbonate rocks that have varying degrees of fractures. The fractures are enlarged by solution where they are in the groundwater circulation system, generally in the fluctuating zone of the water table and a slight distance below it. The Tertiary limestone system of the Atlantic Coastal Plain and younger limestones of southern Florida have more open pore spaces that are not altogether confined to fractures. These two karst systems have some discharge of fresh water to the sea, but all other U.S. karst regions are interior and have discharge to perennial streams. Some tributary streams have typical losing and gaining karst characteristics.

6. References.

[1] LaMoreaux, P.E., Raymond, D., and Joiner, T.J., Hydrology of limestone terranes, annotated bibliography of carbonate rocks: Geol. Survey of Alabama Bull. 94 (A), 242 p, 1970.

[2] Herak, M., and Stringfield, V.T., Eds., Karst, important regions of the northerm hemisphere: Amsterdam, Elsevier Pub. Co., 551 p, 1972.

[3] Sweeting, M.M., Karst landforms: London MacMillan, 362 p, 1972.

[4] Jennings, J.N., Karst, M.I.T. Press, Cambridge, Mass., 252 p, 1972.

[5] International Association of Scientific Hydrology, Hydrology of fractured rocks: Proc. Dubrovnik Symp., 1965, v. 1 and 2, Int. Assoc. Sci. Hydrol. Gentbrugge, 689 p, 1967.

[6] Grund, Alfred, Der Geographische Zyklus im karst: Zeitschs. der Gesellschraft fur Erdkunde zu Berlin, p. 621-640, 1914.

[7]   Cvijic, Jovan, The evolution of lapies: A study in karst
      physiography: Geog. Rev., v. 14, p. 26-49, 1924.

[8]   White, W.B., Conceptual models for carbonate aquifers:
      Groundwater, v. 7, no. 3, 7 p, 1969.

[9]   Meinzer, O.E., Groundwater in the United States, a summary
      of groundwater conditions and resources, utilization
      of water from wells and springs, methods of scientific
      investigation, and literature relating to the subject: U.S.
      Geol. Survey Water-Supply Paper 836-D, p. 157-232, 1939.

[10] Davies, W.E., Map of karst areas, in National Atlas of
      the United States of America: U.S. Geol. Survey, p. 77,
      1970.

[11] Stringfield, V.T., Artesian water in the Florida Peninsula:
      U.S. Geol. Survey Water-Supply Paper 773-C, p. 115-195,
      1936.

[12] Warren, M.A., Artesian water in southeastern Georgia, with
      special reference to the coastal area: Georgia Geol.
      Survey Bull. 49, 140 p, 1944.

[13] Stringfield, V.T., Artesian water in the Tertiary lime-
      stone in the southeastern states: U.S. Geol. Survey Prof.
      Paper 517, 226 p, 1966.

[14] Stringfield, V.T., and LeGrand, H.W., Hydrology of lime-
      stone terranes in the Coastal Plain of the southeastern
      United States: Geol. Soc. America Special Paper 93, 46 p,
      1966.

[15] Green, M.G., Artificial recharge to the Edwards Limestone
      aquifer in south Texas: in Hydrology of fractured rocks,
      Proc. Dubrovnik Symp. 1965, v. 2, p. 465-481, 1967.

[16] Strahler, A.N., Valleys and parks of the Kaibab and
      Coconino Plateaus, Arizona: Jour. Geology, v. 52, no. 6,
      p. 361-387, 1944.

ON THE NATURE AND SIGNIFICANCE OF FRACTURE TRACES AND LINEAMENTS IN CARBONATE AND OTHER TERRANES

by

Richard R. Parizek
Professor of Hydrogeology and Assistant Director,
Mineral Conservation Section,
The Pennsylvania State University
University Park, Pennsylvania, USA

Synopsis. Fracture traces and lineaments observed largely on stereo paired, high altitude, black and white and colored aerial photographs and photo mossaics have been the subject of studies in North America since about 1950. Early studies were concerned with their potential application to oil and gas and mineral exploration, structural analysis at the local and regional scale and by 1960 to groundwater exploration and to various geotechnical and geomorphic investigations. The utility of fracture traces has been demonstrated for carbonate and other rocks and is reviewed here. This prospecting technique is receiving increased application worldwide. Only with the added platforms of observation afforded by U-2 overflights, LANDSAT (ERTS-1) and SKYLAB has it been possible to map lineaments in excess of 5 to 150 km in length on a consistent basis in all terranes.

Evidence for establishing the analogous relationship between fracture traces and major lineaments in defining increased zones of permeability and porosity development for carbonate and other rocks is presented. Thirty-seven water wells tested for yield under controlled conditions and under known construction and geologic conditions were ranked by lineament and nonlineament location for the same lithologic unit. A one km width was assumed for structure controlling lineaments compared with a 5 to 40 foot width for fracture traces. Wells were located in upland, valley wall and valley bottom settings with similar bedrock dips, on and off fracture traces and fracture trace intersections, and yields adjusted for well depth.

Yield probability plots show that both lineament and nonlineament wells can be highly productive particularly when the penetrate zones of fracture concentration revealed by fracture traces. However, lineament wells were more consistent in yield and displayed less yield variability for the same setting. The maximum, minimum and 50 percent yield values were 9.3, 0.002, and 0.3 gpm/ft/foot of saturated rock penetrated for lineament wells compared with 2.2, 0.003, and 0.07 gpm/ft/ft for nonlineament wells. These data together with other observations presented proves that a positive benefit can be derived

when selecting well sites or attempting to locate zones of
increased weathering by combining both fracture trace intersections with lineament and lineament intersections where ever
possible. The density and distribution of lineaments and fracture traces are such that their controlling structures are
within easy reach of most population centers, hence should be
used for water supply exploration, waste management and
geotechnical investigations.

1.   Introduction.

Fracture traces (lineaments less than 1.5 km in length)
have been mapped for the purpose of locating zones of increased
weathering, porosity, and permeability development within bedrock under a wide variety of geological settings. Fracture
traces are known to reveal narrow zones (2 to 20 meters wide)
suitable for groundwater prospecting, high permeability and
porosity avenues 10 to 1,000 times that of adjacent strata
where water can escape from below dams, from lagoons and reservoirs. They define flood and roof stability hazard areas within mines, tunnels and quarries, landslide prone areas, and
areas of potential foundation instabilities.

Lineaments in excess of 1 km and up to 150 km in length
are far more numerous than hitherto for been recognized [1].
They are analogous in all respects. An attempt is made to
describe their nature and the potential application of lineaments in groundwater and geotechnical studies, with emphasis on
carbonate rocks. Significant literature on fracture traces is
reviewed.

Fracture traces and lineaments appear to be universal in
their distribution and will have their greatest utility in
rocks where secondary permeability and porosity dominate and
where intergranular characteristics combine with secondary
openings influencing weathering, and soil-water and groundwater
movement.

2.   Lineaments Developed Within Bedrock.

Lineaments owe their expression to aligned surface sags
and depressions, gaps in ridges, soil tonal changes revealing
variations in soil moisture, aligned springs, seeps, and
perched surface ponds, alignments in vegetation, in vegetation
type and height changes, straight stream and valley segments,
abrupt changes in valley alignment, and gully development.
These surface features help to reveal zones of fracture concentration within bedrock even when blanketed by residual and
transported soils in excess of 95 m in thickness. Linear
features have been classified in various ways. Those believed
to be underlain by nearly vertical zones of fracture

concentration expressed continuously for slightly more than 1 km in length but generally in excess of 300 to 600 m in length were defined as a *photogeologic fracture trace or fracture trace* [2]. Those greater than one mile (>1 km) are termed *lineaments*. More recently, it was recognized [1] the tentative groupings of lineaments as mapped on ERTS-1 (now referred to as LANDSAT-1) images that are measured in kilometers, to tens of kilometers to in excess of 150 km in length.

Previous work. A considerable amount of work has been done to date to establish the nature and significance of fracture traces and to apply this knowledge to groundwater exploration and foundation engineering and related studies. These investigations were reviewed by Siddiqui [3] and Parizek [4,5] and are highlighted below.

Surface lineations observed on aerial photographs have been studied by Kaiser [6], Blanchet [7], Mollard [8,9], Kupsch and Wild [10], Lattman [2], Lattman and Nickelson [11], Hough [12], Meisler [13], Lattman and Parizek [14], Parizek and Drew [15], Lattman and Segovia [16], Lattman and Matzke [17], Keim [18], Boyer and McQueen [19], Setzer [20], Wobber [21], Calkins [22], Trainer [23], Trainer and Ellison [24], Deike [25], Parizek [26], Parizek and Voight [27], Brown and Parizek [28], Parizek [4,5], Siddiqui [3], Lovell and Gunnett [29], Brown and Lambert [46], Cline [47], Gwinn [48], Hamilton [49], Howard [50], Kayne [51], Mandel [52], Stringfield and Le Grand [53], Thomas [54], Weise [55], and others.

Fracture traces and lineaments are frequently straight in plan, unaffected by topography, hence are considered surface manifestations of vertical to near-vertical zones of fracture concentration [9,12,14,27,4] as shown in Figs. 1 and 2(a). In carbonate terranes, surface sags and depressions smaller than 1-3 m deep may develop along fracture traces or open sinkholes 3 to over 20 m deep may occur. The width of these depressions appears to vary with the thickness of weathered mantle above bedrock, degree of weathering and the width of the zone of fracture concentration. Calkins [22] found that fracture traces in granite represent linear depressions smaller than 1-2.7 m deep and 5 to 66.6 m wide. The author has measured zones from 3 to over 33.3 m wide in various rock types in the United States, locally has found zones 2 to 20 m wide in folded and faulted rocks of the Central Appalachian region. In siltstones and shales of northeastern Pennsylvania they varied from 3 to over 20 m wide, and averaged 13 m and were slightly inclined, 2 to 3 degrees from vertical [4]. Individual joints may be closely spaced, 5 to over 60 in number, subparallel to parallel, and cut all beds equally well, or be concentrated in

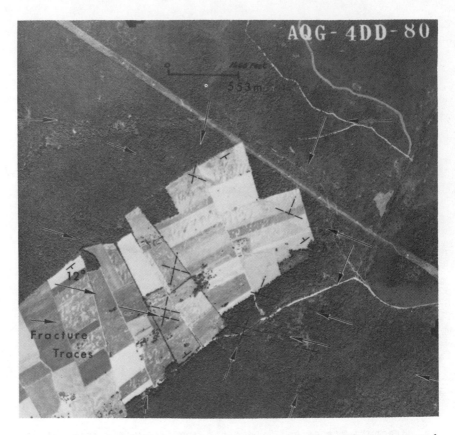

Fig. 1. Fracture Traces Expressed on 5 to 80 m of Transported
        Soils Developed on Faulted and Faulted Dolomite,
        Sandy Dolomite and Limestone of Cambrian and
        Ordovician Age, Centre County, Pennsylvania. Swell
        and Swail Topography Obvious in Cultivated Areas
        Reflect Differential Weathering Along Joints,
        Fractures, Bedding Planes, Zones of Fracture Concen-
        tration and the Intersection of Two or More of These
        Features, from Parizek [26].

selected bedrock units when viewed in cross section, and poorly
developed to scant in number in overlying and underlying units.

Five or more distinct high-angle joints have been observed
under fracture traces in limestone and dolomite bedrock in the
Central Appalachian area (Fig. 2(b)). At other sites, bedrock
contained hundreds of joints that were so closely spaced and
intersecting so as to impart a shattered appearance to the rock.

The width and depth of bedrock weathering underlying
fracture traces varies with rock type and regional setting.

Fig. 2.   Slightly Inclined Zone of Fracture Concentration
Within Siltstone and Shale of Devonian Age, Siver
Thread Falls of East Central Pennsylvania (a) Within
the Stone Henge Limestone of Ordovician Age, (Upper
Photo), (b) And Highly Fractured Nittany Dolomite of
Ordovician Age, (Lower Photo). In (a) Joints Are Well
Developed, Cut All Beds Nearly Equally and Dip Approx-
imately 87 to 89°. In (b) Joints Are Few in Number,
Some Cut All Beds Exposed, Others Only Single Beds
[4,5].

The character of drill cuttings, well-yield and caliper log
data obtained from wells completed 66 to 166 m deep in interbedded dolomites and sandy dolomite of Cambrian and Ordovician
age suggest that weathering may extend laterally for 66 to 93 m
along bedding planes and within selected beds of some carbonate
rocks. In fresh granite, metamorphic rocks, sandstone, shale,
siltstone, and other rocks weathering may extend but a few
inches or less beyond the zone of fracture concentration.

Application to hydrologic and engineering studies.
Lattman and Parizek [14] established the important relationship
between the occurrence of groundwater and fracture traces for
carbonate aquifers, and in particular that fracture traces are
underlain by zones of localized weathering, increased permeability and porosity.

Meisler [13] was unsuccessful in correlating high well
yields and well locations with respect to fracture trace sites
in carbonate rocks in Lebanon Valley, near Harrisburg,
Pennsylvania, and Meiser in 1975 obtained similar results for
carbonate rocks near Altoona, Pennsylvania. This should be due
to the fact that most wells ranked as on fracture traces were
not close enough to their center lines, and hence showed no
significant increase in yield; fracture traces were not mapped
correctly; or their width of influence was not known. An
alternate explanation that they are not of value in prospecting
is rejected because the method has been applied successfully by
others in their study areas.

Setzer [20] studied fracture traces and well yields in
Sao Paulo, Brazil and reported but did not document a favorable
relationship between well location and yield. Wobber [21] suggested that fracture traces may be useful in locating zones of
increased permeability in bedrock in Illinois overlain by
glacial drift. He found an association between fracture trace
orientations, and that of bedrock joints buried by up to 50 m
of drift.

Parizek and Drew [15] mapped fracture traces in a greater
than 27 km^2 carbonate area near State College, Pennsylvania
(Fig. 3). Three models were assumed to determine the probable
success of randomly located wells drilled in that area. Zones
of fracture concentration were assumed to be 8.3 m wide and as
long and as numerous as mapped, 16.6 m wide and as numerous as
observed, and twice as numerous and 16.6 m wide. Expectable
yields at fracture trace intersections or single fracture
traces, and at interfracture trace areas were assumed based on
well-yield data obtained locally, and the probability of penetrating each setting determined using a computer, and
expectation equation.

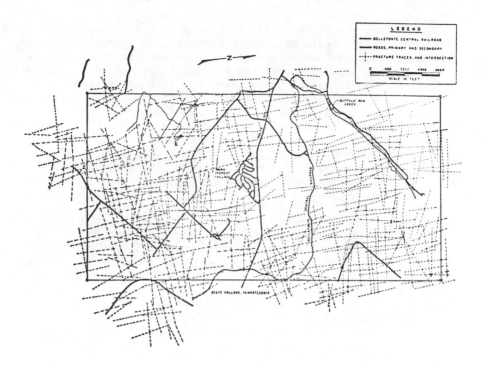

Fig. 3. Fracture Trace Density Within Folded and Faulted
         Cambrian and Ordovician Aged Carbonate Rocks, Centre
         County, Pennsylvania. Bedrock Strike Is to the
         Northeast, from Parizek and Drew [15].

     Probability plots were obtained not unlike ones observed
using actual well-yield data collected later. The need to map
and protect potential high-capacity well sites in advance of
urban and industrial sprawl was stressed because criteria for
the recognition of fracture traces are readily obscured even by
minor changes in landscape.

     Cline and Parizek [30] showed that fracture traces could
be used to locate high capacity wells in folded siltstones,
shales, and sandstones within the east Mahantango Creek Watershed of east-central Pennsylvania. No association between well
yields and fracture traces was found when fracture trace widths
were assumed to be 13.3 m. Later, data collected by Parizek
showed that 10.4 m width for the zone of fracture concentration
is a better approximation for the region. Ten fracture trace
intersections were mapped by Parizek, wells drilled and tested
for yield by Cline, with the result that a positive
relationship was found [30].

Parizek and Voight [27] and Parizek [26,4] showed that fracture traces could be used in geotechnical investigations to predict zones of increased weathering in advance of foundation exploration; areas of potential roof collapse and excess water in mining and tunneling operations; and leakage beneath dams and into excavations within bedrock. Zones of fracture concentration also could be mapped to account for seepage pressure variations, risk of blowouts and piping, and strength variations within bedrock. Detailed knowledge of the significance and distribution of zones of fracture concentration also is useful in planning, designing, and conducting grout or cut-off wall operations, and in locating highly-effective pressure and drainage wells.

The most complete study of the relationship among well yields and other well hydraulic and geologic factors in Cambrian and Ordovician-Aged, folded shale, limestone, dolomite, and sandy dolomite aquifers was conducted by Siddiqui and Parizek in central Pennsylvania and was reported upon by Siddiqui [3] and Siddiqui and Parizek [31,32]. They classified water wells for which controlled pumping test data were acquired according to their hydrogeological setting to establish which, among many possible geologic variables contributed to the yield of wells, hence groundwater occurrence and movement in folded and faulted sedimentary rocks with emphasis on carbonate rocks. Secondary openings predominate in their control of groundwater movement in their study region.

Fracture zones form an interlaced highly transmissive network (Fig. 3) in most terranes; serve as local groundwater feeder-routes from more massive blocks of rock in interfracture areas; and supply water to more-regional conduits, which in turn may be localized by these same features (Fig. 4).

Parizek [5], Koppe and Thompson [33], Lovell and Gunnett [29] showed how fracture traces could be used in controlling and abating mine drainage produced from deep coal mines, how they relate to mine seals, and groundwater inflow to mines.

Whether similar relationships exist for lineaments observed on LANDSAT (LANDSAT has been adopted in replacement of ERTS.) and SKYLAB images that are in excess of ten's of kilometers in length still must be more adequately established. Some of the control points used by Siddiqui and Parizek [31,32] are located on linear features in excess of one kilometer in length, hence, are lineaments by Lattman's [2] definition.

The problem with lineaments. The topographic expression of some linear features are sufficiently well developed to allow them to be distinguished on oblique aerial views. The majority are indistinguishable on the ground even after

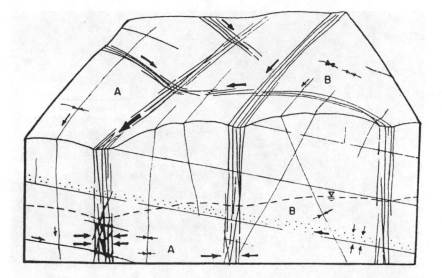

Fig. 4. Massive Blocks of Carbonate Rock Interlaced With
High Avenues of Permeability Development Along Zones
of Fracture Concentration. Transmission and Storage
Properties Afforded by Intergranular and Vugular
Openings Within Selected Beds, Bedding Plane Partings,
Joints and Fault Zones, from Parizek [4].

prolonged field work and detailed analysis of underflight
photos. The significance of landforms that reveal lineaments
can be appreciated, however, after the lineament has been
detected in advance on images.

This problem of optimum scale of view, and elevation of
vantage point has been all but eliminated through the LANDSAT-1
and SKYLAB programs. Hundreds of lineaments of various lengths
are now mapped for Pennsylvania where previously only a few
were known; compare Gold, Parizek and Alexander [1] with Koppe
and Thompson [33] (Fig. 5). Of the number of questions that
remain unanswered concerning the nature and significance to
groundwater; (1) The nature of the structural features that
underlie lineaments, their width and depth and the genetic
relation of lineaments and other structures of larger and
smaller scale must be established. (2) Lineaments observed on
LANDSAT and SKYLAB images must be accurately located on the
ground to allow direct observation and use in field studies,
and (3) Their significance to geological and engineering
applications must be further established under controlled
conditions rather than by inference.

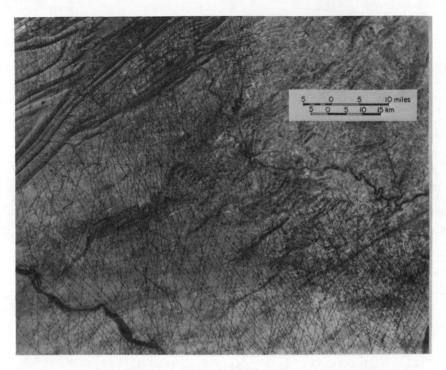

Fig. 5.   Mega Lineaments of Pennsylvania Mapped on LANDSAT-1
Images, from Gold, Parizek and Alexander [1].

Many factors combine to influence well yields at a
particular location (well radius, well depth and diameter,
casing length, method of drilling, degree of well development,
depth to water table, presence of various changes of rock type,
dip of beds, topographic setting, rock type, type of fold
structure, presence and type of joints, faults, number and type
of zones of fracture concentration, etc.). Comparison of
yields of but a few wells on or off a lineament will not
suffice to establish a significant relationship even though a
strong inference may have been established. Similar variables
influence depth and extent of weathering and permeability
development of importance in engineering foundation studies,
mine and tunnel roof stability analyses, and similar other
investigations.

Optional procedure. Strong conclusions have been drawn in
this paper that relate lineaments to zones of increased
permeability and porosity development in bedrock. A fool proof
determination has been made using LANDSAT-1 and SKYLAB imagery
and controlled pumping test data. This was attempted using
intermediate levels of data obtained from SKYLAB, U-2, and
underflights by transferring or matching lineaments mapped on

LANDSAT-1 and SKYLAB images with their mapped or transferred
locations on photographs taken from U-2 or lower altitudes
(Fig. 6,a,b,c,d). Lineaments initially mapped on LANDSAT-1
images can be transferred to the ground with sufficient
accuracy by this procedure to allow well control points to be
ranked as being on or off lineaments, and direct field observations.

Fig. 6(a). Operational Procedure for Mapping Lineaments and
           Fracture Traces. Megalineament Map of Pennsylvania,
           Plotted on a Mosaic Base of Channel 7 LANDSAT-1
           Images. The dashed Lines Represent Known Faults
           Which Exhibit Displayments on this Scale. The
           Physiographic Provinces-the Allegheny Plateau to
           the North and West, the Curved Appalachian Folded
           Belt Through the Central Section, and the Piedmont
           and Coastal Plain to the Southeast-Show up Well.
           The Dark Crescent-Like Area in the North-Eastern
           Part of the State is the Anthracite Coal Basin
           Around Scranton and Wilkes-Barre. Lake Erie and
           the Atlantic Ocean are Shown. (After Gold, Parizek,
           Alexander, [1]).

   Joint density studies beneath lineaments are underway
along ridges crests of Bald Eagle Mountain, Centre County,
Pennsylvania (D. Krohn, in progress). His observed widths of
fracture concentration are being used in the extrapolation.

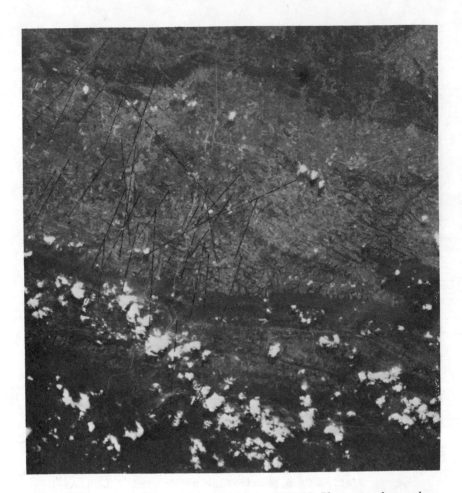

Fig. 6(b). Lineaments are Mapped on SKYLAB Photographs and
Transferred from LANDSAT Images. Individual
Fields, Roads, Bridges, Buildings and Woodlots can
be used for Field Location.

However, the width of the structural zone controlling the
surface expression of lineaments, may indeed, vary from rock
type to rock type within immediately adjacent areas and time
will be required to find favorable circumstances to determine
if variations do exist. The sparcity of outcrops and nearly
ubiquitous cover of residual and transported soil in the humid
eastern U.S. requires that widths measured for one rock type
be extrapolated to adjacent rocks in this initial work. Proof
of the application of lineaments to groundwater prospecting is
offered here for wells completed in folded and faulted dolomites
comprising one formation and folded siltstone, sandstone and shale.

Fig. 6(c).   Fracture Traces and Shorter Lineaments are Mapped
             on Stereo-Paired Aerial Photographs on 1:12,500
             to 1:20,000 Scale Longer Lineaments are Transferred
             From SKYLAB Photographs.

3.   Significant Results.

   Relationship between lineaments and topography. Fracture
traces and lineaments are commonly straight, unaffected by
topography, and hence are considered surface manifestations of
vertical to near-vertical zones of fracture concentrations
(Mollard [8,9], Hough [12], Lattman and Parizek [14], Parizek
and Voight [27], Parizek [4,5], Siddiqui and Parizek [31,32]).
In the ridge and valley province of the Appalachians, for
example, lineaments have been mapped above folded bedrock where
dips are vertical.   There is no evidence of offset of beds on
either side of a fracture trace or lineament, even when beds
are thin, distinct, and relatively well exposed.   The same is
true where fracture zones are observed in cross-section.

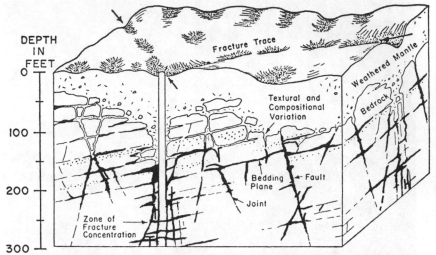

DEPTH IN FEET

(After Lattman and Parizek 1964)

Fig. 6(d). Individual Fracture Trace Intersections and
Lineaments are Field Mapped and Test Well Sites
Staked. The Block Diagram Shows Other Geological
Factors that Favor Weathering and Secondary
Permeability Development (Joints, Bedding Plane
Partings, Faults, Beds with Intergranular Perme-
ability, Etc.).

Parizek [4] and others have observed that fracture traces may
be underlain by relatively few closely spaced joints that cut
one or more beds but not overlying or underlying beds or they
may cut all beds exposed at a given location or they may be
underlain by hundreds of closely spaced fractures that give
the rock a brecciated appearance.

Gold, Parizek, and Alexander [1] reported that lineaments
observed on LANDSAT-1 have the same morphological characteristics as fracture traces except they are longer, appear wider,
are not at all obvious in the field, and exert a major influence on topography. Most lineaments are straight, some
appear to be gently curved and appear to be independent of
regional structural trends.

It may be seen from careful examinations of lineaments on
LANDSAT or SKYLAB images that one of the most pronounced
expression of lineaments results from the alignment of topographic features that reveal valley development, wind and
water gaps, upland sags and depressions, aligned valley segments
of both tributary drainages and master streams and rivers, and
aligned field and woodland boundaries that terminate along
steeper valley slopes. Their anology with fracture traces is

striking with the exception that topographic features associated with lineaments are on a larger and more pronounced scale.

The importance of fracture traces and their significant
control on valley development has been stressed by Parizek
[4,5]. Other controls were also reviewed that include the
interaction of rock type, fold structure, fracture traces and
other structures. It has been shown, for example, that
selected straight valley segments particularly for smaller
tributary valleys are controlled by zones of fracture concentration. These valleys show abrupt to nearly right angle
turns at fracture trace intersections which produces an
apparent meander pattern for youthful, incised valleys (Fig. 7).
Parizek [4] states that from 50-90 percent of selected stream
segments can be shown to be localized by these features in
carbonate valleys in the Central Appalachian Mountain region.
This is particularly evident along headwater tributaries where
the initial control for valley location is still apparent.
In adjacent uplands, solution along zones of fracture concentration allow for subsidence of unconsolidated (residual and transported) soils and produces lines of shallow depressions smaller
than 1 to over 3 m deep... New tributary drainages are
developed adjacent to valley walls as runoff becomes integrated.
New straight valley segments are born in this manner. To a
lesser degree, master joint sets control the same process and
together with zones of intersecting fracture concentrations
and bedding plane openings, they produce irregular offsets in
the new tributaries (Fig. 8).

Lineaments in excess of one but generally less than ten
km in length recognized prior to the LANDSAT program also
show similar controls on valley development. Lineaments
greater than 10 to more than 100 km in length recognized only
recently on LANDSAT images show identical relationships and
it appears safe to conclude that they control valley development for the same reason that shorter lineaments, fracture
traces, and fault zones do, namely, lineaments are underlain
by zones of fracture concentration, hence also must control
secondary permeability and porosity development as has been
established for fracture traces.

The anitquity of structures that underlie lineaments is
inferred by the fact that they are impressed across rocks of
many ages in Pennsylvania and elsewhere, they transect local
fold and fault structures and mountain uplifts of known and
varied ages, they appear to have preferred orientations with
mountain belts hence, should be genetically related to them,
and they appear to control the location of known ore bodies
that formed in more deeply buried environments in rocks of
diverse age. These same structures also must have served as
zones of increased permeability in the past. The relationship
between lineaments and structure, association of lineaments

62

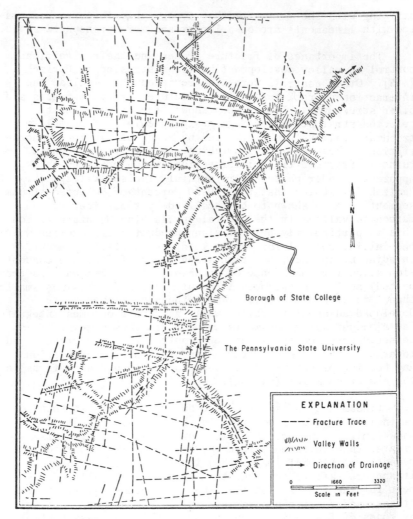

Fig. 7. Valley Development Localized by Zones of Fracture
Concentration with Folded Limestone and Dolomite
of Cambrian and Ordovician Age, Centre, County,
Pennsylvania. From Parizek [4].

and zones of fracture concentration that must be vertical to
near vertical to be expressed as straight lines tens of kilometers in length, and their established control on valley
development led Gold, Parizek, and Alexander [1] to conclude
that structures that underlie lineaments tend to permanently
fix master drainages in a vertical plane. This *permanency of
drainage position principle* must be relaxed in practice because
mechanisms of stream piracy and the changing surface position
of inclined beds of varying resistance must cause spatial

3-16

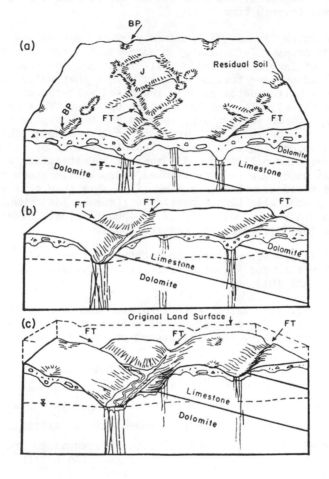

Fig. 8. Valley Development Localized Along Strike of Exposed
Limestone but Later Incised into Underlying Gently
Dipping Dolomite. In (a) Differential Weathering
Along Bedding Planes (BP), Joints (J), and Zones of
Fracture Concentration (Ft.) Produce Surface Sags
and Depressions that Concentrate Surface Runoff,
Facilitates Infiltration and Erosion of Residual
Soils. In (b) Weathering and Erosion are Enhanced
Along Soluable Limestone and a Master Drainage System
is Fixed in its Position. Increased Runoff Facilitates
Infiltration, Solution of Underlying Bedrock and
Erosion Until Groundwater Drains are Established. In
(c) the Land Surface is Lowered and the Valley is
Incised into less Soluable Dolomite Bedrock. From
Parizek [4].

shifts in master stream position as the landsurface is lowered or raised through time.

Fracture traces and lineaments: Their control on ground-water movement: Influence of topography. A second observation is of importance here. Well-yield data obtained under controlled pumping test conditions reveal that wells located in valley bottom settings show increased well-yields when compared with wells located in adjacent uplands. This general rule applies to sedimentary, igneous and metamorphic rocks alike in a wide range of hydrogeological settings. This conclusion is considered a basic principle because of its seamingly universal application. A number of investigators working in areas underlain by consolidated bedrock have shown that the average yield of wells in valleys is higher than that of wells at topographically higher positions (LeGrand [34], Mundorff [35], Dingman and Meyer [36], Poth [37], Johnston [38], Siddiqui and Parizek [31,32], Cline and Parizek [30]).

Yield frequency graphs and statistical analysis of data sets show this for selected sites in Pennsylvania and elsewhere (Figs. 9 and 10).

Productivity values were tabulated and each wells' relative frequency (or percentage) of wells with productivity equal to or greater than the stated value was computed by:

$$P_m = [m/(N_w + 1)] \, 100 \qquad (1)$$

where m = the order number of a well; N_w = the total number of wells falling within that hydrogeological setting; P_m = the percent of wells whose productivities are equal to or greater than the productivity of well number m. The merits of this plotting technique are reviewed by Siddiqui and Parizek [31].

The fact that wells located in valley bottom settings show higher yields than wells located on adjacent uplands and that many valleys are controlled by structural features that manifest themselves as fracture traces and lineaments does not in itself prove lineaments and fracture traces reveal the location of zones of higher bedrock permeability and porosity. Rather, the relationship between increased well-yields and fracture traces and lineaments must first be established on an independent basis because other factors contribute to well yields in valley settings.

Parizek [4] outlined a variety of ways in which permeability and porosity development would tend to be enhanced for carbonate rocks located in the valley bottom setting when compared with the same rock, located beneath a topographic high

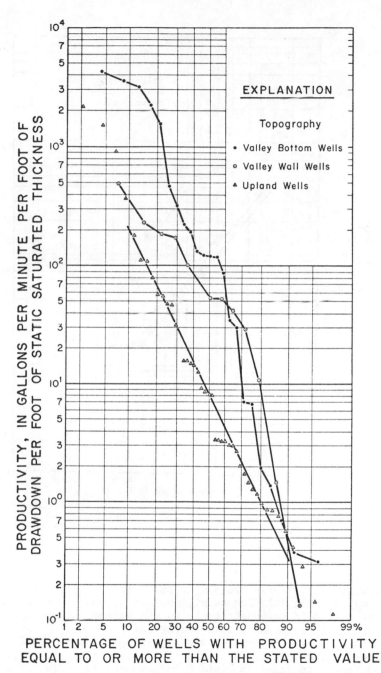

Fig. 9. Productivity Frequency Graphs for Wells Located in
Various Topographic Settings in Folded and Faulted
Shales, Dolomite and Limestone of Cambrian and Ordo-
vician age. From Siddiqui and Parizek [31].

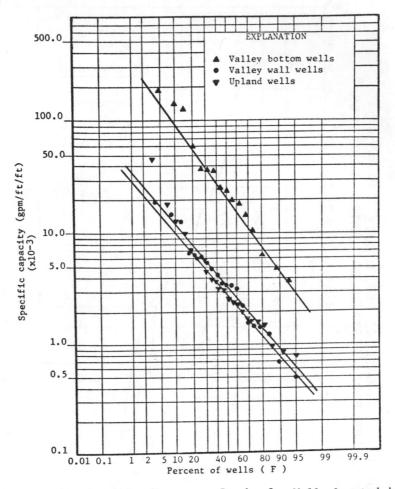

Fig. 10. Productivity Frequency Graphs for Wells Located in
Various Topographic Settings in Folded Siltstone,
Shale, and Interbedded Shale and Sandstone Beds of
Devonian Age.

(Figs. 11-14). These are summarized below. The combined processes favoring solution enlargement of secondary and primary
openings within carbonate rocks in the valley environment may
be easier to comprehend than weathering processes operating
within other rock types. However, well-yield data obtained in
valley bottom settings nearly universally show a statistically
significant increase in yield when compared to yields of wells
located in adjacent uplands no matter what the bedrock type.

Once tributary surface drainages are initiated above
joints, bedding plane openings, faults and fracture zones,
surface runoff is concentrated (Figs. 8 and 11). As erosion

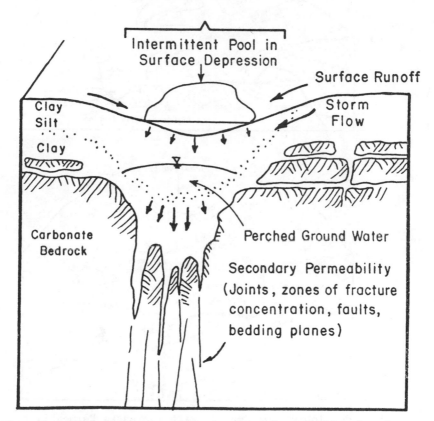

Fig. 11. Various Processes to Increase Permeability Develop-
ment Within the Valley Environment. Differential
Weathering Along Secondary Openings in Bedrock
Result in the Surface Sags and Depressions that Con-
centrate Surface Runoff Perched Ponds, Groundwater
Lenses and Increased Infiltration and Solution of
Bedrock.

progresses the valley eventually may intersect bedrock exposing
clay-filled joints, solution zones, or open channelways. Concentrated infiltration and recharge within swallow holes, and
through residual soils and alluvial sediments along valley
bottoms, foster more rapid solution of underlying carbonate
bedrock which initially was more highly jointed. Rocks beneath
tributary valleys consequently have a high initial permeability
which tends to increase at a more rapid rate when compared to
the permeability development within bedrock located beneath
adjacent uplands. Ultimately, the valley widens by lateral

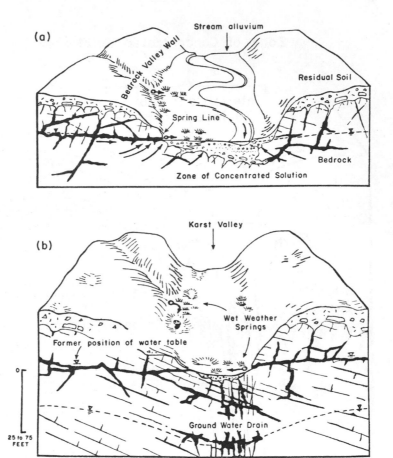

Fig. 12. Development of Regions with Increased Permeability
and Underdrains (Groundwater Sinks) Within the
Valley Environment. In (a) a Valley Has Been Eroded
to the Water Table to Produce a Permanent Groundwater
Drain. Lines of Groundwater Flow Converge on the
Valley and Dissolve Bedrock at a Faster Rate than
for Adjacent Uplands. Less Permeable Residual Soils
and Flood Plain Sediments Promote the Formation of
Springs at the Contact of Bedrock and Valley Fill
Sediments. Conduits Extend Laterally that are Graded
to the Flood Plain and Falling Water Table. In (b)
High Avenues of Permeability Development Beneath
the Valley Favor Conduit Formation and Underdrains
Controlled by a new More Distant Base Level. Upper
Caves and Conduits are Abandoned Often Graded to
Abandoned Terrace Levels and New Conduit Systems
Begin to Form. From Parizek [4].

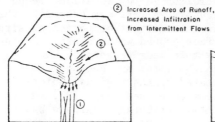

② Increased Area of Runoff,
Increased Infiltration
from Intermittent Flows

③ Increased Volume of Flow
Per Unit Volume of Rock

① Structural Control on Valley Location
(Joints, zones of fracture concentration,
faults, bedding plane openings)

⑤ Swallow Hole Development, Turbulent Flow
in Conduits, Expansion of Ground Water
Drainage Basin, Increased Volumes of Discharge
in Under-drains, Inwash of Organic Matter as
Source of CO_2, Zone of Mixing of Various
Waters to Increase Solution Potential

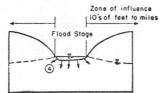

Zone of influence
10's of feet to miles

Flood Stage

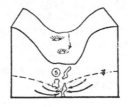

④ Reversal of Ground Water Flow, Surface Water
added to Bank Storage

Fig. 13.   Summary of Five Processes that Favor Permeability
Development Within the Valley Environment.   From
Parizek [4].

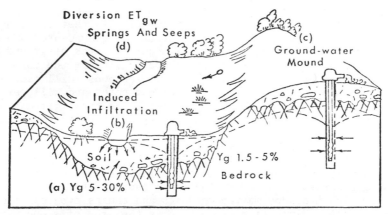

Fig. 14.   Summary of other Factors that Account for the Increased
Yield of Wells Located in the Valley Environment.
Flood Plain Soils and the more Highly Weathered Top
of Bedrock all to the Storage and Transmission
Potential of Shallow Saturated Deposits (a), Induced
Streambed Infiltration Sustains Pumping (b), Wells
in Groundwater Troughs Display less Drawdown than for
Wells on Mounds (c) and Wells in Valleys Divert Water
from Springs, Seeps and Groundwater Evapotranspiration
(d).

erosion and the initial control on valley location frequently
becomes obscured. Some tributary valleys may extend to the
water table producing either intermittent or permanent streams
and both surface and subsurface ground water sinks. As the
solution process continues within bedrock beneath the valley
environment, tributary drainages later may become karst drainages or underdrained as dictated by the regional water-table
base level and conduit systems developed (Fig. 12). At this
stage in development, the entire tributary drainage basin
becomes a collector of chemically corrosive surface water.
Numerous sinks open to accept this drainage and again the rocks
beneath the valley bottom dissolve at the expense of adjacent
strata. In this manner valley bottoms tend to localize
groundwater drains and conduits, influence cave development,
and begin to exert regional influences on the hydrogeologic
setting of carbonate terrains (Figs. 12, 13-5). Thus, secondary
fracture and fault permeability along with the evolving topography, combine to localize areas of increasing weathering
and solution. Once groundwater drains are established flow
patterns are set between recharge and discharge areas. This
condition of through flow is necessary to the overall solution
process.

The valley environment is especially well suited in
inducing flow lines to coverage in the manner described by
Theis [39], Rodes and Sinacori [40], Bedinger [41], and others.
Theis [39, p. 44] stated that even in the initial stages of
groundwater circulation in carbonate rocks, lines of flow are
modified from the ideal. The circulation in the discharge
area, together with the greater velocities in that area, may
result in an enlargement of the outlet for groundwater and a
consequent shallowing of the more accurate paths of groundwater
flow channels. Further, solution openings along the more
direct flow paths, normally the shallower ones, will become
larger than those along the less direct paths and will permit
progressively larger volumes of water to be transmitted along
the more rapidly developing passageways at the expense of other
openings being robbed of their groundwater. Rhodes and
Sinacori [40, p. 794] also stressed the importance of increased
solution along shorter flow lines which occur in upper zones
of saturation. They state that progressive flow concentration
of undersaturated water in the upper part of the zone of
saturation produces master conduits and causes eventual flow
and solution diminution at depth. As the area of groundwater
diversion supplying water to conduits increases, the flow
volume increases and hence, the opportunity for solution increases.

Add converging groundwater flow channels to this setting
(Fig. 13-5), and one can see that a greater volume of groundwater passes through a given volume of rock within the valley
environment than for an equal volume of rock located beneath

an adjacent upland. Bedinger [41] stressed that the exact
configuration of these flow lines in carbonate rocks must not
resemble those for the ideal porous media illustrated by
previous authors. He investigated the solution process in the
valley environment with the aid of an electrical analog. He
assumed that limestone is impermeable (not entirely true except
in relative sense) but contains joints, fractures, bedding
plane partings and solution channels; that at depth, limestone
is underlain by impermeable rock; the system is under water
table conditions; recharge is by infiltration of precipitation
through overlying rock to the zone of saturation; discharge
is by seeps and springs; and that the medium constantly
changes as solution progresses. Through his electric analog
study Bedinger [41] concludes: that the most active zone of
solution is at shallow depths beneath the water table and
near the point of groundwater discharge; that void size
decreases with depth, increases with proximity to the point of
groundwater discharge; that solution channels have a greater
lateral than vertical extent; and that regional groundwater
flow modified by rock structure and heterogeneities of the
aquifer control the areal solution pattern whereas hydraulic
and geochemical factors largely control the vertical position
of solution channels and solution pattern in the vertical plane
at right angles to the perennial stream.

Recharge beneath intermittent and karst valleys may reach
rates of millions of gallons a day within individual swallow
holes during peak runoff events. Water levels in wells located
in the underdrained valley environment may rise 10 or more
meters accompanying a single period of snow melt or rain as
surface water is recharged through swallow holes. Water levels
in wells beneath adjacent uplands may continue to decline during
these brief recharge periods, especially where thick accumula-
tions of residue soils promote runoff and retard infiltration
and vertical movement of soil moisture to underlying bedrock.
Directions of groundwater flow are even reversed temporarily
in some settings and are from water-table mounds beneath
valley bottoms to water-table lows beneath uplands during
peak events. Major amounts of groundwater recharge are possible
in the karst valley environment. These surface waters are
particularly aggressive in the solution of carbonate strata.
Where underdrains are sufficiently well developed and regionally interconnected, localized groundwater mounds that form
beneath valley bottoms during periods of high recharge may
be quickly bled off to nearby conduit-fed springs and the influence of groundwater recharge short-lived. The flashy flow
of these systems is reflected in flow and chemical behavior of
spring waters (Shuster and White [42]).

Various stages of this continuous process of porosity and
permeability development in the valley environment may be
observed within a particular drainage basin as one traces a
valley to its headwater region.

Solution is further augmented in some valleys by infiltrating surface waters which accompany rising river stages
during peak runoff (Fig. 13-4). Where the water table is
nearly horizontal and graded to low river stages as is common
in carbonate areas, abrupt rises in river stage are accompanied
by a reversal in groundwater gradients, a halt in groundwater
discharge, and, in fact, direct recharge to the aquifer by
chemically aggressive surface water. The reversal in flow may
influence the aquifer for only a few 10's of meters to possibly
kilometers adjacent to the river depending upon circumstances.
Infiltration of flood waters as bank storage must aid solution
in the valley environment at least immediately adjacent to
the river channel and intermittent drainages. As bedrock
permeability increases in the vicinity of the channel, a
greater volume of subchannel flow becomes possible further
augmenting permeability development. This is accentuated
where flow becomes turbulent. Inwash and backwash of organic
matter in swallow holes and spring outlets may further augment
solution by providing a source of CO_2 during decomposition.

Twigs, leaves, organic-rich muds and similar materials are
common within conduits fed by swallow holes.

A basic principal emerges, namely valley environments
favor increased local and regional permeability development in
a wide variety of carbonate and other terranes and represent
excellent sites for potentially high capacity wells. Well
yield data presented by various workers support this conclusion
as does information on cave distribution; theoretical groundwater flow data obtained from an electric analog model that
shows convergent flow adjacent to groundwater discharge areas;
observations on the distribution and topographic control on
springs in carbonate rocks located down valley from underdrained valleys; water table maps showing troughs parallel to,
and below karst valleys; the realization that joints, zones
of fracture concentrations and fault zones localize valley
development hence, contribute to initial secondary permeability
and porosity development; and the chemical character of spring
water discharged from some conduits located below underdrained
valleys that show that rapid recharge and through flow occurs
within these conduits when compared to springs draining more
distant uplands where diffuse flow dominates.

Other factors also can contribute to favorable well-yields
encountered within the valley bottom environment. Mechanical
and chemical weathering extends below topographic highs and lows
alike to produce a weathered mantle of completely to partly
weathered rocks. Although not necessary equally weathered nor
of the same thickness, the mantle is more apt to be saturated
when located in topographic lows. Wells penetrating these
shallow and more extensively developed openings should be more
productive and their pumping rate should be sustained for a
longer period by the rock's higher storage potential and

increased hydraulic conductivity (Fig. 14a). Saturated flood
plain deposits can contribute to the groundwater storage
potential of aquifers in the valley bottom setting. Specific
yield values of 5 to 20 percent are not unreasonable for
unconsolidated sediments, whereas specific yield value of 1.5
to 3.5 percent are typical for more dense limestone, dolomite,
shale and sandstone within the central Appalachian region
(Parizek [4], Konikow [43]).

The induced streambed infiltration potential is also
higher for wells located in valley bottoms than for wells
located within adjacent topographic highs (Fig. 14b). This
adds to a well's specific capacity potential. Saturated valley
train sand and gravel, coarse-grained point bar deposits,
channel fill sediments and the mechanically weathered top of
bedrock also contribute to the sustained yield of valley
bottom wells drilled into underlying fractured bedrock because these overburden sediments have high storage characteristics and act as sources of recharge to underlying joints,
fractures and bedding plane openings that otherwise are more
easily dewatered.

Wells drilled on topographic highs rather typically encounter groundwater mounds. Pumping cores of depression
migrate in all directions around the mound as water is withdrawn from storage (Fig. 14c). The drawdown required to obtain
a particular volume of water from storage is greater for
wells located on groundwater mounds than for the case where
cores of depressions are developed within groundwater lows or
troughs or where the water table slopes only in one direction,
because groundwater divides bounding the cone must continually
expand to reverse gradients and extract water from storage.

Wells may also divert groundwater from natural seepages
and springs thereby reducing their flow or eliminating them
entirely (Fig. 14d). Groundwater evaporation and transpiration
losses also are reduced as shallow water tables are lowered
below the root zone (1 to 30 or more meters). Water diverted
from natural discharge areas, i.e., springs, seeps or as
evapotranspiration areas helps to sustain pumping levels and
act as if recharge has been increased.   38, 50 or more cm
of groundwater evapotranspiration may be salvaged per unit
area in this manner in more humid regions receiving 88.9 to
152.4 cm of annual precipitation.

*Relationship between well yields and fracture traces for
folded and faulted carbonate rocks (Conclusions of the Siddiqui-
Parizek Study). Fracture traces versus nonfracture traces.*
Despite the many factors that help to account for the increased
yield of wells located in the valley bottom setting, the relationship of zones of fracture concentration revealed by fracture traces and shorter lineaments is now indisputable
(Siddiqui and Parizek [31,32]).

To evaluate the relative importance of fracture traces in controlling well productivity, Siddiqui and Parizek segregated well yield data into various fracture trace categories, subjected yield data within and between categories to nonparametric statistical tests, and presented probability yield plots for four categories (Fig. 15). The following discussion was extracted from their study.

The fact that the line of best fit for fracture trace wells is widely separated from the one for nonfracture trace wells means that fracture trace wells are far more productive than nonfracture trace wells and that the probability of obtaining a certain productivity is greater in fracture trace wells than in nonfracture trace wells. The median and geometric mean productivity values for fracture trace wells are greater than those for nonfracture trace wells (Table 1).

The Mann-Whitney U test shows that the productivities of fracture trace wells are significantly different from those of nonfracture trace wells (Table 3 of Siddiqui and Parizek [31]).

Fracture trace versus randomly located wells. To evaluate the importance of fracture traces in locating wells, wells were segregated into two categories: (1) wells located by means of fracture traces and (2) wells located randomly. Productivity-frequency graphs (Fig. 15) indicate that wells located by means of fracture traces are better producers than wells located randomly. However, the slopes of the two lines, which intersect in the high productivity range, are different. It may be concluded from the slopes of these graphs that wells located by means of fracture traces are more consistent in production than wells located randomly. The two graphs show that the probability of a productivity greater than 100 gpm/ft/ft is almost the same in wells located randomly and by means of fracture traces, because some randomly located high productivity wells in the analysis fell on fracture traces by accident. However, for the low productivity (< 10 gpm/ft/ft) wells, the probability of certain productivity is less in wells located randomly than in those located by means of fracture traces.*

The median and geometric mean productivities of wells located by means of fracture traces are about three to four times greater than those of wells located randomly (Table 1), and these differences are statistically significant. The Mann-

---

*Note: A gallon per minute/foot of drawdown/foot of saturated rock penetrated, system of units is used here because Table and Figures of published data included below are in these same units.

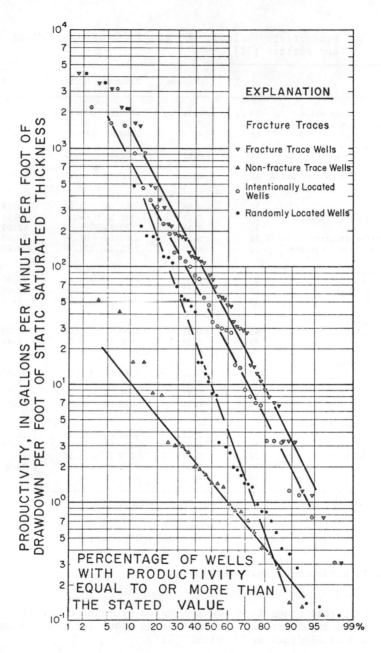

Fig. 15. Productivity - Frequency Graphs for Wells Grouped
with Respect to Fracture Traces for Folded and
Faulted Limestones, Dolomites and Shales. From
Siddiqui and Parized [31,32]. (All Data in the Plot
have been Multiplied by 10^3).

Table 1. Productivity Values, 10^3 gpm/ft/ft (From Siddiqui
and Parizek [31]).

	n	Minimum	Maximum	Median	Geometric Mean*
Fracture trace wells	53	0.31	4360.68	79.59	72.20
Intentionally located	35	0.31	2271.71	34.26	34.43
Accidentally located	18	10.72	4360.68	148.12	194.10
Nonfracture trace wells	27	0.11	52.64	1.45	1.74
All randomly located wells	45	0.11	4360.68	8.43	11.69
Rock type					
Shale	10	0.56	85.65	3.10	3.98
Bellefonte dolomite	22	0.11	180.14	4.45	3.51
Limestone	11	0.31	323.73	7.89	11.09
Nittany dolomite	15	0.85	4360.68	68.30	79.43
Upper Sandy dolomite	22	0.70	2202.56	122.35	123.30
Topography					
Valley bottom	23	0.31	4360.68	120.81	70.47
Valley wall	13	0.13	491.45	53.64	45.08
Upland	44	0.11	2202.56	7.95	8.55
Structure					
Anticline	45	0.11	4360.68	52.64	45.20
Syncline	35	0.14	930.00	7.00	7.41
Dip of bedrock strata					
<15°	30	0.31	4360.68	128.25	125.90
15°-30°	27	0.14	193.30	12.43	8.72
30°-60°	13	0.11	491.45	2.00	3.78
60°-90°	10	0.70	323.73	5.87	10.00
Depth to water table					
<50 feet	35	0.11	4360.68	10.72	16.37
50-100 feet	16	0.13	232.42	14.04	13.34
100-150 feet	16	0.41	172.34	28.18	15.42
<150 feet	13	0.85	2202.56	111.89	91.62

*Geometric means were computed from grouped data.

gpm/ft/ft is defined as gallons per minute per foot of draw-down per foot of exposed saturated rock penetrated by the well bore.

All data have been multiplied by 10^3.

Whitney U test shows that wells located by means of fracture traces are significantly different from those located randomly (Table 3 of Siddiqui and Parizek [31]).

Eighteen of 45 randomly located wells fell on or near fracture traces, and 27 did not. Thus 60% of the randomly located wells missed fracture traces, for a success ratio of 4:6. Thus the probability of missing a fracture trace (i.e., a potentially good well site) by randomly locating a well is

greater than hitting one. If fracture traces are absent from
a property on which water is required, the use of expert advice
would not help except to point out the increased risk of obtaining a low yield.

*Intentionally located versus accidentally located fracture
trace wells.* One may conclude Fig. 15 and Table 1 that it is
better to locate a well randomly than to use fracture traces.
However, this conclusion cannot be supported, because the success
ratio of hitting a fracture trace accidentally is 4:6. Moreover, accidentally located fracture trace wells are located in
restricted areas (The Pennsylvania State University well field
area (seven wells) and the State College Borough well field
area (three wells), rather productive areas compared to other
well settings. On the other hand, intentionally located
fracture trace wells were distributed over a larger area and
along a wider spectrum of hydrogeologic settings, often in
poorly productive strata. More recent well yield data obtained
for intentionally located wells in more productive rock reverses
this association.

Although aerial photographs and fracture traces were not
used to locate some wells in the two well fields, they were
located by means of other geologic observations. Because
most of these wells are located very close to each other,
initial success guided the location of subsequent wells.
Initial failure might have changed the entire balance; for
although other unsuccessful wells were located, they were
abandoned, and no yield data are available.

Importance of rock type. Wells located in the Upper Sandy
Dolomite Member of the Gatesburg Formation are more productive
than those in the Nittany Dolomite of Ordovician Age (Fig. 16).
Nittany Dolomite wells are more productive than wells in any
of the remaining three categories. The geometric mean and
the median productivities of wells in shales, Bellefonte
Dolomite, and limestones are relatively close to one another
(Table 1). The slope of the graph for Nittany Dolomite wells
is steeper than that for Upper Sandy Dolomite wells. Thus
wells located in the Upper Sandy Dolomite member of the
Gatesburg Formation are more consistent in production.

The Kruskal-Wallis test shows that the productivities of
wells in different rock types are significantly different
(Table 4 of Siddiqui and Parizek [31]); hence variation in rock
type had a significant influence on well productivity. The
Kruskal-Wallis test also shows that fracture trace wells in
different rock types are significantly different, whereas wells
in shales, limestone, and Bellefonte Dolomite are not.

Well yields adjacent to other water gaps. Further data
in support of the significance of lineaments in groundwater

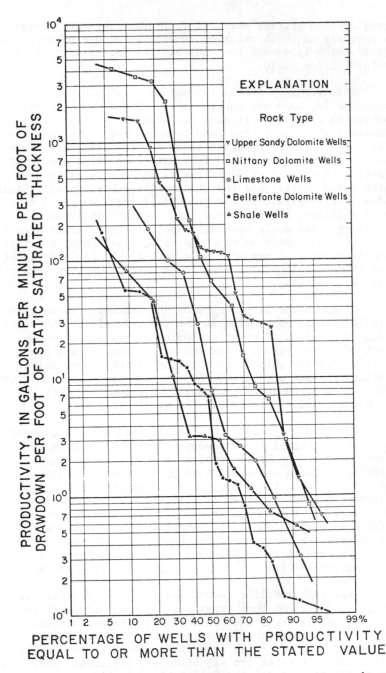

Fig. 16. Productivity-Frequency Graphs for Wells Grouped
with Respect to Rock Type. From Siddiqui and Parizek [31,32]. (All data multiplied by 10^3).

prospecting can be made for scant well-yield data obtained opposite or within other water gaps.

The following example is cited for an underdrained valley that is oriented transverse to bedrock strike and lacks a permanent stream. A gap is developed in a mountain ridge underlain by resistant sandstones and quartzite (Tussey Mountain near Shingletwon, Centre County, Pennsylvania) at the head of the valley (Fig. 17). The regional trend of this youthful karst valley was known to be linear and related to the Shingletown Gap. A new well field was recommended by the author for the lower reach of this valley because of its close proximity to existing wells (Thomas Well Field, Borough of State College, Pennsylvania), pipe and power lines, bedrock was gently dipping and among the most productive dolomites available in the area, a valley bottom setting was available that would increase permeability development and high rates of seasonal recharge following snow melt, the field would be close to the confluence of a small stream that would further augment recharge and water levels were expected to be shallow, and a zig zag offsets in the regional valley alignment assured well developed fracture traces were available to pin point high capacity test well sites that were favorable clustered on a single property available for purchase. No major pollution threats existed in the immediate area.

Prospecting was guided by the favorable combination of factors listed above and by a knowledge of the optimum set of field conditions that favor permeability development. That is the best targets in the area were at fracture trace inter- sections, within the Upper Sandy Dolomite Member of the Gatesbury Formation (Late Cambrian Age) or the next best Nittany Dolomite, on crests of anticlines or at least in beds with less than 15° dips, where water tables are shallow, but in carbonates, and within valley bottoms. Most of these conditions were satisfied at the proposed site. The opposite extreme or poorest sites were expected within interfracture trace areas, on upland, on synclinal troughts, where bedrocks dips were in excess of 30°, the water table is deep, and shales, the Bellefonte Dolomite or limestone bedrock was exposed. The Middle Ordovician Series limestones are excluded from this idealization because of their known cave and conduit development (See Rauch and White [44], Parizek [4]), but for which few water well yield data are available end member conditions favoring the best and poorest permeability develop- ment on a regional scale are summarized in Table 2.

Test wells (25, 26 and 27 of Table 2) were drilled at high priority fracture intersection test sites, developed and pumped tested using air rotary and cable tool methods of drilling. These were completed as final production wells. The specific capacities (gpm/ft) found to be 200 for screen length of 40

Fig. 17. Location of a Three Well (6 Million Gallon a day)
          Well Field in Gently Dipping Dolomite that is
          Located at Fracture Trace Intersections and on a
          Lineament Assumed to be 1 km Wide. Dashed Lines
          Show Fracture Traces, Arrows the Lineament not
          Readily Apparent on Conventional Photographs, and
          Well Locations.

feet and 16 in. diameter for well 25, 400-500 for the same
length and diameter for well 26, and 525, 200 and 300 for the
same length and diameter and different depths for the well 28.

Table 2.   A Guide to Groundwater Prospecting.
End Member Classification Summarizing the Optimum
Combination of Conditions Favoring groundwater
Occurrence and Movement Within Folded and Faulted
Carbonate Rocks of the Central Appalachian Type.

Best conditions at top.   Poorest aquifer conditions at bottom.

Rock Type	Structure	Topographic Setting

(1) Nealmont Formation
   (a) Center Hall Member
   (b) Rodman Member
	Fracture trace intersection combined with lineament intersection.	Valley bottoms opposite wind and water gaps controlled by zones of fracture concentration and faults.

(2) Benner Formation
   Valentine
   Valley View
   Oak Hall
   Stover
	Normal and thrust faults.	Valley bottoms with rivers and creeks, shallow water tables and saturated overburden deposits.

(3) Hatler Graiser	Anticlinal crests.	Base of mountain slopes favoring high rates of recharge and conduit development.

(4) Gatesburg Formation
   Upper Sandy Dolomite
   Member Nittany Dolomite
	Beds with dips of <15°	Underdrain valleys.

(5) Other Limestones
   Axmann
   Stonehenge
   Warrier
	Synclinal troughs.	Valley walls.

(6) Bellefonte Dolomite	Beds with dips >15° to 90°	Uplands
(7) Reedsville and Antes Shale.		
(8) Coburn - Salona Limestones.		

For wells 7, 8, 11 and 14, these values were 142.8, 114.3,
235.7, and 136.3, respectively. The wells were amongst the
most productive wells ever drilled in the region which is in
part due to the drilling and well development skills employed
by the contractor. The specific capacity values for the wells
on the lineament and fracture trace intersections (25, 26 and
27) are considerably higher than for wells located adjacent
to the lineament (7, 8, 11 and 14) but within the same rock
type, same dip, in a valley bottom setting just over 1 km
away. Wells 7 and 8 are on single fracture traces by chance
and wells 11 and 14 at fracture trace intersections (11 by
chance, 14 by design). Productivity values adjusted for depth
of saturated rock penetrated appear less conclusive because the
non lineament wells were all shallower hence did not get de-
valued by extending into less productive rock. Study of
driller's and caliper logs of these wells revealed that cavity
distribution diminished markedly within the lower 100 feet of
each well (25, 26 and 27). Although wells 25 and 27 were
found to be caved and filled above their original depths
following pumping, the depth of saturated rock penetrated was
taken to be the initial drilled depth hence, productivity
values appear lower than they otherwise would have been. The
specific capacity values alone however, should provide con-
vincing evidence of the added significance of the lineament

present. Wells 25, 26 and 27 were drilled by air rotary and cable tool methods and were developed more extensively than wells 7, 8, 11 or 14. However, the former are screened and gravel packed which reduces their efficiency when compared to unscreened rock wells.

LANDSAT-1 and SKYLAB images became available after the well field was located. A comparatively minor lineament when compared to more obvious lineaments that are longer in length was mapped for this water gap and aligned valley verifying what had been suspected from analysis of conventional photographs.

Relationship among well yields, lineaments; and a single rock type. Figures 18 a and b displays the probability frequency distribution of well yield data obtained for the same formation, Upper Sandy Dolomite Member of the Gatesburg Formation of Late Cambrian Age. Well yield data were obtained under controlled conditions for wells located on fracture traces, at fracture trace intersections and remote from fracture traces, within beds with various dips, and for wells within valley bottom, valley wall and upland settings (Tables 3a and 3b). Well-yield data are adjusted for depth of saturated rock penetrated or saturated rock exposed below the well casing. Further, wells were considered as on lineaments if they fell within a 1 km wide belt as defined from LANDSAT and/or SKYLAB images and off lineaments if they fell beyond this assumed width. Both generations of immergy were required because of the partial cloud cover that existed on SKYLAB images where the well yield data base was best developed.

It is apparent that some wells were highly productive no matter whether they fell on or off lineaments. In both cases nearly all of the more productive wells were located on fracture traces or fracture trace intersections, hence, derived the benefit of penetrating zones of fracture concentration. The slope of the line for wells considered to be on both fracture traces and lineaments is less steep when compared to the slope defined by wells remote from lineaments. This implies that wells will be more consistent in their yield and display less variability when located on lineaments combined with fracture traces and favorable topographic settings.

The maximum, minimum and 50 percent yield values were 9.3, 0.002 and 0.3 gpm/ft/ft for lineament wells compared with 2.2, 0.003, and 0.07 gpm/ft/ft for non lineament wells.

It may be concluded from this study that a positive benefit can be derived when selecting water well sites by combining both fracture trace intersection, or fracture trace sites with lineaments and lineament intersections where ever possible. The graphs further reveal that some variability in yield still remains for wells located on lineaments. This is

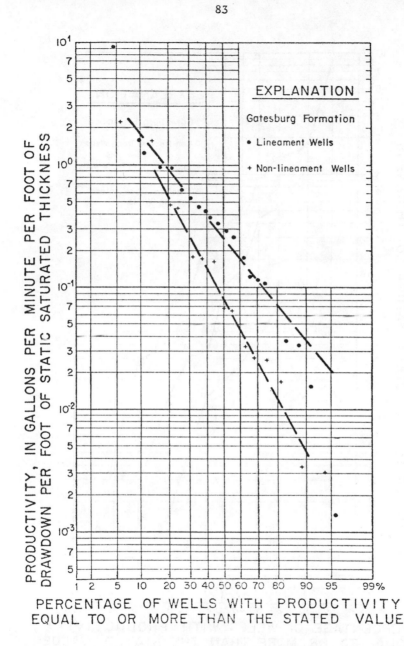

Fig. 18a. Comparison of Productivity Frequency Graphs for
Wells Located on Lineaments Assumed to be 1 km Wide
and Nonlineament Sites. All Wells are Located in
the Gatesburg Formation of Late Cambrian Age and
Under Similar Topographic, Fracture Trace and
Nonfracture Trace Settings.

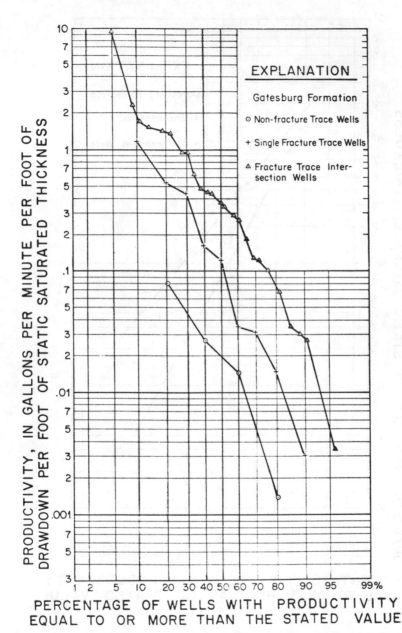

Fig. 18b. Comparison of Productivity Frequency Graphs for Wells
Located on Lineaments Assumed to be 1 km Wide and
Nonlineament Sites. All Wells are Located in the
Gatesburg Formation of Late Cambrian Age and Under
Similar Topographic, Fracture Trace and Nonfracture
Trace Settings, With the Same Well Data as in Fig.
18a but Grouped by Fracture Trace Setting.

3-38

Table 3a. Wells Completed in the Gatesburg Dolomite of Late
Cambrian Age. Wells were located in Valley Bottoms,
Valley Walls, Uplands and on a Lineament Assumed
to be 1 km wide. Dips Ranged from 0 to 45°.

Interfracture Trace Area.

Well Number	Casing Length (ft.)	Depth (ft.)	Diameter (inches)	Screen Length (ft.)	Yield (gpm)	Specific Capacity (gpm/ft)	Productivity (gpm/ft/ft)	Test Duration (hours: min.)
UN-20	32	400	12				.00145	

Single Fracture Trace.

Well Number	Casing Length (ft.)	Depth (ft.)	Diameter (inches)	Screen Length (ft.)	Yield (gpm)	Specific Capacity (gpm/ft)	Productivity (gpm/ft/ft)	Test Duration (hours: min.)
UN-2	37.5	325	12				.1239	
UN-3	47.4	288	7		528	40.4	.016	5
UN-16	63	453	10		278	6.8	.036	1:15
FC BSH-1	33' 8" of 16"	125	15		780	111.4	1.22	16:0
FC BSH-1	33' 8" of 16"	125	15		2000	95.23	1.04	9:0
FC BSh-2	35' of 16"	140	15 to 125		2000	57.1	0.53	

Fracture Trace Intersection.

Well Number	Casing Length (ft.)	Depth (ft.)	Diameter (inches)	Screen Length (ft.)	Yield (gpm)	Specific Capacity (gpm/ft)	Productivity (gpm/ft/ft)	Test Duration (hours: min.)
415	284.4	298	10				.930	
443	37.	250	7					
UN-17	31.	188	12.8		680	29.6	.114/.125	20
UN-25							.030	
UN-24	23	300	12	100	524	43.7	.17/.18	31
UN-26	40	400	12				.1199	
FC-1	12	147	12" to 34" 8" to 147"		840	42	0.343	24
FC-2a	17.5	146	12"		1080	34.8	0.27	5
FC-2b	17.5	146	12"		1640	37.3	0.29	17.30
FC-3	38	150	13		1850	50	.466	37
393	24.4	313	6				.034	
SC-18	358.8	500	10				1.590	
SC-19	434	470	14				.3715	
Imbt Quarry	164	304	7 7/8		600		0.10	0.75
Imbt Quarry	164	304	7 7/8		1000	9.61	.068	
FC LSH-2	38' of 14"	150	13 1/4		1800	34.61		11.45
FC LSH-2	38' of 14"	150	13 1/4		1850	49.45	0.45	34.0
FC USH-1	35' 8"	100	18 O.D.		1600		0.622	24.0
FC USH-1	35' 8"	Caved at 40'	14		1600		9.30	24.0
FC USh-2	24' 8" of 18' O.D.	100	17		1850	71.15	0.944	24:30

probably due to the fact that joints, fractures, bedding plane
partings and secondary weathering is not equally well developed
beneath lineaments and an element of chance and variability of
penetrating openings will always remain when drilling on fracture concentration variable fracture development has been observed in cross-sectional views. A hole, for example, might
have been placed within the general zone of fracture concentration and at the same time penetrated by chance a relatively

Table 3b. Wells Completed in the Gatesburg Dolomite on
          Fracture Traces or Interfracture Trace Areas and
          in Valley Bottoms, Valley Walls and Uplands and
          Remote from Lineaments where Dips Ranged from 0°
          to 45°.

Interfracture Trace Area.

Well Number	Casing Length (ft.)	Depth (ft.)	Diameter (inches)	Screen Length (ft.)	Yield (gpm)	Specific Capacity (gpm/ft)	Productivity (gpm/ft/ft)	Test Duration (hours: min.)
Donsborough	130	195	6		6.5	1.82	0.028	3:15
L.G. Appt.	378	411	8 5/8		60	0.51	0.016	48:0
I-80 #31	236'6"	316	6		60.86	8.68	0.048	0:31
I-80 #31	236'6"	316	6		42.8	7.68	0.084	1:0

Single Fracture Trace

Well Number	Casing Length (ft.)	Depth (ft.)	Diameter (inches)	Screen Length (ft.)	Yield (gpm)	Specific Capacity (gpm/ft)	Productivity (gpm/ft/ft)	Test Duration (hours: min.)
UN-22	95	343	6				.0313	
SC-2								
408	27.8	170	6				.003	
P.G.C.	179	506	12" to 419	8"				
			8" to 506	179-419 ft.	510		0.44	48:0

Fracture Trace Intersection

Well Number	Casing Length (ft.)	Depth (ft.)	Diameter (inches)	Screen Length (ft.)	Yield (gpm)	Specific Capacity (gpm/ft)	Productivity (gpm/ft/ft)	Test Duration (hours: min.)
UN-23	102.5	270	6		27	3.9	.12/.15	1:25
UN-14	50	215	12				.172	
SC-16	285.8	453	8				1.6568	
SC-15	361	458	12				.0276	
SC-5	384	365	10				2.2026	
SC-17	297	450	10				0.0033	
UN-14	50	215	12				.172	
G-10	289	320	6				.4715	
409	74	197	.6				.0683	

dense wedge of poorly fractured rock. A few feet away, more
intensely fractured and more productive rock would have been
encountered. The same variability of fracture and joint
development beneath lineaments has not been documented but is
expected to exist even to a greater degree. For this reason
I would recommend that all lineament well sites also be located
on fracture trace intersections or on single fracture traces
to increase the probability of penetrating the maximum number
of secondary openings. On the other hand, wells drilled to
meet minor domestic supplies in carbonate terranes might
better be offset from these sites to avoid costly drilling,
double casing and well development requirements frequently
required at more highly fractured sites.

     Lineaments and lineament intersections combined with
fracture trace intersections together with favorable rock type
and other variables named earlier should be added to the list
of conditions favoring increased permeability development,
hence increased well yields. The above normal distribution
of sinkholes and swallow holes at the base of the Appalachian
Mountain ridges where lineaments transect bedrock strike and
interact with rock units favoring cave and conduit development

represents an entirely different set of supporting evidence
that these features delineate zones of increased weathering
of significance to many geotechnical investigations.

The local and regional controls on permeability and
porosity development and distribution for carbonate terranes
is slowly emerging. A complete understanding of the 'circula-
tory system' governing water movement in these rocks is key
to the rational exploitation of these systems (Fig. 19).

4. The Importance of Exchange of Experience.

Another case study conducted on folded carbonate rocks
of Silurian and Devonian Age in Central Pennsylvania is worthy
of note. The study by (Mundi [45]) was designed to determine
what geological factors contributed to the aquifer properties
of a sequence of folded rocks younger in age than those considered by Siddiqui and Parizek. Again well yield records
were subjected to analysis to isolate controlling variables
that influenced well yields. In this study 300 well records
on file with Pennsylvania Geological Survey were examined for
completeness of information of which only 84 were subjected
to analysis. Intentionally controlling pumping tests were not
conducted during the study nor the drilling locations of any
of the wells used in the analysis picked for the study. Yield
data were that reported by water well contractors. These data
were often obtained under other than ideal or even reliable
conditions. However, records on well depth, casing lengths,
well radius, duration of test, etc. were considered acceptable.

Yield probability plots obtained for four selected formations penetrated by the wells were prepared. The Catskill
Formation of Late Devonia age is largely composed of shale,
with interbedded shale and sandstones, Middle Devonian aged
Hamilton Formation is composed of shale, the Orskany of Early
Devonian age is of conglomerate and sandstone overlain by
siliceous and cherty limestone and the Keyser-Tonoloway
Limestone of Late Silurian age of thick bedded limestone and
thin bedded to laminated fine-grained limestone. Yields of
wells drilled largely for domestic purposed may be read from
these graphs to give an indication of the probability of obtaining a given well yield based on available well data. Well
productivities ranged from 0.00005 gallons per minute per foot
of drawdown per foot of saturated rock penetrated (gpm/ft/ft)
to 0.050 gpm/ft/ft. The 50% probability values taken from the
plots shows that the Catskill productivity is 0.001 gpm/ft/ft.,
the Keyser is 0.002, the Hamilton is 0.007, and the Oriskany
is 0.004 gpm/ft/ft.

These data imply that the shales of the Hamilton are more
productive as an aquifer than either the limestone of the
Keyser or limey sands and sandstones of the Oriskany Formation.

88

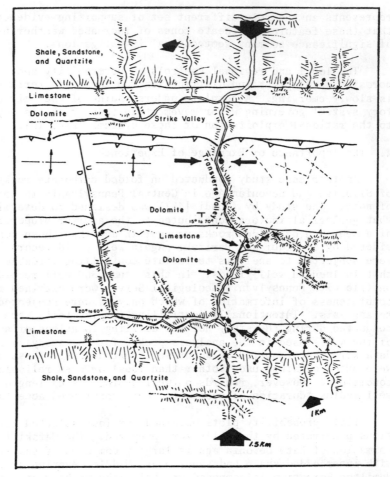

Fig. 19. Summary of Regional and Local Controls on Permeability
and Porosity Development in Folded and Faulted Car-
bonate Rocks of the Central Appalachian Type. This
Includes the Interaction of Rock Type Where Petro-
graphic Properties Favor Intergranular Permeability
Preservation and Weathering, Tilt and Sequence of
Beds that Favor Region Patterns of Anistropic Perme-
ability Distribution, Folds that Produced Anticlines
and Synclines, Normal and Thrust Faults Development,
Zones of Fracture Concentration Revealed by Fracture
Traces and Lineaments and Interaction of all these
Features to produce Topographic Variations that
Accentuate, Recharge, Flow, Weathering and Solution.
(Expanded from Parizek [4]).

Further, one is led to conclude that none of the rocks are particularly important as aquifers, because all are highly cemented, compact and contain limited to negligible inter-granular permeabilities with the exception of the Oriskany Sandstone.

The 84 wells used in the analysis were drilled largely to produce an adequate supply of water for domestic and farm purposes rather than to evaluate the true yield potential of these strata to meet larger municipal, industrial, or irrigation demands. Few if any of the wells were located with the aid of a trained geologist, few were drilled to exploit the full saturated thickness of the fractured aquifer system under study except where an insufficient yield was obtained at a shallower depth and few wells were developed adequately to improve the efficiency of the well beyond that resulting from the normal act of drilling using air rotary or cable tool methods.

The true nature of these fractured aquifers is inadequately understood based on these data and the potential yield of individual wells to be drilled into these rock units totally misrepresented.

By applying current knowledge of the geological factors influencing the occurrence and movement of water within these strata, a totally different insight emerges. Table 4 summarizes the results of pumping tests conducted on only 12 wells drilled to exploit the full yield potential of a well site in the Oriskany and Keyser Formations. Each well was drilled at a fracture trace intersection or on a single fracture trace, drilled to a depth designed to maximize the chances of penetrating shallow openings developed within the zone of weathering and developed with various surging techniques, sequestering agents to breakdown drilling muds and cavity fill sediments, etc.

The highest specific capacity observed in the domestic wells completed in these same strata was only 3.0 gpm/ft after one hour of pumping as compared to 100.0 gpm/ft. after 50 hours of pumping for the larger wells (Table 3). This serves to dramatize the significance of applying our current geological insights and knowledge when prospecting for water within complex fractured carbonate and other rocks and draws attention to the significant potential of aquifers previously believed to be of limited value in meeting greatly expanding water demands. It is interesting to note that the wells reported upon in Table 3 were drilled by one water well contractor who has adopted the fracture trace method of prospecting explained by Lattman and Parizek in 1964 [14].

Table 4.   A Summary of Available Specific Capacity Data from
Wells Located in Fracture Trace Within the Oriskany-
Tonoloway Aquifer (Modified from E.K. Mundi 1972).

(The theoretical maximum yield is computed based upon
a safe available drawdown of 50 feet)

Well Field	Well Number	Diameter of Well (inches)	Water Level (ft)	Well Depth (ft)	Saturated Thickness (ft)	Pumping Duration (hrs)	Pumping Rate (gpm)	Specific Capacity (gpm/ft)	Maximum Yield (gpm)
City of	1	6.25	36	540	504	24	300	18.7	940
Altoona	1	6.25	36	540	504	24	280	28.0	1400
(Blair Co.	1	12.00	36	549	513	24	1350	45.0	2250
Penna.)									
	2	6.25	32	575	543	24	200	2.4	120
	2	6.25	32	625	593	24	250	8.3	415
	3	6.00	45	280	235	24	200	18.0	900
	3	12.25	45	545	500	24	1400	46.0	2300
Claysburg	1	8.00	1	494	493	21	250	2.6	130
(Blair Co.	1	8.00	1	456	493	34	250	2.8	140
Penna.)	3	8.00	1	690	689	18	150	1.1	55
Boggs	5	8.00	20	385	365	50.5	550	100.0	5000
Township	6	8.00	20	385	365	81.0	500	13.0	650
(Centre Co. Penna.)									

All farm and domestic wells
completed in the Oriskany and
Keyser as were all municipal
wells listed above.

Range 0.00005 to 0.050 gpm/ft/ft
50% value Keyser 0.002 gpm/ft/ft
50% Oriskany 0.004 gpm/ft/ft

5.   Environmental Planning.

The surface evidences of zones of fracture concentration
underlying fracture traces and short lineaments and probably
long lineaments as well are obscure and readily destroyed by a
variety of changes in landuse. Parizek and Drew [15] stressed
the importance of mapping fracture traces in advance of industrial and urban sprawl, strip mining etc. and documenting their
locations so that test drilling can be guided in the future
at a time when the demand for water increases. This is still
true today for fracture trace and lineaments that define
avenues of increased porosity and permeability in a great
variety of rock types and settings. These features should be
included on all maps that show aquifer distribution and on
engineering hazard maps for urban and rural areas alike aimed
at delineating areas with risks of foundation instability, dam
and reservoir failures, excessive flows to mines and quarries,
tunnel and mine roof instability, land settlement, sinkhole
collapse, etc. Knowledge of the number, spacing and presence
of zones of fracture concentration and their precise field
location will be important in planning and laying out new mines,
and their successful flooding when abandoned, prospecting for
ore bodies, potential sites for increased oil and gas production, for the design of secondary oil recovery operations,

the placement of recharge and dewatering wells, groundwater monitoring wells, waste-water injection wells, delineating landslide hazard areas and similar other applications. The applications of this knowledge are indeed numerous and are only now being more fully exploited.

6. Conclusions.

Several highly significant conclusions can be drawn:

(1) Namely, wells within the valley bottom setting encounter rocks with increased permeability and porosity when compared to the same rocks located beneath topographic highs for a wide range in rock types and geographical areas. An important conclusion also can be drawn concerning fracture traces.

(2) A significant percent of a valley's length (60 to 80 percent), particularly tributary valleys, can be controlled by or localized by differential weathering along zones of fracture concentrations revealed by fracture traces. Water wells, therefore, located within narrow valley bottom settings.

(3) Have an increased probability of penetrating zones of fracture concentrations by chance when compared to wells randomly located on wider, adjacent uplands. For the latter, zones of fracture concentrations tend to be more widely scattered and they present a small target to randomly located wells in view of the large percentage of land area represented by non-fracture trace areas.

(4) Other factors in addition to the presence of zones of increased jointing and fracturing account for increased permeability and porosity development within the valley bottom environment hence, increased well yields. Therefore, it cannot be concluded that all wells located in valley bottoms owe their yield solely to the presence of zones of fracture concentration.

(5) The relationship between valley development and fracture traces is similar to that for valley development and lineaments. This implies that zones of structural weakness also underlie lineaments hence, lineaments favor differential weathering and solution of bedrock.

(6) The proven relationship between fracture traces and permeability development and close analogy between lineaments and fracture traces implies that a strong relationship should also exist between lineaments and permeability development. However, other factors in addition to structure should also account for permeability development and well yields within lineament controlled valleys as was true for fracture trace controlled valleys.

3-45

(7) Lineaments manifest themselves in all terranes in
Pennsylvania and elsewhere and crosscut rocks of all ages and
fold-fault complexity. Their utility in delineating potential
zones of increased permeability and porosity is expected to
be similar to that established for fracture traces. Preliminary
data presented here proves that lineaments will be useful in
groundwater exploration and foundation engineering related
studies wherever increased weathering, porosity and permeability
development is significant, i.e. planning tunnels, mines,
exploration and grouting programs below dams and foundations,
etc.

(8) Lineaments and fracture traces related to bedrock
fractures manifest themselves in areas with residual and
transported soils in excess of 88 meters in thickness as
near State College, Pennsylvania and areas with an overburden
of glacial drift. They may be seen when colluvium, alluvial
fans and stream alluvium exceed 33 meters in thickness and are
apparent where glacial drift mantles the bedrock surface. It
is not known if fracture zones located in bedrock are propagated
through unconsolidated overburden sediments as increased joint
development.

(9) Increased soil moisture and perched groundwater and
perched surface water bodies are frequencly aligned along
lineaments where residual soils are well developed above
carbonate bedrock. Although shallow groundwater supplies may
be obtained from perched groundwater bodies developed with
soils overlying lineaments, lineaments should be more significant in delineating zones of potentially productive bedrock
for a wide range of rock types and in delineating areas likely
to experience surface drainage problems.

(10) Fracture traces should be combined with lineaments
and lineament intersections to maximize the change of locating
fracture zone, zones of more intense chemical weathering and
permeability development in all terranes containing cemented
sedimentary, igneous and metamorphic rocks. Lineaments are
expected to be underlain by zones of joint and fracture concentration that are less evenly distributed than for zones
underlying fracture traces. Wedges of intact rock should occur
beneath lineaments more so that beneath fracture traces, hence
well yields are likely to display a greater range in values
for some rock type when compared to fracture traces.

(11) Productivity frequency graphs are provided that con-
clusively prove the significance of lineaments as a means of
delineating zones of increased permeability and porosity. The
data were corrected to a common well radius, well depth and
pumping period and all control points are for the same formation in a limited geographic region. Wells are included for
fracture trace intersections, single fracture traces, and

nonfracture trace areas on and remote from lineaments. The dip of beds was less than 45 degrees in nearly all cases, and wells were on uplands, valley walls and valley bottoms. These similarities in hydrogeologic setting allow for the positive conclusion drawn.

(12) Lineament wells show a greater consistency in yield in that the slope of the yield probability plot is less than for nonlineament wells. Less difference in yield appears for the higher productivity portions of the two graphs. The non-lineament wells show a greater range in yield from the least to most productive wells, hence a greater variability in yield. These graphs prove that a positive benefit can be gained by using lineaments when prospecting for groundwater. Further, the highest yields appear for wells that fall on both linea-ments and at fracture trace intersections and in valley bottom settings. It should be clear that other geological factors should be used in addition to lineaments when prospecting for groundwater where ever possible.

(13) A preliminary lineaments map has been prepared by Kowalik and Gold for Pennsylvania. This map shows that lineaments are in close proximity to most cities, towns, and villages within the state. Yield data presented in this report establishes the fact that lineaments can be used with advantage in groundwater prospecting to increase the chance of obtaining maximum well yields available within a given terrane. However, test well sites must be selected to take into consideration other geological controls that favor groundwater occurrence i.e. rock type, topographic setting, dip of beds, existing and possible future pollution potential and other factors.

(14) Lineaments will have far broader application to groundwater prospecting throughout the nation and world than many hydrogeologist still realize. All sedimentary rocks, even with moderate to limited amounts of cement will yield increased amounts of water when fractured. For metamorphic and igneous rocks, zones of fracture concentration offer the best hope of obtaining maximum well yields at least economic risk.

(15) The Pennsylvania lineament map shows an uneven distribution of lineaments for sections of the state. In particular, southeastern and northwestern Pennsylvania shows fewer lineaments than other regions of the state. These vari-ations may be more due to operator bias than due to geological causes and subject to operator interpretation and culture in more densely populated regions. For this reason multiple operators should be used to increase the chances of detecting more subtle lineaments.

(16) To maximize the recognition of fracture traces, more
than one set of aerial photographs are routinely used by the
author. These may be for different seasons for the same year
or different years. Five to even ten percent more fracture
traces not recognized previously have been shown to be enhanced on a second set of photographs either as the reflectance
characteristics of the landsurface changes (due to soil vegetation changes) or as trees and shrubs become re-established or
mature following clear cutting. For somewhat similar resons
multiple remote sensing coverage of the same region as expected
to add new information on the abundance of lineaments.

(17) Multiple operator mapping and ranking of lineaments
has been accomplished for only selected areas to date. Continued work of this type is required to provide the most meaningful and accurate lineaments map of a state or region. For
ultimate accuracy, complete SKYLAB coverage should be combined
with LANDSAT coverage of the area under study preferably with
repetative coverage.

(18) The fact that two distinctive plots are shown in
Figs. 18a and 18b when wells are ranked on and off lineaments
need not prove that a 1 km assumed width for lineaments is
correct. Many wells fell in narrow valleys controlled by
structure that is revealed by lineaments hence may have hit
the structure even if it were less than 1 km wide. Additional
studies are required.

(19) There is no doubt that lineaments are underlain by
structural features that increase the physical and chemical
weathering of bedrock of all types. The damage caused by
improper waste management along lineaments is likely to cause
more regional groundwater pollution than for adjacent areas
where bedrock is less permeable. Lineament mapping, therefore,
will be of significance in planning waste treatment and management facilities and monitoring water quality changes below and
adjacent to such facilities.

(20) Sinkholes, swallow holes, cave entrances, influence
streams, and land subsidence is occurring along lineaments and
at lineament intersections in carbonate terranes. These
structures combined with other details of depth of water table,
seasonal variation in water table position with respect to
residual and transported soils, distribution of surface water,
groundwater development, details or rock type, and other
structural features combine to define hazardous subsidence
and leakage areas. Lineament maps will help to delineate risk
areas for various structures but in themselves cannot be used
to predict when and where subsidence and cave-in's and severe
leakage are precisely going to occur. However, they can be
used to flag areas where caution should be exercised in landuse planning and where more detailed test drilling and foundation exploration work are justified.

7. Acknowledgments.

Organizers and supporters of the Bilateral United States--Yugoslavian Seminar in Karst Hydrology and Water Resources are greatfully acknowledged for financing my trip to the seminar and for extending an invitation for this paper. The studies summarized are the result of ongoing investigations by the author, his associates and students and sponsored by the Mineral Conservation Section, Pennsylvania State University, by the U.S. Department of Interior as authorized under the Water Resources Act of 1964, P.L. 88-379, Project A-005, through the Institute for Research on Land and Water Resources, and the Office of Remote Sensing through grants provided by NASA Contract NAS 5-23133 of the ERTS-1 program and NASA contract NAS 9-13406 of SKYLAB/EREP (G.J. McMurtry and G.W. Peterson, Principal Investigators).

Special acknowledgement is extended to Mr. Roy Frank, Ben Whitacre and others of the Pennsylvania Fish Commission, Bellefonte, Pennsylvania for making records available for wells located in various hatchery facilities under their jurisdiction. Appreciation is extended to R. Landon, formerly of Moody and Associates, Meadville, Pennsylvania for providing similar records for wells constructed by their firm.

8. References.

[1] Gold, P. P., R. R. Parizek, and S. A. Alexander, Analysis and application of ERTS-1 data for regional geological mapping: Symposium on Significant Results Obtained from ERTS-1, NASA, 12 p., 1973.

[2] Lattman, L. H., Technique of mapping geologic feature traces and lineaments on aerial photographs: Photogrammetric Eng., Vol. 24, pp. 568-576, 1958.

[3] Siddiqui, S. H., Hydrogeologic factors influencing well yields and aquifer hydraulic properties of folded and faulted carbonate rocks of central Pennsylvania: Ph.D. dissertation, The Pennsylvania State University, 502 p., 1969.

[4] Parizek, R. R., Hydrogeologic framework of folded and faulted carbonates--Influence of Structure, pp. 28-65, in *Hydrogeology and Geochemistry of Folded and Faulted Use Problems*: Parizek, R. R., W. B. White, and D. Langmuir, Mineral Conservation Series Circular 82, College of Earth and Mineral Sciences, The Pennsylvania State University, University Park, Pennsylvania, 182 p., 1971.

[5] Parizek, R. R., Prevention of coal mine drainage
     formation by well dewatering: Special Res. Report 82,
     Coal Research Section, The Pennsylvania State University,
     1971.

[6] Kaiser, E. P., Structural significance of lineaments:
     (Abs.), Bull. Geol. Soc. America, Vol. 61, No. 12,
     pp. 1475-1476, 1950.

[7] Blanchet, P. H., Development of fracture analyses as
     exploration methods: Bull. Am. Assoc. Petrol. Geol.,
     Vol. 41, pp. 1748-1759, 1957.

[8] Mollard, J. D., Aerial photographs aid petroleum search:
     Canada Oil and Gas Inc., Vol. 10, pp. 89-96, 1967.

[9] Mollard, J. D., A study of aerial mosaics in southern
     Saskatchewan and Manitoba: Oil in Canada, Winnepeg,
     Issue of August 5, 1957.

[10] Kupsch, W. O. and J. Wild, Lineaments in Avonlea area,
     Saskatchewan: Bull. Am. Assoc. Petrol. Geol., Vol. 42,
     No. 1, pp. 127-134, 1958.

[11] Lattman, L. H. and R. P. Nickelson, Photographic
     fracture-trace mapping in Appalachian Plateau: Bull. Am.
     Assoc. Petrol. Geol., Vol. 42, No. 9, pp. 2238-2245,
     1958.

[12] Hough, V. N. D., Joint orientation of the Appalachian
     Plateau in southwestern Pennsylvania: Unpublished M.S.
     thesis, The Pennsylvania State University, 82 p., 1960.

[13] Meisler, H., Hydrogeology of the carbonate rocks of the
     Lebanon Valley: Pennsylvania, Pennsylvania Geol. Survey,
     4th ser., Ground-Water Report, W17, 81 p., 1963.

[14] Lattman, L. H. and R. R. Parizek, Relationship between
     fracture traces and the occurrence of ground-water in
     carbonate rocks: Journal Hydrology, Vol. 2, pp. 73-91,
     1964.

[15] Parizek, R. R. and L. J. Drew, Random drilling for water
     in carbonate rocks: Proceedings of a symposium and short
     course on computers and operations research in mineral
     industries. Min. Industries Experiment Station, Vol. 3,
     (Special Publication 2-65), The Pennsylvania State
     University, University Park, Pennsylvania, pp. 1-22,
     1966.

[16] Lattman, L. H. and A. V. Segovia, Analysis of fracture trace pattern of Adak and Kagalaska Islands, Alaska: Bull. Am. Assoc. Petrol. Geol., Vol. 45, No. 2, pp. 249-263, 1961.

[17] Lattman, L. H. and R. H. Matzke, Geological significance of fracture traces: Photogrammetric Eng., Vol. 27, No. 5, pp. 635-638, 1961.

[18] Keim, J., A study of photogeologic fracture traces over the Bisbee quadrangle, Cochise County, Arizona: Unpublished M.S. thesis, The Pennsylvania State University, 42 p., 1962.

[19] Boyer, R. E. and J. E. McQueen, Comparison of mapped rock fractures and airphoto linear features: Photogrammetric Eng., Vol. 30, pp. 630-635, 1964.

[20] Setzer, J., Hydrologic significance of tectonic fractures detectable on air photos: Ground Water, Vol. 4., No. 4, pp. 23-27, 1966.

[21] Wobber, F. J., Fracture traces in Illinois: Photogrammetric Eng., Vol. 33, No. 5, pp. 499-506, 1967.

[22] Calkins, J. A., The geology of the west limb of the Hazara-Kashmir Syntaxis, West Pakistan and Kashmir: Unpublished Ph.D. dissertation, The Pennsylvania State University, 142 p., 1966.

[23] Trainer, W. F., Measurement of the abundance of fracture traces on aerial photographs: U.S. Geol. Survey Prof. Paper 575-C, pp. C184-188, 1967.

[24] Trainer, W. F. and R. L. Ellison, Fracture traces in the Shenandoah Valley, Virginia: Photogrammetric Eng., Vol. 33, pp. 190-199, 1967.

[25] Deike, G. H., The development of caverns of the Mammoth Cave region: Unpublished Ph.D. dissertation, The Pennsylvania State University, 235 p., 1967.

[26] Parizek, R. R., An environmental approach to land use in a folded and faulted carbonate terrane: *Environmental Planning and Geology*, U.S. Dept. of Housing and Urban Development and U.S. Dept. of Interior, pp. 122-142, 1969.

[27] Parizek, R. R. and B. Voight, On remote sensing investigations for dam and reservoir construction in karst terranes: Question 37, Commission Internationale des Grands Barrages, Montreal, G.R.Q. 37, (Manuscript submitted for symposium volume), 1970.

[28] Brown, R. S. and R. R. Parizek, Shallow ground water flow systems beneath strip and deep coal mines at two sites, Clearfield County, Pennsylvania: Special Res. Report SR-84, Coal Research Section, The Pennsylvania State University, p. 13, 1971.

[29] Lovell, H. L. and J. W. Gunnett, Hydrogeological influences in preventive control of mine drainage from deep coal mining: Special Res. Report SR-100, Coal Res. Section, The Pennsylvania State University, 89 p., 1974.

[30] Cline, G. D. and R. R. Parizek, Factors influencing well-yields in a folded sandstone-siltstone-shale terrane, Northumberland and Schuylkill Counties, Pennsylvania: (In press), 1975.

[31] Siddiqui, S. H. and R. R. Parizek, Hydrogeologic factors influencing well-yields in folded and faulted carbonate rocks in central Pennsylvania: Water Resources Res., Vol. 7, No. 5, 1971.

[32] Siddiqui, S. H. and R. R. Parizek, Variations in well-yields and controlling hydrogeologic factors: pp. 87-95, In College of Earth and Mineral Science, Mineral Conservation Series Circular 82, The Pennsylvania State University, 182 p. 1971.

[33] Koppe, E. F. and D. R. Thompson, Progress in the recognition of fractured rock zones in prevention and abatement of mine drainage: 4th Symposium on Coal Mine Drainage Res., Mellon Institute, Pittsburgh, Pennsylvania, pp. 41-47, 1972.

[34] LeGrand, H. E., Sheet structure, a major factor in the occurrence of ground-water in the granites of Georgia: Econ. Geol. Vol. 44, pp. 110-118, 1949.

[35] Mundorff, M. J., Geology and ground-water in the Greensboro area: North Carolina, North Carolina Mineral Res. Bull., Vol. 55, 108 p., 1948.

[36] Dingman, R. J. and G. Meyer, The water resources of Howard and Montgomery Counties, Maryland: Maryland Dept. of Geol. Mines and Water Res., Bull. 14, 260 p., 1954.

[37]   Poth, C. W., Hydrology of the metamorphic and igneous
       rocks of Central Chester County, Pennsylvania:
       Pennsylvania Geol. Survey, 4th ser., Bull. W-25, 84 p.,
       1968.

[38]   Johnston, H. E., Ground-water resources of the Loysville
       and Mifflintown quadrangles in south-central Pennsylvania:
       Pennsylvania Geol. Survey, 4th ser., Water Resource
       Report W-27, 96 p., 1970.

[39]   Theis, C. V., Ground water in south-central Tennessee:
       U.S. Geol. Survey Water Supply Paper 677, 182 p., 1936.

[40]   Rhoades, R. and M. N. Sinacori, Pattern of ground-water
       flow and solution: Journal Geol., Vol. 49, No. 8,
       pp. 785-794, 1941.

[41]   Bedinger, M. S., An electrical analog study of the
       geometry of limestone solution: Ground Water, Vol. 5,
       No. 1, pp. 24-28, 1967.

[42]   Shuster, E. T. and W. B. White, Seasonal variations   in
       ground-water chemistry: pp. 121-126, In *Hydrogeology and
       Geochemistry of Folded and Faulted Carbonate Rocks of the
       Central Appalachian Type and Related Land Use Problems*,
       College of Earth and Mineral Science, Mineral
       Conservation Section, Circular 82, 182 p., edited by
       R. R. Parizek, W. B. White and D. Langmuir, 1971.

[43]   Konikow, L. F., Mountain runoff and its relation to
       precipitation, ground water, and recharge to the
       carbonate aquifers of Nittany Valley, Pennsylvania:
       M.S. thesis, Dept. of Geol. and Geophys., The
       Pennsylvania State University, 128 p., 1969.

[44]   Rauch, H. W. and W. B. White, Lithologic controls on
       the development of solution porosity in carbonate
       aquifers: Water Resources Res., Vol. 6,   pp. 1175-1192,
       1970.

[45]   Mundi, E. K., The physical characteristics of some
       fractured aquifers in central Pennsylvania and a digital
       simulation of their sustained yield: Ph.D. dissertation,
       Dept. of Geosciences, The Pennsylvania State University,
       250 p., 1971.

[46]   Brown, R. F. and T. W. Lambert, Reconnaissance of
       ground-water resources of the Mississippian Plateau
       Region, Kentucky: U.S. Geol. Survey Water Supply Paper
       1603, 58 p., 16 pls., 10 figs., 15 tables, 1963.

[47] Cline, G. C., Geologic factors influencing well-yields in a folded sandstone-siltstone-shale terrane within the East Manhantango Creek Watershed, Pennsylvania: M.S. thesis, Dept. Geol. and Geophys., The Pennsylvania State University, 180 p. 1968.

[48] Gwinn, V. W., Thin-skinned tectonics in the Plateau and Northeastern Valley and Ridge Provinces of the Central Appalachians: Geol. Soc. of Am. Bull. 75, pp. 863-900, 1964.

[49] Hamilton, D. K., Some solutional features of the limestone near Lexington, Kentucky: Econ. Geol., Vol. 43, pp. 39-52, 1948.

[50] Howard, A. D., The development of karst features: Natl. Speleo. Soc. Bull., Vol. 25, Pt. 2, pp. 45-65, 1963.

[51] Kayne, C. A., The effect of solvent motion on limestone: Journal Geol., Vol. 65, pp. 35-46, 1957.

[52] Mandel, S., A conceptual model of karstic erosion by ground water: Bull. of the Inter. Assoc. of Scientific Hydrology, Vol. 11, No. 1, 1966.

[53] Stringfield, V. T. and H. E. LeGrand, Hydrology of limestone terranes in the coastal plain of the south-eastern United States: Geol. Soc. of Am. Special Paper 93, 46 p., 1966.

[54] Thomas, G. E., Grouping of carbonate rocks into textural and porosity units for mapping purposes in classification of carbonate rocks: Am. Assoc. Petrol. Geologists Memoir 1, pp. 193-224, 1962.

[55] Weise, D. V., Regional and sub-continental sized fracture systems detectable by topographic shadow techniques: Geol. Survey Canada Paper 68-52, pp. 175-199, 1968.

DISCUSSION

Yevjevich. The research results presented in the paper are impressive. They coincide with similar findings elsewhere. As a support to this approach, the experience in the Trebisnijica River basin shows, that a particular borehole (PB-1) on the intersection of large fractures (faults) provides significant hydrologic information.

Full spectrum of remote sensing can be used in karst areas. When water flow increases in a karst formation, the air must be replaced by water. The cold air would then escape at the nearest outlets to atmosphere. The infrared photography might then discover these places, indicating the locations of major underground karst channels.

In comparing the investigations in hydrogeology and in hydrology of karst formations, it seems a safe approach to expect the hydrogeologic investigations to lead to advancement of the most plausible hypotheses, and then by a use of the quantitative hydrologic investigations to test, accept or reject, these hypotheses.

Pavlović. I was impressed by the similarity of the author's approach to the solution of the problems posed with the approach used by Professor Bać of Sarajevo. By using the fracture trace method for the last he was very successful in locating ground water, both for water supply and for an increase of thermal and mineral waters. Therefore, an exchange of experience on the uses of fracture trace method is very beneficial, regardless that Professor Bać did not have on his disposal the satellite pictures.

Avdagić. Professor Bać, working within the Institute of Water Resources Engineering in Sarajevo, used very successfully, the fracture trace method. He was a pioneer in searching for the fresh ground waters, as well as for the thermal and mineral waters in fissured rocks. His approach was very similar as that in this paper. In a large majority of cases he was very successful in this search, obtaining the water flows from the drilled wells of 100 l/s or more in dry periods of the year. Three such projects are underway at present. In addition to general geological and micro-geological maps, used for investigations, the data on fracture traces are identified also by using the topographical maps, by field investigation, because the areal photographs were not available. The boreholes are then located at fracture trace intersections.

Dragović (Dusan). With regard to investigations of the coastal karst zone, as well as the Sinjevina Mountain in Montenegro, maps of a scale 1:25,000 were used in order to establish the river basins boundaries and for the planning of explorations. It was feasible to draw a large number of lines indicating tectonic breaks, faults, and fissures which accompany the funnel-shaped depressions in karst, or the other typical features of the relief establishing thus a likely existence of concentrations of underground channels. Using this information, and by a visual inspection of the terrain from the higher elevations, in the study of water supply of Cetinje, the river basin was defined and the most likely directions of the underground flow of the Cetinje River and its tributaries, as well as the locations of concentration of water usable for water supply were established. Then, it was concluded that the investigations carried out in the Cetinje Polje, could not lead to the identification of water quantities for an economical water supply. This also was confirmed later by well drillings.

The use of the remote sensing techniques for such investigations, as described in this paper, offers possibilities for considerable improvement in the use of the fracture trace method, with better chances of success. In this way, the exploration program for searching for ground water which would then replace the more expensive methods used at present.

Breznik. There are three major water resources areas for economic development of karst regions: (i) flood control of karst poljes, (ii) hydroelectric power generation, and (iii) use of ground water for water supply and irrigation.

The floods are usually decreased in karst poljes by hydroelectric power developments. This effort is fully applied in the Yugoslav karst at present. The development of karst ground water needs much more investigations for their full use.

Research and investigation of karst aquifers and underground courses is well developed in some countries, such as Syria and Greece. In Syria, the limestone is rich with water. The capacity of wells reached usually between 1-20 l/s. In Greece the results varied, depending on the type of karst, as pointed out by Prof. Herak. Much more attention should be paid to the investigation and utilization of karst ground waters in Yugoslavia. To obtain better results the method proposed by Professor Parizek should be followed.

Faulkner. This paper is a very good evaluation of the role of fracture analysis for identifying important permeability in the subsurface. In my judgement a detailed statistical proof of the value of fracture analysis as a means for optimum location of water-supply wells in carbonate rocks in the United States is hardly needed. I would judge that the method would have important applications in Yugoslav karst, although there are others here with much more knowledge of the Yugoslav karst who could make a better judgement of this than I.

Early in his presentation, the author indicated that remote-sensing fracture analysis had value in locating zones of high permeability that could be used for high-rate large-volume injection and storage of liquid wastes. This seems a contradiction to the generally accepted concept that a subsurface liquid-waste storage zone should be overlain by an essentially impermeabile confining layer. If traces of fractures indicative of a highly permeable zone in the subsurface are observed on the surface, a permeable connection with the proposed storage zone and the land surface would seem to be suggested. I know of one area where regional fracture lineaments are being analyzed by remote sensing methods with the object being to avoid waste injection operations where a high risk of significant upward leakage along faults or fractures could exist.

Parizek. I entirely agree that thermal infrared sensing and other remote sensing procedures can be useful in detecting the location of sinkholes, shallow holes and shallow caves and conduits under Yugoslavian conditions. This should be possible even when there is an overburden of unconsolidated soils or tree cover obscuring direct field observation. A discussion on conduit detection using geothermal means was prepared following our seminar to further elaborate on this point (See comments by Ebaugh, Parizek and Greenfield in the written discussion submitted on the paper by Arandjelović et al).

Zones of fracture concentration have been shown to localize weathering, solution development and avenues of increased permeability and porosity in a wide variety of terrances. In carbonate terranes these structural controls are particularly significant because they control the location of cave and conduit systems, and zones of more intense differential chemical and physical weathering near the bedrock surface. Caliper log data show this for wells located on fracture traces and fracture trace injections (Fig. 20). These high avenues of permeability in turn, control soil water and groundwater movement and air flow within bedrock hence, should be useful when attempting to vent compressed air trapped by overlying less permeable residual and transported soils and by a rapidly rising water table. Not uncommonly unconsolidated overburden sediments are 1 to 10 more times thicker along zones of fracture concentration when compared with adjacent bedrock areas. This is revealed by casing lengths in Fig. 20. These deposits may help to retain compressed air within underlying bedrock voids to help produce the hazardous blowouts and *inverse* piping failures described by several Yugoslav colleagues.

I agree with you Professor Yevjevich, that fracture trace and lineament mapping procedures should be evaluated as a means of locating potential pockets of trapped air beneath poljes and flooded karst plains. These voids could be penetrated by a number of boreholes and air vents constructed to prevent piping erosion. A relatively few boreholes located along interlaced avenues of high bedrock permeability should serve to control air pressures within adjacent less permeable blocks of bedrock where voids are more difficult to locate on a consistent basis.

Figure 20 shows typical caliper logs of water wells drilled on and adjacent to zones of fracture concentration. They clearly show that dry solution cavities can be well developed and

numerous above and below the water table (beneath fracture
traces) even for less cavity prone dolomites, hence, should
serve to control air flow above the water table. Blowouts
actually may occur immediately adjacent to these zones of
weathering where the soil cover is thin.

    To evaluate the potential use of fracture traces and
lineaments for this purpose, high altitude stereo paired black
and white or color photographs at a 1:10,000 to 1:20,000 scale

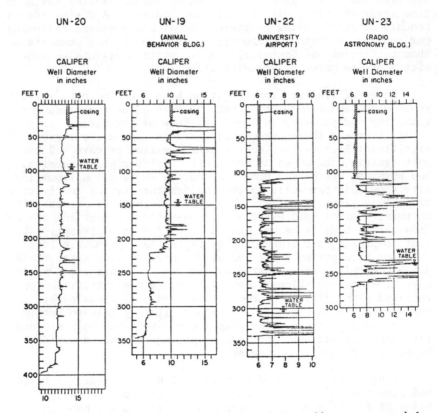

Fig. 20. Caliper logs of wells drilled into limestone or dolo-
          mite. UN-19 and 20 are at interfracture trace sites,
          UN-22 on a single fracture trace and UN-23 at a frac-
          ture trace intersection. The residual soil thickness
          is revealed by the casing length. (After Lattman and
          Parizek 1964)*

* Latman, L. H., and R. R. Parizek, Relationship between
          Fracture Traces and the Occurrence of Groundwater in
          Carbonate Rocks: Journal of Hydrology, Vol. 2,
          p. 73-91, 1964.

is all that is required for initial work. Lineaments could be
mapped on an independent basis and lineaments, fracture traces,
fault zones, bedding planes and other intersecting structural
and stratigraphic features mapped to define areas of potential
cavity development. These could be compared with known areas
of *blow outs* sinkhole formation, subsidence areas and data obtained from drill holes, tunnels and foundation excavations.

Fracture traces and lineaments are underlain by zones of
structural weakness hence have been shown to localize gulley
development, valley and stream positions, surface sags and
depressions and other elements of surface and subsurface drainage networks. Using lineation features that have pronounced
topographic expression on maps to identify possible fissure
locations means using a reliable guide in prospecting efforts.
Additional information, however, can still be gained through
photo analysis because many lineaments and fracture traces
or segments of them have little or no obvious topographic expression and are entirely overlooked when studying topographic
maps. Further, it is often possible to discriminate among
various features that control topography and have linear expression on topographic maps that are not controlled by near
vertical zones of fracture concentration. For this reason I
strongly urge that a photo analysis be made in all cases where
definition of zones of increased permeability and porosity development and differential weathering are required. Information base may be more than doubled by this procedure.

The saying that *there is nothing new under the sun* or that
new discoveries are made only when one fails to read history
undoubtedly applies to this matter of using lineaments and
fracture traces when prospecting for groundwater. Bedrock is
well exposed in the mountainous and sparcely vegetated area of
Yugoslavia and lineation features are particularly well exposed by width and length under such circumstances. A trained
individual may be quick to make these observations and under-
stand the association between zones of fracture concentration,
their surface expression, and their importance in controlling
groundwater movement. An early awareness could be gained in
semi arid to arid regions where vegetation highlights lineaments and where water supplies have been obtained from lineament controlled springs. The alignment of springs, valleys,
sinkholes, shallow holes, and vegetation patterns is
particularly apparent in semi arid areas underlain by limestone.
Experience by Professor Bać undoubtedly belongs to this category and our exchange of experience is worthwhile.

Poor well yields are the rule rather than the exception in
carbonate and other rocks where intergranular permeability and
porosity are essentially lacking and secondary openings dominate
in their control of water movement. This point is well illustrated in the paper. The various wells drilled to meet farm,
domestic, industrial and commercial water needs in a region of
Central Pennsylvania, a range of 0.00005 to 0.050 gallons per

minute per foot of drawdown per foot of saturated rock penetrated (gpm/ft/ft) was observed for a number of wells drilled
into the Keyser Limestone. A 50% yield value likely to be
equalled or exceeded for all Keyser wells was only 0.002 gpm/
ft/ft whereas a 50% yield value of 0.004 gpm/ft/ft was observed
for the Oriskany Formation. These data, based on several hundred reliable well points significantly degrade the importance
of these formations as aquifers and they have been all but overlooked as important water supplies in a heavily industrialized
region of Pennsylvania in preference to surface water. Rather
costly surface water storage and treatment facilities have
been developed over the years and to make matters worse, poor
landuse planning and control has resulted in the pollution of
this narrow but elongate folded aquifer system without awareness of its potential significance or presence.

Test drilling is costly in the U. S. and in carbonate
terranes drilling difficulties are the rule. Test holes can
cost from U. S. $10,000 to $50,000 or more, depending upon the
size of test well selected, its location, etc. Often 5 to 10
such test holes have been required to secure an adequate supply
of water from two or three final production wells. When the
number of failures is kept to a minimum, say by the elimination
of one or more unsuccessful wells, frequently will more than
cover the cost of obtaining high altitude photographs for a
large area. Where these photos have multiple uses in topographic map making, planning engineering studies and geological
investigations, their cost can be shared and greatly reduced
when charged to various projects.

Faulkner's point is well taken because for either waste
injection or gas storage to be successful without loss of gas
or fluids to overlying aquifers, a poorly permeable to
impermeable cap rock is required for containment. However, it
is difficult to avoid zones of fracture concentration when selecting subsurface chemical waste storage sites or gas storage
reservoirs. Figure 3 of the paper illustrates the density of
fracture trace-revealed zones of fracture concentration that
are typically present in a given region. Three to five zones
are not uncommon in any 100 acre tract and occasionally more
are present. When it is considered that a large scaled
waste injection project may require the storage space contained
beneath a several hundred area tract of land it is difficult to
avoid these zones of fracture concentration. The intent is to
utilize the increased uptake and delivery efficiency of the
fracture trace intersection injection site for waste water or
gas and the more efficient gas recovery efficiency of such a
site and at the same time selecting a region where the cap rock
is thick, joints and fractures are poorly developed to tight
caps. Hence, rocks are relatively impermeable.

An additional problem remains. Fracture traces are underlain by zones of vertical to near vertical fracture concentra-

tion. However, these zones have been observed to have a 1 to 2 degree deviation from vertical. An injection well located at the center line of two intersecting fracture traces at land-surface need not penetrate the intersection at the depth interval of interest and the well may fail to derive the benefit of the fracture zone. Field conditions frequently do not permit direct inspection of the dip of the fracture zone, hence some element of chance still remains. Also the degree of fracture development with depth of burial is not well established at least in published literature. Oil companies undoubtedly have confidential data that would shed light on this point

Faulkner is correct that I have been attempting in the paper to document the significance of fracture trace features in groundwater and geotechnical investigations since 1961 and more recently lineaments in terranes where secondary permeability and porosity predominate and where it is particularly difficult to pinpoint avenues of permeability development in advance of drilling. Further, only two U. S. authored groundwater text books published in the U. S. in the last 15 years even mention the importance of these features and previous books exclude the concept entirely. Groundwater prospecting in these terrances has been conducted on a rather hit or miss basis for many years and many responsible practicing engineers, groundwater geologists and others have more or less written off vast areas of the USA as important groundwater provinces or have accepted the fact that groundwater prospecting is a risky business and requires a test drilling program as a matter of routine and at considerable expense.

Further research is still necessary for fracture trace method because the geotechnical significance of lineaments of the 10 to 50 km length class is essentially undocumented from a scientific view point. The length, width and depth of these features and fracture density is poorly known as are the three dimensional permeability and porosity distribution characteristics along these zones. Still less is known about the consistency and variability of well yields likely to be obtained along these zones in advance of drilling under the great diversity of field conditions in which they have applications. Meaningful yield data are required to illustrate the extent of the benefits they may derive by using these features.

Similar remarks apply when planning mines and tunnels, quarries, deep highway cuts, and foundations to minimize problems of excessive water and unstable ground. Fracture trace and lineament mapping is still not routine in site evaluation studies for these facilities.

For these and other reasons further work is justified and information transferral must continue. The national interest

in lineaments by U. S. geologists has expanded on a widespread
basis essentially since the first images became available from
LANDSAT-1 and SKYLAB. The documentation of their nature and
usefulness will require additional years of study.

HYDROGEOLOGIC METHODOLOGY FOR INVESTIGATION OF A KARST POLJE

by

Joco Mladenović, Geological Engineer
Energoinvest, Sarajevo, Yugoslavia

Synopsis. This paper relates to investigation methods of hydrogeologic problems of a karst polje which represents a classical example of karst morphogenic development within the region of the outer Dinarides in Yugoslavia. A strong emphasis is put on theoretical aspects of essential factors which have taken part in developments of karst processes, as well as on specific conditions of groundwater drainage, storage and outflow.

The presented hydrogeologic concepts are a synthesis of results of an applied research methodology. The developed criteria for hydrogeologic terrane division and classification of rocks according to intensity of karstification, water permeability, hydrogeologic function of rocks and other parameters are shown.

1. Introduction.

In karst terranes of Yugoslavia, in which the belt of outer Dinarides has a special place as a separate morphologic and geotectonic unit, various micro and macro surface and underground morphologic forms are developed, such as large poljes, deep fossile river valleys, caves, and innumerable sinking streams with large karst springs in water outflowing zones. This is the reason why the belt of the Dinaric Karst is treated as a classical karst development area. The wider area of the Popovo Polje in the lower reach of the Trebišnjica River is only a small piece of this large karst complex. This area was the subject of comprehensive hydrogeologic investigations in the last two years, with the purpose of water resources developments.

Investigations have shown that this region has many common hydrogeologic features with other karst regions. They also proved that it is characterized by certain specific features which are the result of local geologic, tectonic, and geomorphologic terrane conditions. Therefore, this study presents the investigation methodology of the terrane, the approach to interpretation of hydrogeologic conditions and the results obtained.

2. Applied Methodology for Hydrogeologic Investigations.

Since the basic objective of almost all hydrogeologic investigations is the determination of parameters needed for quantitative results on groundwater drainage and storage, it is of importance to determine hydrogeologic functions of litho-stratigraphic members and their spatial positions.

In non-karst terranes, which have simpler geologic structures, as well as in these terranes in which various sediments are lithologicly present, hydrogeologic functions of particular kinds of rocks is self evident. They result from certain kinds of porosity. In order to obtain parameters needed in groundwater investigations, often only a small amount of investigation is necessary, because previous hydro-geologic mappings may have already defined the basic para-meters such as the watershed surface, the thickness and the position of aquifer tables, etc. In a characteristic karst terrane, as in the Popovo Polje, the hydrogeologic classifica-tion of rocks and the approach to groundwater study were more difficult than usual. The reason is that large areas are predominantly built of carbonate rocks of different geologic ages, with these rocks folded, faulted, resulting in reverse positions to each other, so that they form a discontinuous hydrogeologic environment.

The groundwater circulation in such an environment is through concentrated underground channels, so that often the karst springs are the only hydrologic features available for a direct study. In a large number of cases the groundwater outflow is in the form of either strong periodic karst springs or permanent springs with sudden water oscillations, frequently as multiple springs, or as submarine springs. In such condi-tions difficulties exist for collecting data necessary for hydrologic and hydrogeologic analyses. Similarly, difficulties appear during the determination of watershed surfaces of certain springs, or in determining the groundwater discharge zones. Problems that most frequently appear are:

(i) The question of determining the underground water dividing lines, and the surface or subsurface flow from one watershed into another, frequent in the rainy period;

(ii) The influence of water originated over the local watershed and ephemeral surface water which feeds numerous karst springs; and

(iii) The dependence of the mechanism of underground flow on the influence of one or the other watershed, on one hand, and the transmissivity of underground channels, on the other.

This explains the complexity of hydrogeologic problems
in distinctly karst terranes. A successful study of groundwater drainage and storage is nearly impossible without a comprehensive analysis of the generic development of karst
processes. Another factor is that karst appears as a complex
phenomenon created under specific conditions of maintaining
a balance between the opposite effects of permanent activities
of endodynamic and exodynamic forces during the evolution of
a terrane. Therefore, the modern study of the karst must be
approached by the geologic history reconstruction starting
with the geosynclinal sedimentation cycle, then through the
embrio of karstification process after the land emersion, to
the present day.

To find solutions to practical hydrogeologic problems
in the development of the karst region studied, certain investigations were carried out, such as:

(i)   The geologic - tectonic mapping, with a register
of all morphologic and hydrologic karst phenomena;

(ii)   Geomorphologic considerations and speleologic
studies by the classical method, and by the method of lowering
TV cameras in drilled holes;

(iii)   Geophysical studies utilizing the geoelectric
methods;

(iv)   Hydrochemical studies of water at karst water
features;

(v)   Hydrometric measurements along the Trebišnjica River
and of spring flows both in dry and wet periods, and during
water release from the reservoir into the Trebišnjica River.

(vi)   The study of groundwater connections using the
method of natrium fluorescine tracer, spores, radioactive
isotopes, special bombs, etc.

(vii)   Geologic structural and hydrogeologic drillings
for the study of rock permeability and gamma carotage, and

(viii)   The study of oscillations of groundwater levels
in boreholes.

The results of each kind of investigation are not specified in this text. They were used to obtain a general picture
of geologic phenomena and in drawing conclusions about the
general hydrogeologic groundwater drainage and storage conditions.

3.   Results of Hydrogeologic Investigations.

Hydrogeologic research of the Popovo Polje area has
covered a large surface of land. The borders of the terrane
studied were from the lowest erosion bases, on one side (the

coastal line, the valley of the River Neretva, and partly the
Bregava River), and on the other side the mountain massifs
which are drained through karst poljes and other morphologic
features to the lower horizons. This was facilitated by the
fact that in karst terranes such as the Popovo Polje, the
surface water dividing lines have little hydrogeologic
importance. Karst depressions surrounded by mountains represent
morphologically separate units. From a hydrographic point
of view they are most often dry or only periodically flooded.
For example, karst depression of the Popovo Polje with a
distinct position in the center of the terrane, hydrogeologically represents a zone to which groundwaters are drained.
At the same time, the division of groundwater flows in several
directions is performed at this depression, namely towards the
sea and towards the Neretva River. Seen from a regional point
of view the whole area is built of more or less permeable
carbonate rocks of fissure and cavernous permeability type.
In spite of this the circulation of groundwater from higher
to lower horizons is not frontal, but by privileged zone
routes and concentrated underground channels.

To establish the essential factors which have produced
the particular hydrogeologic conditions of the Popovo Polje,
it was necessary to classify rocks according to their
hydrogeologic function in the overall terrane.

In establishing criteria for classification the concepts
developed for karst hydrogeology by M. Herak [1,2,3,4] were
used, attaching a special importance to structural-tectonic
elements, taking into account all the other lithostratographic,
geomorphologic, and hydrologic factors. The results of
hydrogeologic investigations are given in maps and by cross-
sections. Graphically a modern hydrogeologic map is produced
in such a way that the lithology is presented by lineation,
stratigraphy by symbols, and the hydrogeologic function of
rocks by color. In addition the map contains all tectonic
elements of hydrologic phenomena, and the established and
general directions of groundwater flow. All these factors
cannot be presented only in black and white. Therefore, the
lithostratigraphic members are designated by symbols, and
the hydrogeologic function of rocks by lineation in the
geologic and corresponding hydrogeologic cross sections of
Figs. 1 and 2.

4. Hydrogeologic Classification of Rocks.

Hydrogeologic classification of rocks has been made by
the analysis of lithological content, morphologic and
structural-tectonic position of every stratigraphic member
in the terrane, their influence on the intensity and develop-
mental direction of karstification process, as well as on the
mechanism of groundwater drainage.

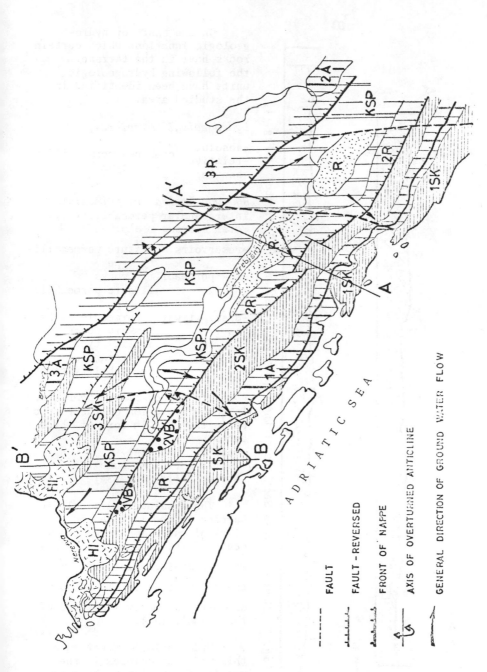

Fig. 1. Hydrogeologic Map of the Popovo Polje Region.

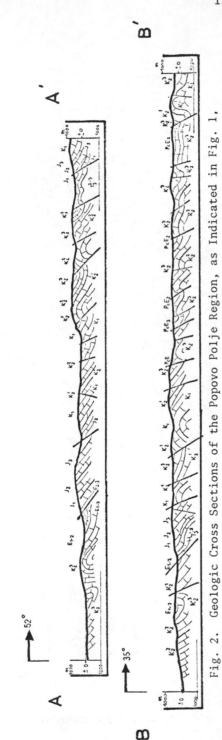

Fig. 2. Geologic Cross Sections of the Popovo Polje Region, as Indicated in Fig. 1.

On the basis of hydro-
geologic functions which certain
rocks have in the terrane,
the following hydrogeologic
units have been identified in
the studied area:

Hydrogeologic barriers:

-absolute
-relative   combined permeability
-hanging   type

Hydrogeological roof insulators:
intergranular permeability type
Water bearing rocks:

-reservoirs   fissure permeability type
-low permeability rocks
fissure permeabili-
ty type
-distinct water permeable rocks
fissure perme-
ability type,
intergranular
permeability type

Absolute hydrogeologic barriers.
In the wide region of the Popovo
Polje they are in form of three
zones:
-coastal zone (1A)
-Lastva anticline zone (2A)
-Stolac Polje zone (3A)

The absolute hydrogeologic
barrier in the 1A zone consists of water impermeable sediments of the Eocene flysch (E_3),
low permeability dolomite of
the upper Triassic (T_3^{2-3}), and
dolomite and marly limestone of
the Liassic (J_1).

Hydrogeologic function of
this sediment complex is the
result of lithologic characteristics of the sediment, on one
hand, and tectonic manifestations, on the other. Namely,

the stratigraphically younger sediments of the Eocene flysch are lowered deep beneath the erosion basis (the sea) and over them, along the front of the fold of the high karst, the formation of the upper Triassic is found. Because of such a position in the terrane this Triassic formulation has the role of setting up groundwater directions, in the hydrogeologic sense, which causes a large number of karst springs along this belt.

The absolute hydrogeologic barrier in the 2A zone consists of the upper Triassic dolomite (T_3^{2-3}). In the structural sense these rocks form the well known Lastva anticline. This is again the case where the lithologic content, and especially the tectonic structure of the terrane have produced the positive hydrogeologic function of the rocks, which has been proven by numerous dye tests done in the watershed of the Trebišnjica River. The positive hydrogeologic function of the Lastva anticline has determined the Trebišnjica River to have surface flow all the way to Trebinje where its waters start sinking underground. The Bileća Reservoir is partly located over the Lastva anticline.

In the syncline zone 3A the Eocene flysch is hypsometrically much lower than the local erosion basis, the Bregava River. This was produced by the tectonic lowering of the whole Stolac syncline block along the reversed fault. Because of this the movement of groundwater in this direction is not possible.

Relative hydrogeologic barriers. In the studied region they are expressed in several isolated zones of the Dinaric direction as:
- coastal belt zone (1R)
- Zavala anticline zone (2R)
- Ljubomir anticline zone (3R).

The relative hydrogeologic barrier in the 1R zone consists of the lithologic-stratigraphic members (T_3^{2-3}, J_1, E). From the structural-tectonic point of view they have also the same position with the fold characteristics, but here the impermeable Eocene flysch is not locally situated deep below the Triassic dolomite. Therefore, in these spaces and in the parts of the terrane where the dolomite is tectonically broken, the groundwater can move under the flysch and drain to springs and submarine springs along the coast.

In the 2R zone the relative barrier consists of dolomite and limestone of the upper Jurassic and the lower and upper Cretaceous $(J_3, K_1, K_2^1, \text{and } K_2^2)$. The anticline structure, and lithologic characteristics have contributed to the positive hydrogeologic function. It can be seen by the direction of groundwater flow to points in which the barrier is broken by the fault tectonics.

In the 3R zone, which is actually a deformed continuation of the zone 2A, the relative barrier consists of a group of lithostratigraphic members. It includes dolomite and limestone of almost all stratigraphic members of the Jurassic and Cretaceous. The positive hydrologic function of the mentioned complex of sediments 3R zone has been influenced by the tangential tectonics. This can be seen in the reverse movement of the older sediments of the Jurassic and Cretaceous over the younger upper Cretaceous and Eocene formations. By such a mechanism of rock mass movements deeper sediments of the Triassic are brought on a higher hypsometric level, which caused an underground watershed in this zone. From this watershed groundwater drains in several directions: to the Popovo Polje, to the Trebišnjica River upstream of Grančarevo, and to the Bregava River.

Hydrogeologic hanging barriers (HB). These are terranes which are built of impermeable flysch of the Eocene in the syncline of smaller karst poljes. Since the flysch is of small thickness and are laid as a thin cover over water permeable and karstified limestones of the upper Cretaceous, they are by their positions an obstacle to flow of high waters of rainy period, while the low waters flow beneath them. This is the reason why during the rainy period small springs appear along the boundaries of the polje, which leads to the periodic flooding.

Hydrogeologic insulators (HI). They consist of poli-facial complex of impermeable Quarternary sediments (clayish gravel, clay, peat, and others) which cover the depression along the Neretva River valley. Even though they belong to the highest stratigraphic level in the geological column, they still have, because of their low position in the terrane (1-2 meters above the sea level) and their thickness of more than 80 meters, a special significance in the hydrogeologic sense as a factor in directing the groundwater.

Hydrogeologic function of water-bearing rocks as reservoirs. They give favorable hydrogeologic conditions for the groundwater storage. Such terranes are in sectors 1KR, 2KR, 3KR.

These areas are built of predominantly karstified, strongly permeable, limestones with rare strata of the upper Cretaceous dolomite. Their structural position is such that in their foundation and boundaries less permeable sediments are situated with the hydrogeologic function of relative barriers which prevent or slow down the flow of stored groundwater from these areas. On the other hand, free groundwater

flow from higher horizons is made possible through terranes
with the hydrogeologic function of water-bearing rocks or
along tectonically predetermined flow directions.

Low permeability rocks. They are parts of lithologic
compositions due to their structural position, or due to the
superposed order of sediments, as low permeability formations.
Such areas are:

- narrow belt along the coast (1SK) where the Cretaceous
  and Eocene limestone and dolomite are located under
  the absolute or relative barriers, respectively;

- the belt of the limestone - dolomite plateau (J_2, J_3)

  (2SK) which is inserted between the south and the north
  hydrogeologic barriers;

- smaller isolated occurrences (3SK), made of the Paleo-
  cene and Eocene sandy and marly limestones, preserved
  in the synclinal parts of the terrane.

Function of permeable rocks - conductors. This is
characteristic of the Cretaceous and partly Jurassic limestone and dolomite, which make the geologic structure of the
terrane, sector KSP. Hydrogeologic function of the rocks is
the product of their tectonic damage, a strongly expressed
degree of karstification, with a very important factor being
the elevation. It is a mountain chain with points up to 1400
meters high, which lowers abruptly towards the depression of
the Popovo Polje (elevations of 225-250 m), and somewhat more
moderately towards the Bregava and the Neretva Rivers.

From this place groundwater drains in several directions
which are:

east sector towards the Trebišnjica Springs above
Trebinje,
- during high water towards periodic springs
in the depression of the Popovo Polje
- during low water the drainage takes place
below the polje to springs of the coastal
belt.

west sector towards the springs of the Svitava Depression,
the Neretva River and partly the Bregava
River.

It should be pointed out that circulation of groundwater
even under these conditions of distinct hydrogeologic water-
bearing formations is not frontal, but takes place along the
tectonically predetermined directions, namely along faults or
structures.

Quarternary (alluvial) sediments are also treated as hydrogeologic water-bearing formations. They usually consist of clayish gravel and sand as an intergranular type of permeability. Such formations in the considered area are usually karst morphologic depressions such as the Popovo, Trebinjsko, Ljubomirsko and Ljubinjsko poljes. The thickness of these water bearing formations is usually small, except at the bottom of the Popovo Polje where it is up to 30 m. The base of these formations usually consists of karstified limestone in which the groundwater level is deep beneath the surface of the terrane, so that these formations are usually dry and only periodically saturated by water.

5. Conclusions.

The following conclusions can be drawn:

The wider area of the Popovo Polje is a classical example of morphogeneric development of karst phenomena within the carbonate formations in the zone of the outer Dinarides in Yugoslavia. It is characterized by the occurrence of karst forms such as: deep swallowholes, sinkholes, springs, estavelas and submarine springs, with a maze of interconnected underground channels.

Hydrogeologic problems of karst terranes, and especially of the Popovo Polje, are very complex. The study of groundwater drainage and water storage conditions is almost impossible without an analysis of the genesis of karst.

The study of karst phenonena is to be approached by the method of geologic tectonic history reconstruction, using the results of a wide range of investigations in various scientific disciplines: geologic, geomorphologic, geophysic, hydrologic, and others.

Classification of types of terranes and formation of the area concerned represents a synthesis of results obtained by previous comprehensive investigations.

Summarized results of investigations show that in a karst region such as the Popovo Polje region, built of carbonate rocks (fissure-cavernous type of porosity), the groundwater circulation from higher horizons to lower ones is not performed only through concentrated underground channels.

The main influence on the directions of water circulation and the general mechanics of drainage and groundwater storage are determined by hydrologic functions of rock formations. This is a result not only of lithologic composition and rock porosity, but mainly depend upon the structural tectonics and morphologic positions of certain rock formations.

The division of the terrane and the hydrologic classification of formations is shown on maps and various cross
sections according to water permeability parameters, the
intensity of karstification and hydrogeologic functions of
formations.

6. References.

[1] Herak, M., O nekim hidrogeološkim problemima Male
    Kapele (On some hydrogeologic problems of the Mala
    Kapela): Geološki vjesnik (Geologic Bulletin), 8-9,
    Zagreb, 1956.

[2] Herak, M., Geološka osnova nekih hidrogeoloških pojava
    u Dinarskom kršu (Geologic base of some hydrogeologic
    phenomena in the Dinaric Karst): Transections, II Congress
    of Yugoslavian geologists, 523-539, Sarajevo, 1957.

[3] Herak, J., Tektonska osnova hidrogeoloških odnosa u
    izvorišnim područjima Kupe i Korane (Tectonic base
    of hydrogeologic relations in the upper part of Kupa
    and Korana Rivers): Proceeding the Vth Congress of
    Yugoslavian geologists, Belgrade, 17-75, 1962.

[4] Herak, M., Pozitivni i negativni uticaji na razoj krša
    u Hrvatskoj (Positive and negative influences in the
    development of the karst in Croatia): Krš Jugoslavije
    (Yugoslav Karst), Jug. akad. 6, Zagreb, 1969.

[5] Bahun S., Fritz F., Hidrogeologija Ličkog polja (Hydro-
    geology of the Ličko Polje): Krš Jugoslavije, Yugoslav
    Karst, Jugosl. akademia (Yugoslav Academy of Sciences),
    8/3, 43-55 Zagreb, 1972.

[6] Stepanović, B., Principi opšte hidrogeologije (Principles
    of General Hydrogeology): Beograd, 1962.

DISCUSSION

Breznik (Marko). This discussion relates not only to the
paper by Mladenović but also to the ongoing work of sealing
water losses at the pondage of the power plant being built in
the Popovo Polje region.

There are two types of sealings for decreasing water
losses in a pondage: (a) surface sealings, developed with the
basic idea of closing the existing sinkholes by technical means,
which greatly rely on impermeability of the clayey layers covering the bottom of a karst polje; and (b) deep located closings
which use grouting curtains to make a permeable rock mass
impermeable with a partial filling of large channels in the
cross section of grouting curtains.

The experience with construction of many reservoirs in the karst areas of Yugoslavia, as well as in the other countries, over the last 24 years, shows that deep located closing were successfully carried out, such as for the Peruća, Kruščica, Grančarevo, Gorica, Slano, and other reservoirs, whereas the attempts for surface closings failed in many cases, such as Vrtac at the Nikšić Polje, Cerkniško Jezero in Slovenia, Deckersberg in Germany, and Perdikas in Greece.

The project for construction of the pondage for the Čapljina hydroelectric power plant calls for a use of surface closing. The closing of sinkholes along the pondage rim is planned, along with a protection of the bottom by using a plastic foil, while the other parts of the clayey bottom remain unprotected. It is well known that the karst channels which have a capacity for water flow, will produce due to the closing of sinkholes with which they have been communicating, an erosion of clayey bottom from beneath. This will open up new sinkholes in the clayey bottom of the pondage. Such new sinkholes at the bottom of the pondage should be expected in the future. For this reason the final successful realization of the project will be extremely difficult.

Mladenović. The discussion by Breznik is related to the subject not treated in the paper. However, to answer it, the practice shows that each case in making the karst peaking power ponds impermeable is a specific case, which depends on various local conditions. The generalization usually leads to a pessimistic assessment as it concerns the construction of hydraulic structures in karst areas, which pessimism was not supported by a vast experience on many karst cases. The use of grouting curtains in case of the Čapljina Power Plant pond would be a much more expensive proposition. Besides, it would lead to flooding of larger areas in the Popovo Polje than would be acceptable.

The concept of the alternative presently being implemented is based on: (i) a detailed regionalization of macro-sinkhole zones and zones without sinkholes, (ii) the positive function of the impervious clayey cover of the pond area; and (iii) the fact that during the entire year the water levels are below the contact between the soil and the rock for about 10-45 m, making the erosion from beneath to upward less likely. The problem of the air under pressure at this contact is the major problem. To solve it, special tubes have been and will be built to enable the air to escape without damaging the impervious layer or its cover.

ESTIMATION OF PERMEABILITY AND EFFECTIVE POROSITY IN KARST ON THE BASIS OF RECESSION CURVE ANALYSIS

by

Konstantin Torbarov, Geologist,
Civil Engineering Department
University of Sarajevo, Sarajevo, Yugoslavia

Synopsis. The decomposition of water recession curves at the springs of the Trebišnjica River for a number of years pointed out distinctly to the existence of three, or at least two, periods of different characteristics of groundwater outflow. It is highly probable that different hydraulic regimes or groundwater flow occur during these periods. Sudden large flow and high rate of decrease in flow in a short time at the outflow zone makes the first period. The second and the third periods are characterized by lower flows, a slow rate of flow decrease during the second period, and a very low flow with still a smaller gradient of flow decrease during the third period. The recession process in this decomposition was expressed mathematically according to the basic equation given by E. Maillet.

The recession curves of groundwater level in piezometric boreholes during the same time were similar to the outflow recession curves. Certain simultaneous changes of groundwater level corresponded to each of the three characteristic periods, with different permeability and effective porosity. In analogy with pumping tests of unsteady groundwater flow, the permeability data for the above three periods could be computed by the Theis equation. The graphical solution of the equation by a logarithmic approximation gives permeability and effective porosity for these periods. The effective porosity is also estimated as the ratio of total spring water outflow to the volume of the involved rock mass for these periods. To check the results, the effective porosity was calculated also as the ratio of the decrease of groundwater levels, as measured in piezometers, and the estimated decrease from the ratio of the total water outflow and the catchment surface for any characteristic recession period. Since the same input data were used, the obtained values for the effective porosity were either the same or very close to values obtained as described above.

1. Introduction.

In karst conditions, rock shape, size, spatial position and number of fissures vary from place to place, with small or large total groundwater storage. This makes the description of basic hydraulic parameters, such as permeability and porosity, difficult and complex. The estimate of these parameters

by pumping tests at wells and boreholes gives usually values
that are valid only for a narrow space around these test holes.

Various karst possibilities of estimating the water
permeability and porosity for large areas have been often
suggested. One such possibility is based on the application
of the well-known Theis equation in logarithmic approximation.
That approach was used for this study, and the test case was
the Bileća Spring and the catchment area of the Trebišnjica
River.

By making an analogy with the pumping tests for variable
discharges under the natural flow conditions, or under the
nonstationarity conditions, such an approach limits observations
to periods of no groundwater recharge only, i.e., to recession
dry-season periods [1]. In this way the values of permeability
and effective porosity are obtained for a narrow area around
the Trebišnjica River Springs, using the measured flows at
springs and the decrease of groundwater level in the piezometer
L-1 of the borehole directly in the background of the Bileća
Springs.

The effective porosity of the whole catchment area for
the recession periods only was calculated as a proportion of
the volume of water flowing out of the springs and the
volume of the involved rock mass. It has been also calculated
as a proportion of simultaneous groundwater level decrease,
obtained from the volume of outflowing water and the catchment
surface, and the average decrease of the corresponding groundwater level in piezometric boreholes of the catchment. This
approach was used to check the above methods of estimation.

The decomposition of recession curves for a number of
years (1956-1963) pointed out to the existence either of two
or three periods with different characteristics of groundwater
discharge. The first period, at the beginning of recession,
has large outflows and high gradient of flow decrease at the
Trebišnjica River Springs. The second and maybe the third
periods were characterized by low and prolonged outflows,
with the gradient of flow decrease in the springs area,
smaller, or considerably smaller, than during the first period.
The curves of decrease of the groundwater level in piezometric boreholes over the catchment were of similar characteristics. It can be then concluded that different values of
permeability and effective porosity corresponded to two or
three periods of different flow characteristics. Such a conclusion and the outline of characteristics of emptying the
karst water system were commensurate with the karstification
process. It has been already found by a number of complex
investigations that karst porosity was greatest near the
ground surface and that it decreased with the depth. The first
period of rather large flows most likely corresponded to the

outflow from the rock mass with largest karst openings, and maybe, with the highest total effective porosity. In karst, it is possible to have two, even more, such zones at various levels.

To single out the periods of different flow characteristics or different flow micro-regimes, the recession curves were approximated by straight lines in semi-logarithmic scales. Figures 1, 2 and 3 show such recession curves for years 1961, 1962 and 1963 with the most reliable observational data. To demonstrate that groundwater levels of piezometers show a similar decrease during the recession period, Fig. 4 presents the level decrease in piezometer L-1 during the recession period of 1961.

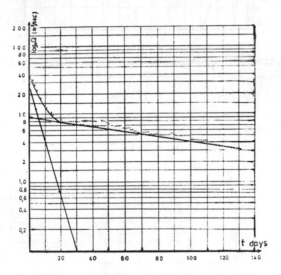

Fig. 1. Fitted and Decomposed Recession Curve, Bileća Springs, 1961. Total Recession Equation:

$$Q_t = 27.60e^{-0.1825t} + 9.20e^{-0.0079t}$$

22 days later: $Q_t = 7.75e^{-0.0079t}$

The decomposition of flow recession curves was made next, showing that the recession period in 1961 had two, in 1962 three in 1963 two micro-regimes. The duration of these micro-regimes of recession periods was:

Year	Micro-regime duration (in days)		
	I	II	III
1961	0-22	22-114	-
1962	0-10	10-24	24-127
1963	0-22	22-76	-

124

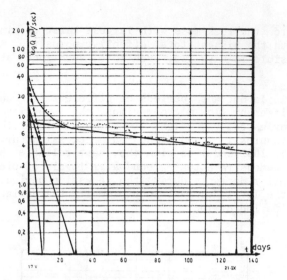

Fig. 2. Fitted and Decomposed Recession Curve, Bileća Springs, 1962. Total Recession Equation:

$$Q_t = 19.25e^{-0.625t} + 17.00e^{-0.1818t} + 8.55e^{-0.0095t}$$

10 days later: $Q_t = 2.76e^{-0.1818t} + 7.93e^{-0.0075t}$

24 days later: $Q_t = 7.4e^{-0.0075t}$

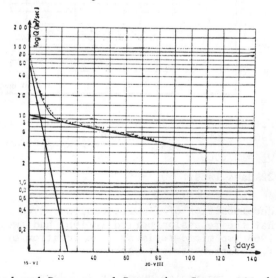

Fig. 3. Fitted and Decomposed Recession Curve, Bileća Springs, 1963.

$$Q_t = 63.60e^{-0.2702t} + 10.00e^{-0.0104t}$$

22 days later: $Q_t = 7.95e^{-0.0104t}$

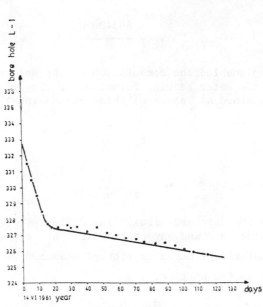

Fig. 4. Curve of Decrease of Groundwater Levels in Piezometer
L-1 During the Recession Period of 1961.

2. Mathematical Formulation.

As given by E. Maillet [2], the general recession equation
is in the form:

$$Q_t = Q_{01}e^{-\alpha_1 t} + Q_{02}e^{-\alpha_2 t} + Q_{03}e^{-\alpha_3 t} \tag{1}$$

in which Q_t = the yield or flow (m^3/sec) at the moment t,
Q_{01}, Q_{02}, Q_{03} = the flows at the beginning of each micro-regime
(m^3/sec), and α_1, α_2, α_3, = the coefficients corresponding
to individual micro-regimes (lit/day), with

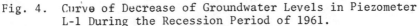

$$\alpha = \frac{\log Q_o - \log Q_t}{0.4343\ (t-t_o)}$$

and t = the duration in days. In case of only two characteristic recession micro-regimes, the third term of Eq. (1) is
omitted.

The integration of the expression $Q_o e^{-\alpha t}$ and some
substitutions give the values of the groundwater volume as
dynamic supplies during a particular day, i.e.,

$$V_t = \frac{86,400 \ Q_t}{\alpha} \ . \tag{2}$$

This volume enabled the computation of the height of the water column of the water bearing formations during the recession period, obtained as ratios of these values and the catchment area

$$h_o = \frac{V_o}{A} \ , \tag{3}$$

and

$$h_t = \frac{V_t}{A} \ , \tag{4}$$

where A = the catchment area. The difference between the initial value h_o and any other value h_t represented the variation of the groundwater storage measured by ΔH_A in a particular period of time, as

$$\Delta H_A = h_o - h_t \ . \tag{5}$$

Permeability and effective porosity were calculated by solving the equation of logarithmic approximation (Theis, 1935):

$$\Delta H_p = \frac{0.183 \ Q}{T} \ (\log \frac{2.25 \ T}{r^2 \ S} + \log t) \ , \tag{6}$$

where ΔH_p and t are variables, with ΔH_p = the groundwater level decrease in piezometer in the period $t(m)$, r = the distance to piezometer (m), T = the permeability (m^2/sec), S = the effective porosity (calculated as a percentage), and t = the pumping period, i.e., the recession period (sec). The function of Eq. (6) was plotted as a straight line in a semi-logarithm of t, the abscissa. Having in mind the general shape of the function $y = m (\log n + \log x)$ and Eq. (6), then the first derivative

$$\frac{d\Delta H_p}{dt} = \frac{0.183 \ Q_{sr}}{T}$$

gave the shape of the straight line (see Figs. 5 and 6) of the relation ΔH_p to $\log t$. The graphic solution gives the following expression:

$$T = \frac{0.183 \ Q_{sr}}{c} \tag{7}$$

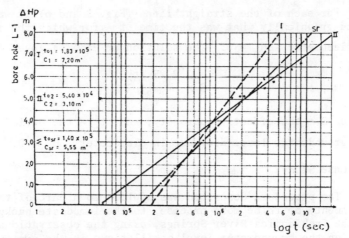

Fig. 5.   The Graphical Solution of the Equations of Logarithmic
Approximation, Bileća Springs, 1961, with ΔH_p = the
Groundwater Level Decrease in Piezometer, t_o = the
Period when ΔH_p = 0; c = the Interval when log t = 1.

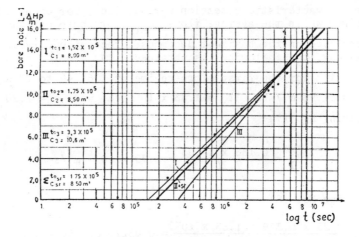

Fig. 6.   The Graphical Solution of the Equations of Logarithmic
Approximation, Bileća Springs, 1962, with ΔH_p = the
Groundwater Level Decrease in Piezometer; t_o = the
Period when ΔH_p = 0; c = the Interval when log
t = 1.

where Q_{sr} = the average yield in a corresponding recession
micro-regime (m^3/sec) and c = ΔH_p the interval in which
log t = 1 (m).

For each of the straight lines (Fig. 5 and 6) it was found graphically what was the time t_o for which the decrease in piezometer $\Delta H_p = 0$. The solution of Eq. (6) gave

$$S = \frac{2.25 \, Tt_o}{r^2} \tag{8}$$

where S = the effective porosity, and t_o = the period when the groundwater level decrease in piezometer $\Delta H_p = 0$.

3. Case Study.

The procedure described was applied to a part of the catchment, or to be more precise, to the immediate background of the Trebišnjica River Springs, using the observational data on the groundwater level oscillations in the piezometric borehole L-1 at the distance of 2200 m from the Springs. Since the observational data were reliable only for years 1961 and 1962, the diagrams of the relation ΔH_p to log t, were presented in Figs. 5 and 6 for these years. From these diagrams the corresponding values t_o and c were obtained for each characteristic recession period, i.e., for each micro-regime, while the average flows Q_{sr} for these periods were calculated on the basis of decomposed recession curves. In this way, the following was obtained:

(i) For the first micro-regime of 1961 (0 to 22 days): Q_{sr} = 14.93 m^3/sec, t_o = 1.83 x 10^5 sec and c = 7.20 m, applying Eq. (7):

$$T_1 = \frac{0.183 \times 14.93}{7.20} = 3.79 \times 10^{-1} \, m^2/sec.$$

Applying Eq. (8)

$$S_1 = \frac{2.25 \times 0.379 \times 1.83 \times 10^5}{4.84 \times 10^6} = 0.0322, \text{ or } S_1 = 3.22 \text{ percent.}$$

(ii) For the second micro-regime of 1961 (22 to 114 days): Q_{sr} = 5.75 m^3/sec, t_o = 5.40 x 10^4 sec, and c = 3.10 m, with

$$T_2 = \frac{0.183 \times 5.57}{3.10} = 3.29 \times 10^{-1} \, m^2/sec$$

and

$$S_2 = \frac{2.25 \times 0.329 \times 5.40 \times 10^4}{4.84 \times 10^6} = 0.0082 \, ,$$

or, $S_2 = 0.82$ percent.

The average values for the whole recession period is

$$T = 2.43 \times 10^{-1} \, m^2/sec, \text{ and } S = 1.58 \text{ percent.}$$

(iii) For the first micro-regime for 1962 (0 to 10 days):

$$T_1 = \frac{0.183 \times 19.05}{8.0} = 4.36 \times 10^{-1} \, m^2/sec,$$

and

$$S_1 = \frac{2.25 \times 0.436 \times 1.52 \times 10^5}{4.84 \times 10^6} = 0.0307 \, ,$$

or $S_1 = 3.07$ percent.

(iv) For the second micro-regime of 1962 (10 to 24 days):

$$T_2 = 1.87 \times 10^{-1} \, m^2/sec \text{ and } S_2 = 1.52 \text{ percent.}$$

(v) For the third micro-regime of 1962 (24 to 127 days):

$$T_3 = 8.66 \times 10^{-2} \, m^2/sec \text{ and } S_3 = 1.32 \text{ percent.}$$

The average values for the whole recession period were

$$T = 1.40 \times 10^{-1} \, m^2/sec \text{ and } S = 1.14 \text{ percent.}$$

The effective porosity of the whole catchment was calculated also as the ratio of the volume of water outflowing at the springs during different recession micro-regimes and the corresponding volume of the involved rock mass. The problem was how to estimate the volume of involved rock, i.e., of the average decrease of the groundwater level in the catchment. These decreases were neither uniform in time or over the catchment. For these reasons, the double weighted values of these decreases were used for the estimates. The catchment area was first divided into two sub-areas, Fig. 7: the sub-area of the Gatačko Polje to Fatničko Polje, or the higher elevations region (and also the region with different characteristics of decrease of groundwater levels in the recession

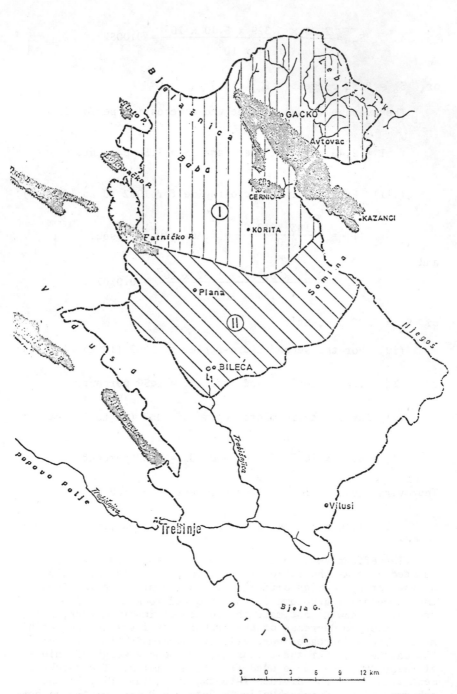

Fig. 7. Topographic map of one Part of Hydrogeologic Catchment of the Trebišnjica River.

period), and the sub-area from the Fatničko Polje to the Trebišnjica River Springs. The data on the groundwater level oscillations were obtained at the piezometric boreholes CR-3 at the edge of the Cerničko Polje, with a high retardation (travel) time, the borehole F-1 on the edge of the Fatničko Polje with the travel time to the springs of about 10 days, and the borehole L-1 in the immediate background of the springs with no retardation time. The first sub-area, from the Gatačko Polje to the Fatničko Polje, has a surface of

668.77 km^2, while the sub-area from the Fatničko Polje to the Trebišnjica River Springs has a surface of 400 km^2. The weighted values of decrease of groundwater levels were used to give the proper weights to times of equal gradients of decrease of groundwater levels in individual recession micro-regimes, for each sub-area separately. This is expressed by

$$\Delta H'_{p1} = \frac{\Delta H_1 \, t_1 + \Delta H_2 \, t_2 + \ldots \Delta H_i \, t_i}{\sum_{i=1}^{m} t_i}$$

where $\Delta H'_{p1}$ = the average decrease of groundwater levels in a borehole; t_1, t_2,...,t_i = the corresponding times for which the decrease of the gradient was approximately the same; and $\sum t_i$ = the time duration of the recession micro-regime.

For only two piezometers in a sub-area (and more when they were available), the average decrease $\Delta H''_{p1}$ in the second piezometric borehole was calculated in the same way. The average arithmetic value of the decrease for the corresponding sub-area was then:

$$\Delta H_{p1} = \frac{\Delta H'_{p1} + \Delta H''_{p1}}{2} \, .$$

The average decrease ΔH_{p2} of groundwater levels for the second sub-area of the catchment was obtained in the same way.

The second weighting used the surfaces of catchment sub-areas, so that the final weighted average decrease of the whole catchment for a given recession micro-regime was

$$\Delta H_p = \frac{\Delta H_{p1} A_1 + \Delta H_{p2} A_2 + \ldots + \Delta H_{pi} A_i}{\sum_{i=1}^{m} A_i} \, . \tag{9}$$

132

Following this procedure and using the data of piezometric
boreholes, the average decreases of individual recession micro-
regimes in 1961, 1962 and 1963 were found to be:

| Year: | Average Decrease of Groundwater Levels (m) | | |
	I	II	III
1961	1.87	3.01	
1962	1.80	3.82	*
1963	2.21	2.18	

*Note that in this estimate, the first and the second
regime were used for 1962.

The further step of the estimates was to calculate the
volume of the engaged rock mass as the product of the average
groundwater level decreases and the catchment surface, which
in this case was 1068.77 km^2. On the basis of differences of
dynamic supplies calculated according to Eq. (2), the values
of drained water volume was obtained and the effective porosity
on the basis of the relation was calculated as

$$S = \frac{100 \ V_v}{V_{st}} \ , \qquad (10)$$

where V_v = the volume of water outflowing during a recession
micro-regime (m^3), and V_{st} = the volume of the involved rock
mass (m^3).

The following values of effective porosity were obtained
for the years 1961, 1962 and 1963:

Year:	Micro-regime	Effective Porosity (%)
1961	I.	$S_1 = 1.41$
	II.	$S_2 = 1.37$
1962	I.	$S_1 = 1.40$
	II.	$S_2 = 1.09$
1963	I.	$S_1 = 1.57$
	II.	$S_2 = 1.21$

For the year 1962 the first and second micro-regime were treated as one.

Finally, the effective porosity was calculated as a ratio of cumulative variations, defined by Eq. (5), and the average decrease of groundwater levels for individual recession micro-regimes, by

$$S = \frac{100 \; \Delta H_A}{\Delta H_p} \; . \tag{11}$$

The estimates of effective porosity for the three years and the individual recession micro-regimes were:

Year:	Micro-regime Duration	ΔH_A (m)	ΔH_p (m)	$S = \dfrac{100 \; \Delta H_A}{\Delta H_p}$
1961	I. 0 to 22 Days	0.026	1.87	1.40
	II. 22 to 114 Days	0.042	3.01	1.38
1962	I. 0 to 24 Days	0.025	1.80	1.38
	II. 24 to 127 Days	0.042	3.82	1.09
1963	I. 0 to 22 Days	0.035	2.21	1.58
	II. 22 to 176 Days	0.027	2.18	1.23

The values of effective porosity obtained by Eq. (11) were almost identical to the values obtained previously by Eq. (10). This was to be expected, because in both cases the data for estimates were nearly the same, and the use of the second method was in fact only a control.

4. Conclusions.

Though the estimates cannot be considered accurate, they point out the differences in permeability and effective porosity between the individual recession micro-regimes of the immediate background formation of the Trebišnjica River Springs. The same results are obtained for the whole catchment. For example, in the immediate background of the Springs the effective porosity for the first micro-regime is within the range 3 to 3.2 percent, for the second micro-regime from about 1.0 to about 1.5 percent, and for the third micro-regime about 1.3 percent. The corresponding permeability ranges from 3.3×10^{-1} m^2/sec to 4.4×10^{-1} m^2/sec for the first micro-regime, from 1.9×10^{-1} m^2/sec to 3.3×10^{-1} m^2/sec for the second micro-regime, and about 8.6×10^{-2} m^2/sec for the third micro-regime.

The average effective porosity of the catchment (permeability has not been estimated for the whole catchment) was about 1.5 percent for the beginning of the recession period (up to 25 days duration), while for the remaining portion of the recession period was about 1.2 percent.

In conclusion, it should be noted that the basic hydraulic parameters, such as permeability and effective porosity, were space-time variables. During the recession period, they did not depend only on parameters directly used in the formula for their estimates, but also on a number of other factors. Such factors were the time regime and areal distribution of precipitation in the period prior to the recession, and in all probability, on the absolute groundwater levels at the moment when the recession began.

5. References.

[1] Boreli, M., Determination of characteristics of pervious layers by pumping tests in nonstationary regime [In Serbo-Croatian]: Seminar, Budget of Aquifers, Beograd, 1967-1968.

[2] Maillet, E., Essais d'hydraulique fluviale: Paris, 1905.

DISCUSSION

Yevjevich. The complex recession limbs of response hydrographs of karst aquifers were approximated in the paper by three straight lines in the semi-logarithmic scales of their graphical presentation. Practically speaking all transitions in slopes exist between a straight line fit to the extreme low flows and a straight line fit to the highest part of the recession limb. The simple exponential tail of the recession curves for extremely low outflows from a karst underground system point out to a linear reservoir approximation, namely $Q = \alpha V$, with Q = the outflow, V = the stored underground water volume, which empties during the very low flows, and α = the proportionality constant. There is a need to study the relationships of the slopes of recession curves of outflow hydrographs in the semi-log scales and the type of water flow regime and underground storage space involved. If these relationships could be well established, then the properties of outflow hydrographs can produce the information on the type of flow regime and the general hydrologic characteristics of the karst system. This means that the relationship between the hydrogeology and hydrology would not be only in one direction of transferring the information from hydrogeology to hydrology, but the hydrologic characteristics of outflows may serve to advance hypotheses and pass the information from hydrology to hydrogeology.

Bagarić. The Theis'es equation of nonstationary, radial filtration through homogeneous unconfined area of constant transmissivity was used in the paper as a mathematical model for transmissivity estimates. Though the paper presents significant contribution to these estimates, nevertheless, some facts need to be pointed out. In the Theis'es equation the non-dimensional constant 0.183 was calculated by dividing the constant 2.3, which represents the connection between natural and base ten logarithms, by 2π which shows the radial moving to be at the angle of 360°. In considering the water circulation toward the spring at the border of a catchment area (as shown by the sketch), the angle should be closer to 180°. That means that instead of using 2π, one should use π or a corresponding value.

SPRING

If the non-homogeneous area is described by an equation which is valid for the homogeneous area, then one must evaluate the representativeness of transmissivity obtained on the basis of the data of one piezometer for the whole studied area. Owing to differences in transmissivities in various parts of the studied area, the data of another piezometer would supply further transmissivities. Having in mind the actual non-homogeneity in space and the Theis'es equation, one can draw the conclusion that the obtained transmissivity denotes the quality of the relationship between the spring and a certain piezometer. It also gives a possibility to define the strike of the privileged underground flow or an area of high transmissivity, by analyzing data from several piezometers.

The transmissivity so defined at several points of the filtration area can represent the transport characteristics of a karst area. If one wants to define the transmissivity on the basis of data from piezometers, it is necessary that these piezometers be representative. The piezometers would be representative only in case when the transmissivity of the immediate piezometer vicinity is of the same order or a higher order than the transmissivity of a more distant piezometer area. The methods of defining the transmissivity of a closer piezometer area are well known.

Torbarov. Concerning the discussion by Bagarić on the
application of the Theis formula, the following points can
be added. For solution of certain problems under karst
conditions, it is necessary to postulate a model as an
initial assumption, which model approximates the natural
conditions as closely as possible. The immediate vicinity
of the Trebišnjica River Spring, taking into account distinctive tectonic features of the rock mass and the presence of an
intensive karstification around it, was assumed to be a homogeneous environment for which the logarithmic approximation
of the recession curves by the Theis formula is applicable.
The assumption of a homogeneous karst environment should not
be always discarded. Specific conditions at each particular
site must be taken into consideration, such as the case of
the Trebišnjica River Spring. I used the coefficient 0.183
which appears in the Theis equation, however, pointing out that
the change of the coefficient of permeability is not a
decisive factor, because the order of magnitude of obtained
permeability values (10^{-1} m^2/sec to 10^{-2} m^2/sec) remains unaffected.

Only a rough estimate of permeability in one direction
from the piezometric borehole L-1 to the Spring was presented
in the paper. This is, however, the main direction of the
underground flow. It will be useful to estimate the permeability for other directions as well. However, in the
period 1961 through 1963, and at present, there are no other
piezometric boreholes in the immediate vicinity upstream of
the Spring, from which to estimate these permeabilities. Since
the piezometric borehole L-1 as demonstrated by other analyses
also, is located in the zone which is obviously influenced by
the Spring, it was considered as a good, representative
piezometer.

Yevjevich discussed certain aspects of the recession
curve analysis. Results of my decomposition of a series of
recession curves lead me to concur with his points made in
relation to recession curves, underlining that this has been
stressed in the paper.

FLOW ANALYSIS OF KARST SYSTEMS WITH WELL DEVELOPED UNDERGROUND CIRCULATION

by

Glen L. Faulkner, Hydrologist
U.S. Geological Survey, Tallahassee, Florida

Synopsis. With a knowledge of the hydrogeology, and a comprehensive suite of representative basic hydrologic data as background, the use of the specified flow-net analysis technique may be a practical and economical way to analyze the flow regime of a cavernous carbonate aquifer with well developed circulation. The specified flow-net analysis was used to evaluate the spatial variation of aquifer transmissivity in part of the Silver Springs groundwater drainage basin in north-central peninsular Florida by likening the springs to a continuously discharging well whose cone of depression is the entire drainage basin.

There is no integrated surface drainage system in the Silver Springs drainage area. The 1,000 feet-thick (300 meter-thick) Floridan aquifer, composed of cavernous limestone and dolomite of highly variable porosity and permeability, is recharged by infiltration of local rainfall through sand and clayey sand of varying permeability. The top of the aquifer is a karst surface, but in most places it is covered with a few to several tens of feet of the sand and clayey sand.

In the aquifer, most of the groundwater flow is in solution channels that are oriented along a dual system of intersecting tension fractures. Ultimately, the groundwater discharges at Silver Springs; the average discharge is 821 cubic feet per second (23.25 cubic meters per second). The drainage area for Silver Springs, measured from potentiometric surface maps, is about 730 square miles (1900 square kilometers). Average annual rainfall for the area is 53.2 inches (1350 millimeters). Calculated average annual recharge is 15.3 inches (390 millimeters) although it presumably varies significantly from place to place, depending on permeability of the overburden. Direct surface runoff in a year averages about 3 inches (76 millimeters), leaving a balance of about 35 inches (890 millimeters) to evapotranspiration. Most flow to the Springs is in the upper 100 to 200 feet (30 to 60 meters) of the aquifer. Transmissivity as estimated from flow-net analysis ranges from 10,000 to 25,400,000 feet squared per day (1000 to 2,360,000 meters squared per day) among 25 flow cells all within a few miles of the springs. Although the degree of accuracy of estimated transmissivity values for individual cells could be subject to question, the distribution of values is believed to reflect the general qualitative properties of the areal variation in transmissivity. A reasonable approximation of average velocity through a flow cell may be calculated by standard methods. The average of the average velocity of groundwater movement downgradient through 25 flow cells near Silver Springs in May 1968 is approximated to be about between 6 and 10 feet per day (2 and 3 meters per day), depending on aquifer thickness.

1. Introduction.

Permeability and porosity distribution in cavernous carbonate aquifers is extremely variable. This feature places major practical and economic constraints on the use of conventional aquifer pump-test techniques to determine areal variations in the characteristics of karst aquifer systems with well-developed underground circulation. However, part of this problem of heterogeneity may be overcome by examination of large samples of the aquifer by use of a specific flow-net analysis technique applied to a basin where natural discharge is concentrated at a large spring or spring complex that may be likened to a continuously discharging well.

The vicinity of Silver Springs in north-central Florida is typical of the kind of covered karst area where the specific flow-net analysis technique described in this paper may be applied. The technique has been useful for making water resource availability appraisals, evaluating potential groundwater contamination problems and their solutions, and predicting the potential effects of various development proposals, including navigation canals that penetrate the aquifer [1]. Flow-net analysis, as applied to the hydrogeologic environment of the Silver Springs area could be useful for analyzing potentiometric maps of other similar karst areas. Silver Springs and its drainage area are shown on the index map of Florida in Fig. 1.

The paper is based on some results of an investigation in 1966-72 by the U.S. Geological Survey in cooperation with the U.S. Army Corps of Engineers [1]. One of the investigation's main objectives was to predict the effect of the proposed Cross-Florida Barge Canal on the water level, flow, and water quality of Silver Springs, a major tourist attraction and probably the largest fresh-water spring in the United States from the standpoint of average measured discharge. Silver Springs issues from several closely grouped, submerged cavities in the Floridan aquifer, the Florida equivalent of the principal artesian aquifer of the southeastern United States [2], and one of the most extensive carbonate aquifers in the United States. The Floridan aquifer is the principal source of potable water supplies in Florida, except for some coastal areas and parts of southern peninsular and westernmost panhandle Florida [3].

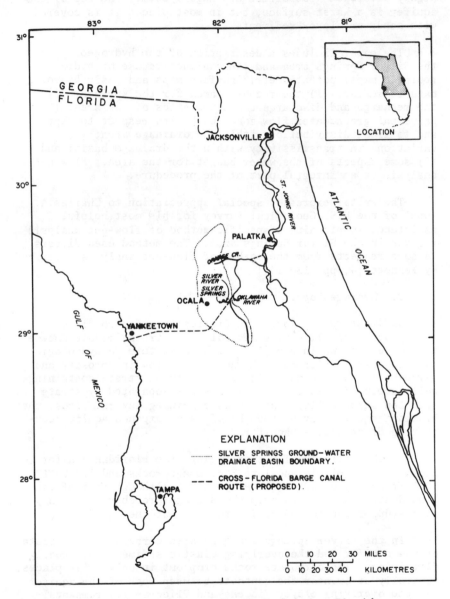

Fig. 1. Silver Springs Area, North Peninsular Florida.

The Silver Springs drainage area is characterized by a highly developed subsurface drainage system. The top of the aquifer is a karst surface, but in most places it is covered with sandy or clayey sediments.

The paper includes a description of the hydrogeology of the Silver Springs area and the conjunctive use of hydro-geologic maps, potentiometric surface maps and basic hydrologic data to define: (1) the recharge area for the springs; (2) the recharge and discharge characteristics of the area; (3) principal groundwater flow zones both with respect to depth and to areal distribution within the drainage area; (4) variations in transmissivity within the drainage basin; and (5) some aspects of the water budget for the area. Flow-net analysis is an integral part of the procedure.

The writer expresses special appreciation to Charles A. Appel of the U.S. Geological Survey for his most helpful assistance in planning a specific method of flow-net analysis for use in the Silver Springs area. The method used differs in some respects from the method of flow-net analysis described by Bennett [4, pp. 139-144].

2. Hydrogeology.

Sedimentary section. The Floridan aquifer consists mostly of marine limestone and dolomite strata, middle Eocene to middle Miocene in age [5], which constitute a hydrologic unit in most of Florida. The aquifer varies in porosity and permeability and in many places consists of strata containing well-developed solution channel systems separated by strata with low permeability that act as confining layers. Thus, the Floridan aquifer may be thought of as a compound aquifer con-sisting of several subaquifers.

In the vicinity of Silver Springs the Floridan aquifer includes only middle and late Eocene age rocks and is about 1000 ft (feet) or 300 m (meters) thick, although most of the groundwater that issues from the springs probably flows only in the upper 100 to 200 ft (30 to 60 m) of the aquifer.

In the Silver Springs drainage area carbonate-rock strata of the aquifer and the overlying clastic sediments are nearly flat lying. The carbonate rocks crop out in only a few places, generally at or near the contacts between rock of the aquifer and the overlying clayey Miocene and Pliocene (?) remnants. The clayey remnants form topographic highs, except near the east edge of the area where they are structurally low, probably in part the result of graben faulting, as shown in Fig. 2. They tend to restrict direct recharge of the carbonate aquifer by local rainfall, although there is some recharge where the remnants are thin or breached by sinkholes. Where the

141

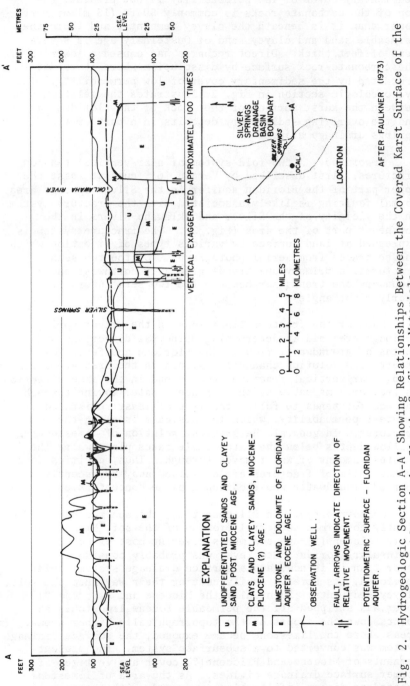

Fig. 2. Hydrogeologic Section A-A' Showing Relationships Between the Covered Karst Surface of the Floridan Aquifer and the Clastic Surficial Materials.

sedimentary cover of low permeability is not present, the
top of the carbonate rocks is commonly 50 ft (15 m) or more
lower than it is beneath the clayey remnants, and there the
permeable sand and clayey sand of Quaternary age is several
tens of feet thick. Direct recharge has caused a lowering of
the carbonate-rock surface by dissolution where it is not
protected by the sedimentary cover of low permeability. The
hydrogeologic section in Fig. 2 illustrates the relationships
between the karst surface of the rock of the Floridan aquifer
and the overlying sedimentary deposits in a part of the Silver
Springs drainage area.

Fractures. A two-fold system of near-vertical tension
fractures, first described by Vernon [6], cuts at least the
upper part of the Floridan aquifer in the Silver Springs area.
Normal faulting is likely associated with the fracture system
in the vicinity of the Silver and Oklawaha Rivers in the
southeast part of the area (Fig. 2). The fracture system is
expressed at land surface by various types of lineation which
can be traced from aerial photographs. Of the two sets of
fractures, a primary one trends generally northwest and a
secondary one trends northeast. The two sets intersect at
nearly right angles.

Maps of the fracture lineations in the Silver Springs
drainage area aid in determining principal directions and
routes of groundwater flow in the Floridan aquifer. Most
caverns and solution channels examined in the area are oriented
along near-vertical fractures that trend in the same direction
as fractures mappable at the surface. Water moving through
the aquifer tends to follow the line of least resistance or
greatest permeability, which in this case is along the
fractures. In general the greatest solution of limestone at
shallow depths below the water table takes place where the
greatest amount of water moves through. Thus, cavities develop
as the walls of fractures are dissolved away by recently recharged groundwater whose carbon dioxide concentration is high.

Geomorphology. In Pliocene time, the sea receded sufficiently to permit subaerial erosion of the soft Miocene and
early Pliocene(?) age sediments covering most of north
peninsular Florida. Sea level was probably considerably
lower than it is now, and a surface drainage system rapidly
developed, its streams easily cutting their way into the soft,
clayey sediments. Eventually the Miocene and Pliocene(?)
cover was stripped off the permeable Eocene limestones at
points down the slopes of the topographically higher areas. In
areas where the limestone became exposed, the surface drainage
system was converted to a subsurface system. The present
remnants of Miocene and Pliocene(?) cover are vestiges of
former surface drainage divides. As the area of limestone
exposed to direct infiltration increased, with the consequent

increase in solution channels in the limestone, a highly developed groundwater storage and drainage system evolved. No interconnected surface drainage system remains in the area.

The permeable sandy materials now covering the limestone karst surface between the Miocene and Pliocene(?) remnants consist partly of residual material that remained after finer constituents were removed by stream transport or downward concentration in filled sinkholes by infiltrating groundwater. Some more or less unaltered Miocene and Pliocene(?) material of low permeability is preserved as slumpage in old sinkholes or as originally deposited sediments in depressions on the erosional surface at the top of the Eocene limestone. Most of the permeable sedimentary cover is considered to be reworked Miocene and Pliocene(?) and some younger coarse clastic material formed into marine terraces by seas covering the area during Pleistocene interglacial periods.

The land surface between the high-standing Miocene and Pliocene(?) remnants is nearly flat to gently rolling--a broadly hummocky, subdued covered karst terrain of low relief with numerous closed sink depressions, most of which have permeable bottoms that do not pond water.

The positions of the old drainage valleys approximately coincide with the lowest parts of the present rock surface. The highest points of the present limestone surface underlie the topographic highs formed by the remnants of the sedimentary deposits of low permeability. The areas where the present limestone surface is lowest not only represent the alinements of the old surface drainage valleys, but the lows also are the locations of the best developed solution channel systems where groundwater flow is now concentrated. Potentiometric maps and flow-net analysis support these determinations.

The zones of concentrated groundwater flow converge on Silver Springs, which forms the head of Silver River. Silver River flows east about 4 mi (miles) or 6 km (kilometers) over confining beds, as shown by Figs. 1 and 3, and joins the Oklawaha River at the east edge of the springs' drainage area. Flow continues northeast over the confining beds down the Oklawaha River, ultimately to discharge by way of the St. Johns River to the Atlantic Ocean.

3. The Potentiometric Surface.

The term *potentiometric surface* as applied to the Floridan aquifer in this paper is that imaginary surface connecting all points to which water will rise in tightly cased wells open to the upper part of the saturated zone of the aquifer, regardless of whether the aquifer is confined or unconfined.

144

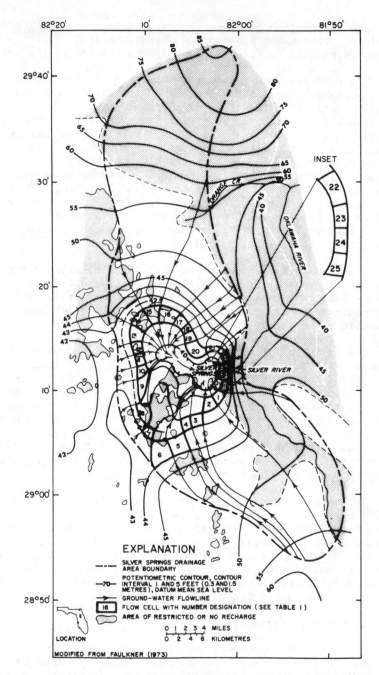

Fig. 3. Potentiometric Surface for May 1968 and Flow Net,
Upper Part of Floridan Aquifer, Silver Springs
Groundwater Drainage Area.

In the Silver Springs area, the potentiometric surface
generally is lowest in late spring and highest in early fall--
corresponding respectively with the end of the seasonal dry
and wet periods. The general configuration of the potentiometric surface changes little from one season to the other,
even though in a given year the surface is usually several feet
higher and gradients tend to be somewhat steeper in the high-
water period than in the low-water period.

A series of contour maps, prepared on a semiannual basis,
of the potentiometric surface of the upper part of the Floridan
aquifer in the Cross-Florida Barge Canal area, including most
of the Silver Springs drainage area, were drawn from water-level
measurements in an approximately 130-well network of observation wells. For the most part, the wells penetrate less than
200 ft (60 m) of the aquifer. The potentiometric surface for
May 1968 and the drainage area for Silver Springs are shown in
Fig. 3. The closed drainage area for Silver Springs is outlined on Fig. 3 by lines drawn along the axes of the ridges
(drainage divides) in the potentiometric surface. Although the
May 1968 surface was lower than the long-term average, it was
used for purposes of this paper because at that time a large
part of north-central Florida was mapped, including the entire
closed drainage area of Silver Springs. The drainage area of
Silver Springs, as outlined on this map, is about 730 mi^2
(square miles) or 1900 km^2 (square kilometers).

Average annual rainfall in the Silver Springs area is
53.2 in (inches) or 1350 mm (millimeters), but for a given
year or series of years the annual rainfall may vary greatly
from the average, resulting in significant variations in
groundwater levels and spring discharge. Water levels tend
to fluctuate least close to the springs and greatest near the
edges of the drainage area. Within 3 or 4 mi (5 or 6 km) of
the springs, groundwater levels will commonly fluctuate 3 or 4
ft (about a meter) between the annual wet and dry periods,
whereas over the long term of 41 years, they have fluctuated
between 10 and 15 ft (3 and 5 m). The long term (1932-73)
average discharge of the springs is 821 ft^3/s (cubic feet per
second) or 23.25 m^3/s (cubic meters per second). The long
term range of record is 539 to 1290 ft^3/s (15.3 to 36.5 m^3/s).

During dry periods, spring discharge declines as the water
levels decline; during wet periods spring discharge increases
as water levels recover. The close relation among rainfall
rates, groundwater levels, and spring discharge is illustrated
by the hydrographs in Fig. 4.

4. Recharge Characteristics.

Most of the Silver Springs drainage area is drained
through the subsurface to the springs. Most of the rain that

146

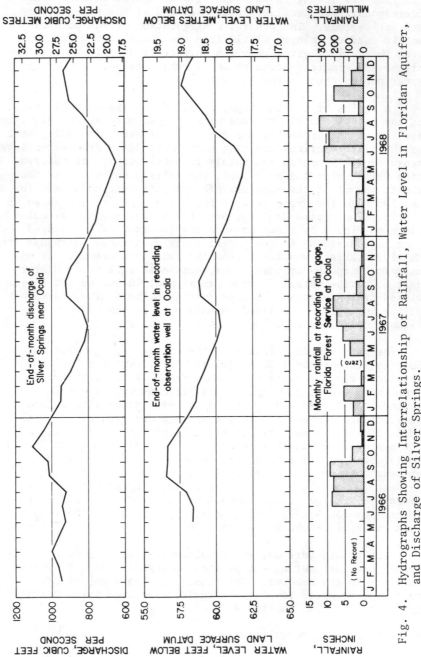

Fig. 4. Hydrographs Showing Interrelationship of Rainfall, Water Level in Floridan Aquifer, and Discharge of Silver Springs.

falls on the area either infiltrates the land surface and
percolates to the aquifer as recharge or is lost to evapotranspiration. Direct surface runoff from the springs' drainage
area is small and is more or less restricted to two streams--
the Oklawaha River in the southeast and Orange Creek in the
northeast part of the area (Figs. 1 and 3).

Except at the springs, significant recharge may occur
anywhere in the Silver Springs drainage area where the aquifer
is not covered by sediments of low permeability. The greatest
rates of recharge are not necessarily at the highest points
on the potentiometric surface, as at the edges of the basin,
but may be in potentiometric lower areas where permeability
of the covering materials and the aquifer are great. Some
such areas are near the springs. Recharge may be rejected
in some potentiometrically high areas during wet periods because
the permeability of the aquifer or of the covering materials is
too low to convey all the available recharge.

The calculated average annual recharge rate for the
Silver Springs drainage area is 15.3 in (389 mm) based on an
average spring discharge rate of 821 ft^3/s (23.25 m^3/s) and a
drainage area of 730 mi^2 (1900 km^2). Because the average
annual rainfall in the area is 53.2 in (1350 mm) and average
annual surface runoff is about 3 in (76 mm), a balance of
about 35 in (890 mm) is lost to evapotranspiration in the
average year. Included in evapotranspiration losses is con-
sumptive use of water withdrawn from wells, estimated at
considerably less than 1 in (25 mm) per year.

Because of wide variation in permeability of covering
materials, recharge rate varies widely from one location to
another within the springs drainage area. No local recharge
rates have been measured directly. The method used for estimating local recharge rates is discussed later in the paper.

5. Circulation and Discharge.

Three-dimensional flow characteristics. Water that re-
charges the aquifer moves downward through the unsaturated
zone along approximately vertical lines, but when it passes
into the capillary fringe of the unsaturated zone and thence
into the zone of saturation, a horizontal component of movement is applied parallel to the down gradient direction of the
potentiometric surface. In a highly permeable aquifer such as
the cavernous limestone of the Floridan aquifer, the horizontal
component is usually dominant. Individual flow paths converge
into gently sloping troughs in the potentiometric surface
as the paths approach points of discharge. The solution
channel systems along which the flow concentrates in a limestone

aquifer, such as the Floridan, may become increasingly well developed as large springs, such as Silver Springs, are approached.

Detailed measurements of head distribution in the vertical in a network of observation wells would provide an ideal basis for defining the three-dimensional groundwater basin that discharges to Silver Springs; but the limited water-level data available do not permit such definition. However, the general knowledge of various geologic and hydrologic controls in the area and a comparison of Silver Springs water quality with the quality of water from wells that discharge from various depths in the aquifer, help define the flow system. These factors support the concept that the Silver Springs drainage area or basin is shallow and of subregional dimensions. Its flow system is to a large degree separate from an underlying, less active, regional flow system. The Silver Springs drainage area or basin may be described as bounded by vertical flow lines at the potentiometric divides, by a nearly horizontal *impermeable* bottom some 100 to 200 ft (30 to 60 m) below the top of the aquifer, and by an irregular top (the potentiometric surface).

The upper approximately 100 ft (30 m) of the Floridan aquifer in the Silver Springs area is composed of upper Eocene age limestone that is subject to active dissolution by circulating groundwater. This upper limestone is underlain by carbonate rock of middle Eocene age that is commonly dolomitized in its upper part. Probably little active dissolution is now taking place in the dolomitic rock, but there is evidence that solution channels that were developed before dolomitization are preserved in the upper 100 feet (30 m) or so of the middle Eocene. This solution channel system is underlain by dolomite of comparatively low permeability that restricts downward movement of groundwater and constitutes the *impermeable* bottom to the basin. Within at least a few miles of Silver Springs, the preserved solution channels probably conduct appreciable flow to the springs. Most flow to the springs probably is in the upper 100 to 200 ft (30-60 m) of the Floridan aquifer, and water tends to travel through a greater thickness near the springs than near the edges of the area draining to the springs.

Theoretical analyses of groundwater flow such as discussed by Freeze and Witherspoon [7,8], Thrailkill [9], and Toth [10] are useful in interpreting flow along vertical planes in the Silver Springs area.

Head distribution is dependent on the locations of recharge and discharge areas. In a recharge area the flow is downward, so that the head decreases with depth. Conversely, in a discharge area flow is upward so the head increases

with depth. Between a recharge area and a discharge area the
flow is nearly horizontal so that the change in head with
depth is slight.

As long as there is additional recharge in the downstream
direction there will remain a vertical component of flow
resulting in a gradual deepening of flow paths, so that recharge
entering at the divide will have to travel deepest in the
aquifer to reach the discharge area. Where there is little or
no recharge, the flow paths will approach horizontal. When
the groundwater then flows from under the covered area of
little or no recharge and enters an area down gradient where
there is recharge, a downward component of flow will again
result because of the higher head at shallower depths resulting
from the recharge. As flow nears the discharge area, the flow
paths turn upward and the hydraulic head lessens toward the
water table. A flow path that reaches the *impermeable* bottom
of the basin will become horizontal and remain so until it
approaches the discharge area. The effect of variable recharge conditions along a flow path is illustrated in the
diagrammatic section in Fig. 5.

Water-quality indicators of flow depth. Certain water-
quality factors support the premise that most of the flow of
Silver Springs is from the top of the aquifer. Dissolved-
solids concentrations in the spring waters are similar to
concentrations in water from wells in the shallow part of the
aquifer.

Like dissolved solids, sulfate concentration increases in
Floridan aquifer water with depth, probably to a large extent
the result of the greater amount of gypsum and anhydrite
(calcium sulfate) in rocks deeper in the aquifer. In the
Ocala-Silver Springs vicinity the average sulfate concentration in water samples collected from 18 wells in the upper
part of the aquifer is 22 mg/l (milligrams per litre). The
well waters range in sulfate concentrations from 0.0 to
92 mg/l and the wells range in depth from 40 to 200 ft (12 to
60 m). About 5 mi (8 km) west of Silver Springs, in the city
of Ocala, a well open to the aquifer from 850 to 1,083 ft
(260 to 330 m) below land surface yields water whose sulfate
concentration is about 260 mg/l. Sulfate concentrations of
about 150 mg/l are found in public-supply wells in Ocala that
are open to the interval 120 to 350 ft (37 to 107 m) deep,
and Silver Springs water has sulfate concentrations ranging
between 30 and 50 mg/l.

Calculations based on average concentrations of 22 mg/l
of sulfate near the top of the aquifer, 260 mg/l near the
bottom of the aquifer and 40 mg/l in Silver Springs water
indicate that the spring water is a mixture of about 92 percent
shallow water and 8 percent deep water. If the foregoing

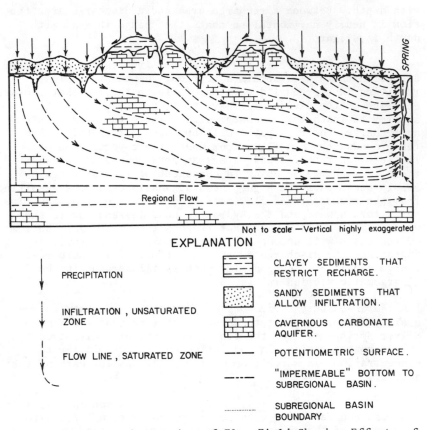

Regional Flow

Not to scale — Vertical highly exaggerated

EXPLANATION

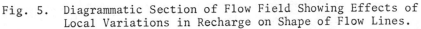

PRECIPITATION		CLAYEY SEDIMENTS THAT RESTRICT RECHARGE.
		SANDY SEDIMENTS THAT ALLOW INFILTRATION.
INFILTRATION , UNSATURATED ZONE		CAVERNOUS CARBONATE AQUIFER.
		POTENTIOMETRIC SURFACE.
FLOW LINE , SATURATED ZONE		"IMPERMEABLE" BOTTOM TO SUBREGIONAL BASIN.
		SUBREGIONAL BASIN BOUNDARY

Fig. 5. Diagrammatic Section of Flow Field Showing Effects of
Local Variations in Recharge on Shape of Flow Lines.

sulfate concentrations for the upper part of the aquifer and
for the springs are compared with 150 mg/l in the upper-
middle part of the aquifer penetrated by the Ocala public-
supply wells, a Silver Springs water mixture consisting of
about 86 percent upper aquifer water and 14 percent upper-
middle aquifer water is indicated.

The temperature of water issuing from Silver Springs is
23°C (Celsius), which indicates that the water comes from
only moderate depth. The normal rate of increase in temperature of groundwater with depth is 1°C for each 115 ft (35 m)
of depth. The mean air temperature in the north-central
Florida climatic division, which includes the Ocala-Silver
Springs area, is about 22°C. Water temperature increases in
wells around Ocala approximately in accordance with the normal
gradient. Therefore, the average depth from which the spring
water comes should be about 115 ft (35 m).

The accuracy of the foregoing analyses is limited because the precise parts of the open-hole intervals that produce most of the water discharged from some of the wells are not known. Nonetheless, the comparisons add supporting evidence that most of the flow in the Silver Springs basin is in the upper part of the aquifer.

A recent investigation by Osmond, Kaufman, and Cowart [11], has utilized activity ratios of two naturally occurring isotopes of uranium, U-238 and U-234, in conjunction with the uranium concentration to *fingerprint* groundwater masses in the Silver Springs drainage area. The groundwater sources and flow patterns indicated in the uranium-isotope investigations are notably similar to those derived from the flow analysis by Faulkner [1] in the Cross-Florida Barge Canal investigations and discussed in the present paper.

Flow net analysis. Average transmissivity of the upper part of the Floridan aquifer along a given potential contour surrounding Silver Springs may be calculated by treating Silver Springs as a discharging well and evaluating its effects upon the potentiometric surface. Through use of Darcy's law expressed by the following equation, average transmissivity based on flow across the full length of a closed potential contour may be approximated roughly by:

$$T = \frac{Q-R}{IL}$$

where T = transmissivity, in feet squared per day; Q = spring discharge, in cubic feet per second - day; R = recharge in cubic feet per second - day in area enclosed by potential contour at which average transmissivity is calculated; I = average hydraulic gradient across potential contour, in feet per mile; and L = width of flow channel or length of closed potential contour, in miles.

Average transmissivity along a 41.5-foot (12.64-meter) potential contour surrounding Silver Springs, as may be inferred on the May 1968 potentiometric map in Fig. 3, was determined by this method to be 1,970,000 ft^2/d (feet squared per day) or 183,000 m^2/d (meters squared per day).

A coefficient of storage for the aquifer in the vicinity of Silver Springs has not been calculated. Continuous discharge and variable, but probably nearly continuous, recharge preclude calculating a storage coefficient by means of an analysis of the relationships between spring discharge and changes in the potentiometric surface.

The aquifer obviously stores vast quantities of water as evidenced by good intergranular porosity (35 to 40 percent as

measured from cores at one location in Ocala vicinity), the
cavernous nature of the limestone, the perennially high flow
at the springs, and a slow rate of decline in groundwater
levels and spring discharge during extended dry periods.

The average transmissivity determined by total flow across
a closed potentiometric contour may serve as a useful generalization, but it is too general where there are needs for
quantifying the variable transmissivity of heterogeneous
groundwater flow systems developed in karst areas such as the
Silver Springs drainage basin. A specific method of flow-
net analysis that, as noted earlier, differs in some respects
from the method of flow-net analysis described by Bennett [4,
pp. 139-144], is used to compute a first approximation of the
variation in transmissivity from one aquifer *flow tube* to
another in the closed groundwater drainage area for Silver
Springs. It is possible through the specific flow-net
analysis used to compare differences in transmissivity within
the drainage area, and thereby further distinguish the major
zones of flow to the springs.

In the method of flow-net analysis used, the following
assumptions are made:

1. Flow in the aquifer is lateral (horizontal), the
component of vertical flow being negligible. Flow in the
leaky beds overlying the aquifer is considered to be vertical,
and when the water gets to the aquifer the direction of flow
abruptly changes to lateral. Flow lines in the aquifer in the
Silver Springs drainage area tend to be nearly horizontal
except at the discharge point where flow lines are vertical.
The gradient of the potentiometric surface is so low in most
places that it is nearly horizontal.

2. The aquifer in the area is heterogeneous and isotropic
with respect to its permeability; that is, the method assumes
that although the permeability can differ from one point to
another in the aquifer, that at a given point in the aquifer,
permeability is the same in all directions.

3. Flow in the aquifer is laminar and Darcy's law
applies despite the concentration of flow in solution channels,
which might lead (at least locally) to turbulent flow.

4. In a heterogeneous and isotropic aquifer the equipotential and stream lines intersect at right angles. It is
assumed that the orthogonality of equipotential and stream
surfaces also holds true when the aquifer receives recharge
vertically.

5. The aquifer is artesian and the flow steady. Inasmuch
as the variation in saturated thickness of the aquifer is small

compared to the estimated total thickness where the aquifer
is under water-table conditions, the assumption of an artesian
condition does not result in large errors.

6. Silver Springs is considered a well which fully
penetrates the upper part of the Floridan aquifer, that part
of the aquifer from which most of the discharge from the springs
is derived. For this analysis, all of the discharge from the
springs is assumed to be derived from the upper part of the
aquifer.

By drawing flow lines perpendicular to the equipotential
lines from the potentiometric divide (drainage area boundary)
to Silver Springs, a pattern of distorted rectangles is produced, each bounded by two flow lines and two equipotential
lines as shown in Fig. 3. Then, by use of the law of continuity
and Darcy's law, an estimate of the average transmissivity in
each rectangle is obtained.

In order to calculate transmissivity, it is first
necessary to estimate how much water flows across the middle
of the rectangular area in question. This flow equals the
sum of the recharge in all the rectangles bounded by the two
flow lines, the potentiometric divide, and the upstream end of
the subject rectangle plus the recharge in the upstream half of
the subject rectangle. Average recharge to the spring drainage
area is considered equal to the average discharge of the spring,
because other withdrawal from the aquifer is negligible. With
the aid of hydrogeologic maps showing variations in thickness
and type of cover over the aquifer, estimates can be made of
the areal variation in recharge.

The method is illustrated by the following diagram:

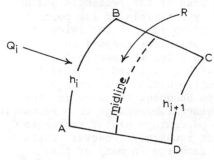

where BC and AD are flow lines,
and AB and CD are equipotential
lines. Q_i is the flow into
the region ABCD, R is the
vertical recharge per unit area,
and h_i and h_{i+1} are potential values. Rather than
the distorted rectangle ABCD,
it is convenient to consider a
rectangular approximation
A'B'C'D', where A'D' and B'C'
are flow lines representing AD
and BC, and A'B' and C'D' are equipotential lines having the
same values as AB and CD respectively:

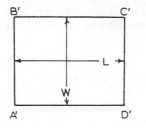

This transformed flow element has the properties where

$$A'B' = C'D' = 1/2 (AB + CD) = W,$$

and

$$A'D' = B'C' = 1/2 (AD + BC) = L.$$

With all other values known, transmissivity, T, may now be calculated for any given locality within the area ABCD by use of the following equation:

$$T = \frac{L (Q_i + 1/2 \; WLR)}{W (h_i - h_{i + 1})} \; .$$

The transmissivity in the rectangle or cell ABCD is treated as if it is constant. Transmissivity can vary from cell to cell.

The closer the shape of ABCD to a rectangle, the more accurate will be the determination of transmissivity. Another factor limiting the accuracy of the method is the difficulty in estimating recharge within the individual rectangles. Average recharge for the entire drainage area may be readily calculated, but that for the individual rectangles must be estimated on the basis of the amount and types of surficial materials and other factors which control recharge. The recharge distribution in terms of percentages of the whole can be estimated. From this it is possible to estimate the recharge in each rectangle.

A first step in estimating recharge to a given rectangle or group of rectangles is to compare, from map measurements (Fig. 3), the percentages of the area of the rectangle and of the total drainage basin covered by materials of low permeability that restrict recharge. Using in part the calculated average recharge to the drainage basin for comparison, a best-judgment estimate of recharge is made for the rectangle. If the percentage of the rectangle with restricted recharge is about the same as that for the entire basin, the average unit-area recharge is estimated to be about the same for the rectangle as for the basin. In general, recharge to a rectangle is inversely proportional to the percentage of the rectangle covered by materials that restrict recharge. However, there are moderate to small amounts of recharge in many of the covered areas, so a best-judgment factor based on hydrogeologic knowledge of the area must be applied in estimating recharge.

Because steady flow is assumed in the flow-net method, the average long term potentiometric gradient and rate of recharge is best to use. However, a map of the average potentiometric

surface was not available when the analysis was made, so the
map of the lower, more gently sloping potentiometric surface
for May 1968 was used. Recharge estimates were based on the
long term average annual recharge for the basin, but were
reduced by 20 percent for transmissivity determinations because the monthly mean discharge for Silver Springs in May
1968 was 653 ft^3/s (18.49 m^3/s), or only about 80 percent of
the long term average discharge rate of 821 ft^3/s (23.25 m^3/s).

Figure 3 is a map of the May 1968 potentiometric surface
in the Silver Springs drainage area on which have been drawn
25 flow tubes converging from all directions on the discharge
area at Silver Springs. Average transmissivity within one
rectangle or flow cell in each of the 25 flow tubes has been
calculated. The cells either abut or are diagonally connected
in a continuous belt around the springs, and they are positioned
on the potentiometric surface at altitudes of 1 to 4 ft (0.3
to 1.2 m) upgradient from the springs. Any number of flow
tubes and flow cells may be used, however, depending on the
detail of analysis desired.

All flow from upgradient of the cells must pass through
a cell in the belt to reach the springs. Thus, the sum of
the flow through all the cells is equal to the flow from the
springs less the recharge down gradient from the belt of
cells.

On Fig. 3 the flow cells for which transmissivity is
calculated are numbered clockwise 1 through 25. The computed
transmissivity and the data used to compute it are listed in
Table 1 for each of the flow cells.

Transmissivity ranges from 10,000 ft^2/d (1,000 m^2/d) in
cell-23, which is located under the confining layer east of
the springs, to 25,400,000 ft^2/d (2,360,000 m^2/d) in cell-15,
through which flow passes from a major part of the north
half of the Silver Springs drainage area. The average transmissivity along the belt of cells is 2,080,000 ft^2/d (193,000
m^2/d). This compares favorably with the 1,970,000 ft^2/d
(183,000 m^2/d) average determined along an inferred 41.5-foot
(12.6-meter) potential contour on the May 1968 map by the
method of analysis based on the flow across the full length
of a closed contour. The inferred 41.5-foot (12.6-meter)
contour passes through the centers of 19 of the 25 flow cells.

The accuracy of the areal variation in transmissivity
estimated by the flow-net analysis is limited both by limits on
available water-level control for development of the potentiometric map and by uncertainty in estimating variation in recharge distribution. Contouring equipotentials becomes less
certain as complexity of the actual transmissivity variation
increases. The computed transmissivities given in Table 1 cover

156

Table 1. Flow-net Analysis Data, Upper Part of Floridan Aquifer, near Silver Springs.

Cell No.	Length L - miles	Width W - miles	Inflow area - miles2	Aver. annual recharge inches	Inflow Q - ft3/s-day	Recharge R to cell - (ft3/s-day)/mi2	WLR - ft3/s-day	Q&WLR - ft3/s-day	$h_i - h_{i+1}$ - feet	Trans. T* ft2/d x10^6	Percent flow of Silver Springs	Trans. T* m2/d x10^6
1	1.0	1.4	94.9	7.2	50.4	0.85	1.19	51.51	1	3.14	7.8	0.292
2	1.4	1.5	82.4	12.0	72.8	1.06	2.22	75.01	1	5.88	11.4	0.546
3	1.4	1.1	14.5	12.8	13.6	1.06	1.63	15.25	1	1.58	2.3	0.147
4	1.4	1.2	14.7	12.8	13.8	1.06	1.85	15.70	1	1.53	2.4	0.142
5	2.0	2.0	14.9	12.0	13.2	0.88	3.54	16.66	1	1.29	2.5	0.120
6	2.6	2.1	8.0	12.0	7.0	0.88	4.82	11.88	1	1.02	1.8	0.095
7	1.0	1.2	4.0	13.6	4.0	0.47	0.59	4.55	0.5	0.62	0.7	0.058
8	2.2	2.1	4.2	11.2	3.4	0.88	4.14	7.60	1	0.51	1.2	0.047
9	2.7	1.4	6.6	14.4	7.0	1.06	4.03	11.09	1	1.47	1.7	0.136
10	1.3	1.2	2.7	14.4	2.9	1.06	1.56	4.41	1	0.35	0.7	0.032
11	1.0	1.4	2.5	14.4	2.7	0.88	1.19	3.91	1	0.19	0.6	0.018
12	1.1	1.3	2.1	14.4	2.2	0.88	1.22	3.46	1	0.20	0.5	0.019
13	1.5	1.6	6.4	12.8	6.1	1.00	2.39	8.46	1	0.56	1.3	0.052
14	1.8	1.7	17.7	9.6	12.5	0.70	2.20	14.70	1	1.30	2.2	0.121
15	1.9	1.4	247.0	12.0	218.3	0.88	2.39	220.73	1	25.41	33.6	2.360
16	1.6	1.8	38.6	16.0	45.5	1.18	3.44	48.99	1	3.68	7.5	0.342
17	1.3	1.1	11.2	14.4	11.8	1.00	1.38	13.14	1	1.27	2.0	0.118
18	1.0	1.0	7.4	14.4	7.9	1.06	1.16	9.09	1	0.80	1.4	0.074
19	1.0	1.0	5.7	14.4	6.1	1.06	1.10	7.17	1	0.56	1.1	0.052
20	0.8	2.7	3.3	14.4	3.4	1.06	2.76	6.22	1	0.13	0.9	0.012
21	0.6	1.3	7.5	14.4	7.9	1.06	0.83	8.75	1	0.35	1.3	0.032
22	0.6	1.2	4.7	4.0	1.4	0.35	0.25	1.61	1	0.07	0.2	0.006
23	0.5	1.2	1.6	1.6	0.2	0.06	0.04	0.29	1	0.01	0.04	0.001
24	0.6	1.3	3.6	4.0	1.0	0.12	0.10	1.09	1	0.04	0.2	0.004
25	0.8	1.1	5.0	6.4	2.3	0.18	0.15	2.53	1	0.15	0.4	0.014
92 mi2--area below cells							81.32	81.32			12.3	
Totals or Averages				12.0			81.32	645.12		2.08	98.04	0.193

* Transmissivity calculations based on potentiometric surface and monthly mean spring discharge for May 1968.

three orders of magnitude and the largest ratio of transmissivities of neighboring cells is about 20. Thus, transmissivity
variation is far from uniform. Considering the large variation
of apparent transmissivity, the uncertainties inherent in preparation of potentiometric maps and that influence the accuracy
of the estimated transmissivities are recognized. However, although computed transmissivity values for individual cells
could be subject to question, the overall configuration of the
computed results are believed to reflect the general qualitative properties of the actual variations in transmissivity.

Time of travel determinations. In the absence of a
practical means for direct measurement of time of travel of
groundwater through a given part of the aquifer, an approximation of velocity through a flow cell may be inferred from
the slope of the potentiometric surface and from the transmissivity.

Assuming that the flow is laminar, one can calculate the
average velocity from the equation:

$$V = \frac{KI}{a}$$

where V = velocity, in feet per day; K = hydraulic conductivity, in feet per day; I = hydraulic gradient, in feet per
foot; and a = aquifer porosity, in percent. Reasonable
estimates of aquifer porosity may be made from a few core
analyses available in the area and judgments of the degree of
solution channel development in the flow cell. Permeability
must be approximated from the calculated transmissivity and
thickness of the flow cell estimated by judgment from a knowledge of the hydrogeology.

The approximated average of the average velocities of
groundwater movement through the 25 flow cells in May 1968 was
about 6.4 ft/d (feet per day) or 2.0 m/d (meters per day) calculated on the basis of: (1) transmissivity of 2,080,000 ft^2/d
(193,000 m^2/d), (2) aquifer thickness of 150 ft (46 m),
(3) hydraulic gradient of 0.74 ft/mi (feet per mile) or 0.14
m/km (meters per kilometer), and (4) aquifer porosity of 30
percent. If the aquifer thickness is considered to be only
100 ft (30 m), the average velocity was about 9.6 ft/d (2.9
m/d). For an individual cell, the velocity approximation may
be appreciably above or below the average. For cell-15, an
average velocity of 77 ft/d (23 m/d) is indicated for May 1968,
while the approximated average velocity through cell-23 was
0.16 ft/d (0.05 m/d).

As stated, the approximations are of average velocity
only and are not necessarily equal to actual velocity between
two points in the aquifer. Actual velocity may vary considerably

along the flow route because of variations in effective
porosity and thickness of the aquifer, among other factors. In
any case, velocity approximations must be used with care because of complications due to the presence of solution channels.

6. Conclusions.

To analyze the qualitative and quantitative flow characteristics of a karst system which has well developed underground
circulation similar to that of the Silver Springs drainage
area, a comprehensive suite of geologic and hydrologic information is needed. A good network of observation wells is
essential for obtaining the necessary subsurface geologic information, groundwater level data and water-quality data.
Historical data for computation of long term averages and
ranges of spring discharge, groundwater level fluctuation, and
rainfall are needed to quantify aquifer recharge, storage
capacity, transmissivity, travel time, and to define a water
budget.

Various types of geologic maps help to define recharge
characteristics, provide clues to the origin of solution
channel systems, and aid in defining the distribution of
porosity and permeability in the aquifer, thereby helping to
define the flow pattern in the aquifer.

Potentiometric maps of the aquifer further suggest variations in porosity and permeability and identify directions of
flow and principal zones of flow. From the map of the potentiometric surface, groundwater drainage basin boundaries are
drawn. If, as in the case of Silver Springs, discharge for a
groundwater drainage basin is concentrated at a single major
spring or spring complex, the springs are like a continuously
discharging well with a cone of depression that includes the
entire groundwater drainage basin. By using the potentiometric
map of the drainage basin in conjunction with measured spring
discharge and estimated recharge rates, first approximations of
transmissivity of the aquifer may be determined for selected
places within the drainage basin by the specified method of
flow-net analysis. The flow-net analysis also identifies
quantitatively the principal source areas for the water discharging at the springs.

Variations in vertical permeability in the aquifer are
important controls on the depth of flow. Good estimates of
depth of flow in the aquifer may be made from knowledge of
changes in permeability and water quality with depth.

Because the method of flow-net analysis permits the
analysis of flow in a large section of an aquifer, it has
important practical and economic advantages over conventional
aquifer-test methods. Flow-net analysis can produce results

that are representative of a basin as a whole, whereas, because of the inherent heterogeneous distribution of the porosity
and permeability in cavernous carbonate-rock aquifers, a conventional pumping test may necessarily analyze too small a
part of the aquifer, possibly a part that is not representative
of a larger segment.

If data are available for good estimates of the average
porosity of the aquifer, reasonable estimates of the groundwater storage capacity of the basin may be made. However, the
aquifer's storage coefficient was not determined from the flow-
net analysis, partly because of difficulties in evaluating the
effects of variable rates of recharge. Also, from good
estimates of porosity, reasonable approximations of average
velocity of groundwater movement through the aquifer may be
made by utilizing data derived from the flow-net analysis.

A comprehensive understanding of the qualitative and
quantitative characteristics of groundwater flow, regardless
of the type of aquifer system, is needed for proper water-
resource development, management and pollution control. There
are special needs inherent in the analysis of flow in karst
systems. The methods described in this paper provide much of
what is needed for understanding the flow in large parts of
the system. With this understanding, conventional aquifer-
test methods may be utilized for detailed local analysis to
solve special problems. Also, the basic understanding of an
aquifer system is a prerequisite to the development of possible
plans for advanced computer modeling of the system.

7.   References.

[1]   Faulkner, Glen L., Geohydrology of the Cross-Florida
      Barge Canal area with special reference to the Ocala
      Vicinity: U.S. Geol. Survey, Water Resources Investiga-
      tions 1-73, 117 p., 1973.

[2]   Stringfield, V. T., Artesian water in tertiary limestone
      in the southeastern United States: U.S. Geol. Survey
      Prof. Paper 517, 226 p., 1966.

[3]   Hyde, Luther W., Principal aquifers in Florida: Fla.
      Board of Conserv., Div. Geology, Map Ser. 16, 1965.

[4]   Ferris, J. G., Knowles, D. B., Brown, R. H., and
      Stallman, R. W., Theory of aquifer tests: U.S. Geological
      Survey, Water-Supply Paper 1536-E, 174 p., 1962.

[5]   Parker, Garald G., Ferguson, G. E., Love, S. K., and others,
      Water resources of southeastern Florida: U.S. Geol. Survey
      Water-Supply Paper 1255, 965 p, 1955.

[6] Vernon, Robert O., Geology of Citrus and Levy Counties, Florida: Fla. Geol. Survey Bull. 33, 255 p., 1951.

[7] Freeze, R. Allan, and Witherspoon, P. A., Theoretical analysis of regional groundwater flow, Part 1. Analytical and numerical solutions to the mathematical model: Am. Geophys. Union, Water Resources Research, v. 2, no. 4, p. 641-656, 1966.

[8] Freeze, R. Allan, and Witherspoon, P. A., Theoretical analysis of regional groundwater flow, Part 2. Effect of water-table configuration and subsurface permeability variation: Am. Geophys. Union, Water Resources Research, v. 3, no. 2, p. 623-634, 1967.

[9] Thrailkill, John, Chemical and hydrologic factors in the excavation of limestone caves: Geol. Soc. America Bull. v. 79, p. 19-46, 1968.

[10] Toth, J., A theoretical analysis of groundwater flow in small drainage basins: Am. Geophys. Union, Jour. Geophys. Research, v. 68, no. 16, p. 4795-4812, 1963.

[11] Osmond, J. K., Kaufman, M. I., and Cowart, J. B., Mixing volume calculations, sources and aging trends of Floridan aquifer water by uranium isotopic methods: Pergamon Press, Geochimica et Cosmochimica Acta, v. 38, pp. 1083-1100, 1974.

DISCUSSION

Boreli. The possible pollution of Silver Springs from the newly planned barge canal was emphasized. Because the plan envisions the water flow towards Silver Springs from a considerable section of the canal, it is not only a potential danger but rather a high probability that the canal construction will lead to contamination of one of the most beautiful karst springs in the United States. This danger exists also for the entire aquifer because, among other things, the end sections of the canal, which are at the sea level, deeply intrude into the Florida peninsula. What protection of Silver Springs and the aquifer as a whole was actually planned?

Yevjevich. Flow field, as shown in Fig. 5 of the paper may be questioned with the curved stream lines shown only in the upper 20-30 meters, though the cavernous carbonate aquifer seems to go much deeper, with the designation *regional flow*. For a deep aquifer, the stream lines and flow may be restricted to the upper 20-30 m layer only if the permeability of lower cavernous carbonate rock is significantly smaller than for the upper layer.

Avdagić. My remarks concern the role which is given to the fissures in the river basin as discussed in this paper. The number of piezometers used to establish the equipotential lines is not adequate to obtain an accurate flow picture for an area of 1900 square kilometers. Assumptions stated in the paper do not appear to be sufficiently restrictive so that certain results should be taken with caution due to the presence of underground channels. In Fig. 2 of the paper a geological cross section is given where a series of faults can be seen. They are mentioned in the paper, as well as of the other type of fissures, but only to give their general description. No data are given as to whether water pressure were measured in these fissures, as to what their relationship is to the medium with fine, primary porosity, as to how water passes through these fissures, or, finally, how the analysis is made of the continuum through which water flows toward the spring, also presented and treated in the paper.

LeGrand. In this symposium we are beginning to notice, in Faulkner's paper, an approach of karst study in the USA that is different from kinds of study in Yugoslavia. Mr. Faulkner and other USA participants refer to karst water level measurements. These water level measurements are obtained from relatively inexpensive boreholes or from existing water wells. The low topographic relief, the relatively shallow water levels (commonly less than 40 meters below land surface), and the dispersion of water wells in rural areas make the production of groundwater maps showing water levels a practicable approach. The water level maps show the direction of flow and allow reasonable quantitative studies of the storage and transmitting capacity of the karst system.

Because of the scarcity of water wells and the great expense of drilling deep boreholes in Yugoslavia, other approaches of study are necessary. Emphasis is placed on water balance techniques in which input and output values are considered in many ways. These studies are very useful, and the uses of tracers to define the catchment areas and the direction of general groundwater flow have been very valuable.

These different approaches to study in the two countries are reasonable and will probably continue to some extent. Yet, this symposium and other means of exchange of information will tend to bring all techniques into focus for best use.

Parizek. Figure 5 of the paper shows a graphical presentation of a groundwater flow system in cross-sectional view. Control points for measuring the fluid potential distribution are not shown nor is it clear from your paper if the flow field depicted was based on a numerical solution based on measured hydrogeological data and hydrologic boundary conditions or if this is a graphically derived estimation of the probable flow field.

Paper shows how important environmental impact studies and environmental considerations have become in the United States when planning, designing and constructing large scale public works projects. The Yugoslavian papers have demonstrated that considerable attention must be given to adverse effects by hydroelectric power projects through diversion of water from springs and streams, the influence of this diversion on agriculture, oyster production, and similar matters. Also, attempts were made to relocate and preserve bridges and other works of historic interest.

The important role of environmental studies in the U.S. such as those for the Cross Florida Barge Canal, should be of a wide interest.

It can be assumed that the canal will eventually be completed more or less as originally planned. This might in-fluence future groundwater development in the area or the amount of water level decline that might be allowed immediately adjacent to the canal. Since the water table controls the water level in the canal and carbonate bedrock is so permeable adjacent to the canal, extensive groundwater development might pose a problem to the maintenance and operation of the canal.

Faulkner. Construction of the canal has been halted since January 1971 because of public concern over possible damage to the environment. A Federal court judge has since determined that a comprehensive environmental impact assess-ment must be made before a decision can be made whether to complete the canal. A comprehensive environmental impact assessment is now underway to evaluate potential effects of the canal on the environment. Included are the canal's potential effects on the water quality at Silver Springs. Among many other things, attention is also given to the impact of the canal on future water use in the area and what effect water development from industrial and population growth in the lifetime of the canal may have on the availability of an adequate water supply for operation of the canal. Informa-tion developed from the environmental impact assessment is expected to have major influence on the decision whether to complete the canal in accordance with its presently authorized design or one of several other alternatives to complete or not complete the canal. The environmental study is expected to cost more than two million dollars and will require about two years to perform with completion of the impact statement anticipated for sometime in the fall of 1976.

It is stated in the paper: "The Floridan aquifer varies in porosity and permeability and in many places consists of

strata containing well-developed solution channel systems
separated by strata with low permeability that act as confining layers." As illustrated in Fig. 5, downward movement
of local recharge is restricted by a dolomitic zone of low
permeability. This zone of low permeability is about 65
meters or less below the top of the aquifer in the Silver
Springs area. Most of the flow to the Springs is restricted
to that part of the aquifer above this permeability barrier.
The regional flow below this zone of low permeability is
thought to be comparatively lethargic in the springs area and
the dissolved solids concentration of this deeper groundwater
is considerably greater than that which discharges at Silver
Springs.

The dual system of near-vertical tension fractures, with
one set of fractures intersecting the other at nearly right
angles, is very densely distributed in the Silver Springs area.
This results in frequent occurrence of intersecting solution
channels oriented along the fractures. Flow in the Silver
Springs drainage area is diffuse. The rock intervening
between the fractures and solution channels is not necessarily
of low permeability, so some groundwater moves down-gradient
through intergranular permeability, although flow through
the solution channels presumably predominants.

It is recognized that the potentiometric surface map
drawn from water-level data collected from a network of observation wells necessarily generalizes the direction of groundwater flow. On a limited local basis, groundwater presumably
flows in the direction of fracture trend which may not
locally be normal to the potentiometric contour lines.
However, because of the high density of fractures and the
intersecting nature of this dual system of fractures, a relatively few well-placed observation wells per unit area, regardless of whether some wells are open to solution channels, provide static water-level data sufficient to draw maps that are
in most places accurate, generalized representations of this
mostly very low-gradient potentiometric surface. Therefore,
the drainage area for the springs and the two-dimensional flow
pattern can be defined with an acceptable degree of accuracy
from the potentiometric map. There may be exceptions, it is
true. In a few places where presently available well control
indicates extraordinarily steep gradients, as in some places
between the Oklawaha River valley and the eastern boundary of
the Silver Springs drainage area, more dense control might
show that some of the head change occurs over an appreciably
shorter distance than indicated in Fig. 3. Most of the change
might take place abruptly across a fault or faults that
parallel the river valley.

The faults shown in Fig. 2 of my paper are, in plan view,
oriented parallel to the fracture systems and represent tension

fractures along which appreciably vertical movement of the
rocks has taken place. The faults in some cases probably
result in permeability barriers rather than zones of higher
permeability. The position of the Oklawaha River valley east
of the Silver Springs drainage area is thought to be at least
in part the result of graben faulting. The valley follows a
rectilinear route paralleling the fracture system. Faulting
may provide at least some indirect control on the position of
the eastern boundary of the Silver Springs drainage area.

Figure 5 is an estimation of the probable flow field. The
line of section is typical of parts of the Silver Springs
drainage basin. The shape of the potentiometric surface near
the top of the Floridan aquifer in the area is well documented
with water-level measurements from a network of observation
wells, although detailed measurements of head change in the
vertical were not available. Detailed data on head distribution in the vertical would provide an ideal basis for defining
the three-dimensional groundwater basin that discharges to
Silver Springs; but since that kind of data was not available,
it was necessary to estimate the shape of the flow field on
the basis of other hydrogeologic information. Coupled with
general knowledge of various geologic and hydrologic controls
in the area, theoretical analyses of groundwater flow such as
discussed by Freeze and Witherspoon [7, 8], Thrailkill [9],
and Toth [10] are useful in interpreting flow along vertical
planes in the Silver Springs area.

Much is known in the area regarding location of recharge
and discharge areas, thus providing indirect knowledge regarding where and how head is most likely to change with
depth. Well-controlled potentiometric surface maps of the
upper part of the Floridan aquifer are the prime source of
information on location of the vertical basin boundaries used
to sketch the section in Fig. 5. Subsurface stratigraphic
information aides identification of the "impermeable" bottom
of the subregional basin depicted in the section. Data on
changes in groundwater quality with depth are also useful in
defining the depth of the basin.

WATER REGIME IN DEEP KARST.
CASE STUDY OF THE OMBLA SPRING DRAINAGE AREA

by

Petar Milanović, Engineering Geologist,
Electric Power Board, Department Trebinje, Yugoslavia

Synopsis. Specific features of water regimes in deep
karst areas are the consequence of hydrogeologic characteristics of the karst underground. Usually the gross porosities
(karst channels and caves) have poor retardation capacities
and they empty quickly.

By analyzing the problems of the Ombla Spring, it has
been found that the immediate catchment area gives the principal water supply to this spring, while the influence of the
percolating water along the Trebišnjica Riverbed is estimated
to be insignificant when looked at from the aspect of the
total undergound water reserves. The 470 days are estimated
to be required for nearly a complete drainage of water
storage in the Ombla River karst aquifer system.

Comparison between the flow hydrograph of the Spring and
the level hydrographs of numerous piezometer boreholes led
to the conclusion that the Ombla River karst system, especially
in the period of high groundwater levels, functions as a
hydraulic system under pressure.

The maximum range in the oscillation of groundwater
levels is about 200 m. The rate of the level rise may sometimes attain 370 cm per hour, that is up to 89 m per day.
The water yields of the spring flow under normal conditions
never decrease below a minimum of 4 m^3/sec, while the maximum
discharge passes 150 m^3/sec.

The catchment area is variable according to flow conditions. This fact complicates the calculation of the water
budget. By analyzing the data collected, the water regime of
the Ombla Spring has all the characteristics of the typical
outflow of a deep karst aquifer system.

1. Introduction.

The water regime in karst hydrogeologic aquifer systems
is the consequence of: (1) hydrogeologic parameters of the
environment; (2) geometry and the position of the aquifer
system; (3) the size of the catchment area, and (4) hydrologic
conditions. The most important hydrogeologic parameters are
the effective porosity and the permeability, which can be
treated as invariables. Geometry and position of the aquifer

system are also invariables. On the other hand, the catchment area can be only conditionally treated as invariable, while the hydrologic conditions fluctuate constantly and both in space and time. This diversity of characteristics of karst aquifer systems results in specific karst water circulations which differ in every respect from the water circulation in intergranular porous media.

Lithological composition, fractures and structures represent geologic characteristics whose role in the formation of the type of porosity of a medium is dominant. Observed from the generic point of view, porosity of the Dinaric Karst is secondary, expressed in the form of karst channels, caves and joints of various dimensions and irregular space positions. Circulation of a larger part of the water runoff occurs through karst underground channels of large dimensions, i.e., of a great transmissivity.

Karstified rocks are not homogeneous porous media. The porosity is the consequence of litho-tectonic factors and the evolution of the karst process. Evolution process is dictated by the position of the erosion base levels, also responsible for the formation of directions of circulation. As a result of these processes, privileged directions in underground circulation are formed. This is one of the principal features of the karst. It is rather difficult to investigate the media of this type of porosity. Since a great deal of data which constitute a karst drainage model is not easily obtainable, part of it is not even feasible to quantify.

The data collected in the course of detailed investigations of a volume of karstified sedimentary rocks, picked up at random, may leave an incorrect impression on hydrogeologic characteristics by relating some of them to the whole aquifer system. Any attempt to identify the representative data may induce gross errors, especially if these data are used as inputs for quantitative hydrogeologic treatments A representative hydrogeologic factor often applies to the whole rock volume, namely to the whole area or catchment that are investigated. To disclose all parameters of these *factors* large investigations are needed, which are rarely justified from an economic point of view. To perform investigations (like drilling piezometric boreholes, carrying out detailed geophysical investigations, etc), those areas must be selected for which one can follow competently all the important results in the investigated sedimentary rocks. These areas may be considered as a kind of strategic zones of the aquifer system. They are generally found in the immediate hinterland of those localities at which water outflows from karst aquifer systems are already concentrated. Determining these zones requires a detailed analysis of complex hydrogeologic characteristics. The concentration of privileged water flow directions

along these zones makes it possible to well plan and undertake
the explorations (mainly by boreholes). Through these zones
the whole drainage area is connected with the dominant erosion
base by relatively narrow, well-karstified parts of the limestone.

2.   Characteristics of the Ombla Spring and its Drainage Area.

The catchment of the Ombla Spring (and River) has all the
characteristics of a typical karst area of the Outer Dinarides
(Dinaric Karst) with very pronounced and deep karstification.
A great volume of sedimentary rocks of about 300 km^3 empties
its water through this spring. The surface of the catchment
area varies because it depends on hydrologic conditions. The
surface of 600 km^2 was estimated to be an optimal value of
this area. In Fig. 1 this surface is marked as a shaded
area, with no clearly established boundaries. Data necessary
for determining this surface were obtained from investigations
of underground connections and hydrogeologic characteristics
of sedimentary rocks which constitute this area. Thickness
of the carbonate rocks in relation to the comparative level
(sea level being zero), varies from about 250 to 1000 m.

The outflow of the underground karst system of the
Ombla Spring, referred here briefly as the aquifer, is at the
elevation of 2.38 m a.s.l. as the permanent spring. Minimum
discharge of the spring, measured under natural conditions
(5 Oct., 1961), was 4.1 m^3/sec. Minimum measured discharge
after the construction of the Bileća storage reservoir and
the Gorica daily pondage was 10.1 m^3/sec (4 Sept., 1970).
Maximum discharge of 88 m^3/sec was measured on 10 April, 1970.
The maximum discharge from the maximum stage and the flow
rating curve was about 165 m^3/sec (17 Feb. 1973).

Very karstified Jurassic and Cretaceous limestones constitute the dominant mass of the aquifer. Eocene flysh
sediments are pretty scarce but are very important for their
hydrogeologic function as are the Triassic dolomites. Two
zones of Cretaceous and Jurassic dolomites between the
Trebišnjica River and the Adriatic Coast play an important
role in the formation of geometry of this water collector
(see Fig. 2). One of the zones follows the direction of
rock structures while the other follows the fractured areas,
somewhat in an oblique direction. Dolomite zone follows
the structure direction assuming a particular position between
the erosion base and the aquifer, causing the concentration of
water flows of the whole drainage area.

In addition to inflows from the immediate drainage area
(shown in Fig. 1), a large part of the remote drainage area
also supplies water under the natural conditions to the Ombla

168

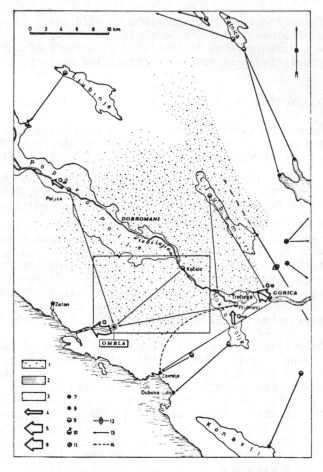

Fig. 1. The Ombla River Catchment Area: (1) Catchment Area,
(2) Storage Reservoir, (3) Karst Polje, (4) Inter-
mittent Surface Inflow into and Outflow from the
Catchment, (5) Constant Surface Inflow into the
Catchment, (6) The point of Concentrated Discharge
of Karst Collector, (7) Permanent Spring, (8) Inter-
mittent Spring, (9) Sinkhole, (10) Estavella, (11)
Borehole, (12) Anticline Axis, (13) Underground
Connection Defined by Dye Tracers, (14) Underground
Connection Defined by Dye Tracers at High Groundwater
Levels.

Spring. Water of this remote drainage area, with a surface
of about 1500 km^2, goes underground through many sinkholes
along the riverbed of the Trebišnjica River, downstream of
Trebinje. When the Gorica Dam was built, the input into the
aquifer became controlled. This controlled inflow into the

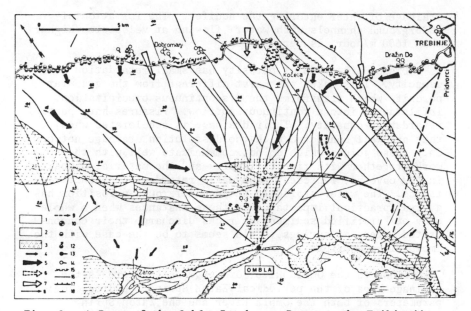

Fig. 2. A Part of the Ombla Catchment Between the Tribisnjica
River and the Ombla River: (1) Karstified Limestones,
(2) Dolomites, (3) Flysh, (4) Circulation Directions
for the Collectors of Zavrelje and Zaton, (5) General
Directions of Underground Circulation, (6) General
Directions of Circulation at high Groundwater Levels,
(7) Circulation Directions Below the Level of the
Trebišnjica Riverbed, (8) Established Underground
Connections (9) Underground Connections Established
at High Groundwater Levels, (10) Piezometric Borehole,
(11) Sinkhole, (12) Estavella, (13) Permanent Spring,
(14) Intermittent Spring, (15) Fault Zone, (16) Fault,
(17) Thrust Face, (18) Beds Altitudes.

groundwater was determined as a biological minimum in form of
a release at the Dam. The remote drainage area is separated
from the immediate drainage area by the anticline structure
with the Triassic dolomite core constituting a hydrogeologic
barrier.

3. Retardation Capacity of the Underground.

     Karst channels, caves, system of joints, enlarged here
and there by karstification, as well as fissures and non-active
channels and caves, often filled by gravel, sand and terra
rosa (a material of intergranulated type of porosity) constitute the effective porosity of the karst. Dissolution type
of porosity in form of channels and caves provide a quick

drainage of water entering the aquifer. The formation of underground channels with water flowing at velocities higher than 1600 m/hour, is very common.

Dissolution type of porosity has small retardation capacity. This makes the karst different from the granular porosity which transforms the discontinuous precipitation infiltration into a continuous outflow. Fissures have partial retardation capacity. Their drainage is accelerated when they are well connected with the dissolution drainage network. Only those joints which do not communicate well with the network, together with finest fissures and the material deposited in the caverns, represent good water retardation characteristics. The water stored in these underground porosities has a great practical importance in those instances when a whole body of karstified sedimentary rocks discharge their concentrated waters at springs. This seems to be the case with the Ombla River aquifer.

Close to the Ombla River drainage basin there is the drainage area of the periodical Zaton Spring. Hydrogeologic parameters of both the Ombla River and the Zaton Spring aquifers are of the same type, differences being only in geometry of underground channels and the size of drainage areas. The Zaton Spring aquifer is completely isolated from the hinterland and intermediary influence of other drainage areas by hydrogeologic barriers. The groundwater dynamic reserves, stored in the rainfall or snowmelt periods in the zone of seasonal fluctuations of groundwater levels recede quickly. Small total water retention in fissure and granular porosity is not sufficient to keep the flow permanent at the spring.

4. Analysis of Fracture Tectonics.

Detailed geologic mapping helped identify the zone in which a concentration of privileged flow directions of underground circulation could be expected. By analyzing the aerial photos (such as Fig. 3), a dense network of fracture tectonics was identified, comprising the area between the Trebišnjica River and the Ombla River, marked as a rectangle in Fig. 1. Large fractures are drawn as thick lines in Fig. 3, while the accompanying secondary tectonics is drawn as thin lines. Prevailing orientation of fractures, normal to the general Dinaric direction, is well shown in Fig. 3. Another dominant orientation of fractures more or less coincides with the directions of underground circulation. Concentration of fractures is well pronounced in the hinterland of the Ombla Spring. In the area analyzed by aerial photos (not counting sinkholes in the Trebišnjica riverbed), 120 pits and caves were recorded. All these forms are connected to fractures.

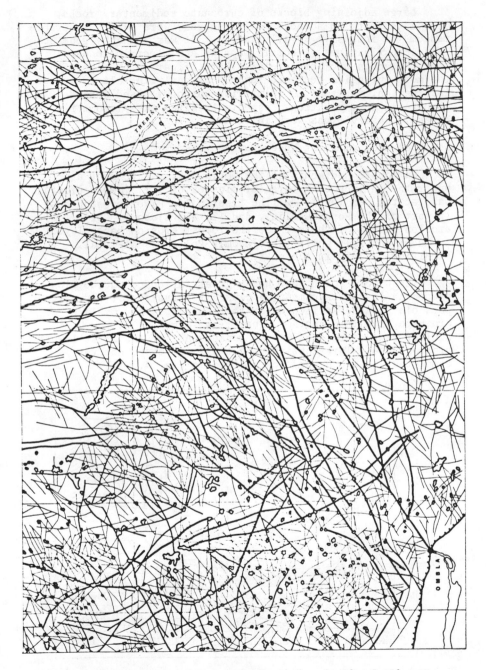

Fig. 3.   The Network of Fracture Tectonics in the Catchment
Area of the Ombla Spring.

Large adjoining blocks of carbonate sedimentary rocks,
dislocated with an abundance of fissures, were a very favorable
medium for intensive karstification. It was found by geoelectric investigations (electric mapping and electric sondage)
that the zones of most intensive karstification overlap with
the most intensive tectonic zones. By analyzing all collected
information, the zone is identified which promised optimal
results in investigations, especially after the piezometric
borehole observations were initiated.

5. Evolution of Karst Underground Systems.

Carbonate sediments of the Ombla Spring catchment are
under the influence of three erosion bases: (1) lowest erosion
base at the sea level, (2) The Trebišnjica River erosion base
(a part of the Popovo Polje), and (3) The Ljubomir Polje
erosion base. Of these three the lowest erosion base played
the dominant role while the Ljubomir Polje was of local
significance only in the past.

The Popovo Polje base has a great influence on the flow
phenomena in the catchment, because it traverses it and makes
possible for the surface water to flow across the Ombla River
drainage area into another area. The formation of the Ombla
aquifer characteristics is the consequence of the karst lowest
erosion base. This continuous geologic process, not yet
completed, is shown very schematized in Fig. 4.

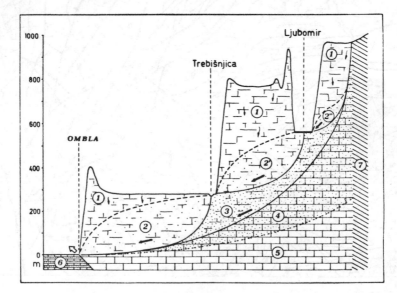

Fig. 4. The Evolution Scheme of Karst Collectors of the Ombla
River, with Three Erosion Bases (Ljubomir, Trebišnjica,
Ombla).

The flysch barrier, (6) of Fig. 4, is responsible for the depth limitation of effective and well expressed porosity of the carbonate rocks. Taking into consideration the possibility of siphon circulation patterns and the conditions responsible for the development of karstification before the Eocene sediment depositions, the Ombla level should not be interpreted as the limit below which it is impossible to find some form of karst porosity. However, the results obtained by drillings and geophysical investigations support the assumption that this deep zone is less pervious (partly due to lesser karstification and partly to sedimentation) than the above-lying zones. This deep zone has all the characteristics of the sedimentary rocks below the base of karstification. The barrier in the hinterland, (7) of Fig. 4, is also affected by the erosion process, because it disturbed the continuity of the karst aquifer, preventing the direct underground connection between the immediate and the remote drainage areas of the Ombla River. Karstification process could not apply on the whole to the rock mass at the great depths and close to the barrier zone due to the emphasized influence of the erosion bases, which predetermined the main evolutions.

In zone (1) of Fig. 4, the evolution process developed in an earlier phase and is now nearly terminated. This zone is of fossil karst forms, with the vertical circulation having the characteristics of an aeration zone. In case of heavy precipitation, the lower parts of this zone of the aquifer between the Trebišnjica River and the Ombla Spring may become filled with water as dynamic groundwater reserves for short periods of time.

Zones (2) and (3) of Fig. 4, which are of the most recent activity in the karst evolution, are characterized by an intensive water circulation. Circulation is emphasized in their lower parts because the main drainage systems are found in these zones. Zones (2') and (2") of Fig. 4 were formed under the influence of higher bases, while the zone (2) (between the Trebišnjica River and the Adriatic Sea) is under the influence of the lowest erosion base. In the course of time the lowest erosion base became dominant for the aquifer with the effect that the process of evolution sank below the level of higher bases forming the main drainage network of the system as the zone (3) of Fig. 4. This is the reason why during the low flow periods the water circulation towards the Ombla Spring runs below the Popovo Polje level (beneath the Trebišnjica riverbed). The higher situated bases once used to have the function of the total drainage permanently. Now these bases are effective only during high water flow periods. Drainage of a part of the karst groundwater is performed at these higher bases only when the groundwater levels attain the positions marked in the scheme as the dashed lines between the zones (1) and (2) of Fig. 4. Zones (4) and (5) of Fig. 4 below the level of the karstification, lead to slow but continuous decrease of the karstification base depth, namely toward the level of the lowest erosion base.

6. Groundwater Level Oscillations.

Although the period in which the piezometric observations were undertaken was not long (1971-1974), it still provided a great deal of data needed for establishing the principal characteristics of the groundwater regime. The maximum and minimum levels in the piezometric profile (Fig. 5) of five boreholes confirmed the assumption that a narrow and very karstified zone had all waters concentrated. The side areas of this zone are less karstified. The fractures in them are well filled by clay, as found in several boreholes. A relatively deep karstification was found in the zone of boreholes O_2 and O_3. Water there practically reaches down to the sea-level. Further in the hinterland, a weakly karstified and low permeability dolomite barrier was found around the borehole O_6 causing a backwater and water retention in the hinterland.

At high levels of the groundwater this barrier is overflown, so it then has no influence on the water regime. At low groundwater levels some sort of overflow is formed with the water level never decreasing below the elevation 70 m.

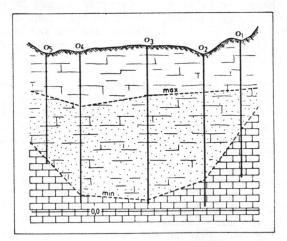

Fig. 5. A Profile with Minimum and Maximum Groundwater Levels.

Since transmissibility of this karst *corridor* is limited and the groundwater is well recharged in the period of precipitation, the groundwater level rises quickly. At high waters the karst channels become active in the upper part of the aquifer, so that one part of the groundwater overflows to the adjacent aquifer and discharges water through the Zavrelje

Spring. The dye tests performed at high levels at Pridvorci
sinkhole confirmed this assumption. In this way, the underground connection was established between the Ombla Spring
and the Zavrelje Spring. In such periods groundwater levels
in the aquifer between the Trebišnjica and the Ombla Rivers
are high as observed in some wells 10-12 km in the hinterland
at the depths varying from 15 to 20 m below the surface. By
dye tests during low flows the underground connection was
established but only with the Ombla Spring (Figs. 1 and 2).

   Oscillations of the dynamic water reserves are rapid,
with the amplitude of level fluctuations great. During the
wet months the response of the groundwater level to the
precipitation was rapid, occurring in 10-15 hours. With
sudden and heavy showers the response was even faster. The
response speed depends on precipitation intensity. In 24
hours the level can rise 42 m (see Fig. 6), and when precipitation is heavy, even 89 meters in 24 hours, with the average
of 370 cm per hour. Such rapid rise of levels was observed
in the borehole O_3 in the period February 3-4, 1974 (Fig. 6,
from point g to point h).

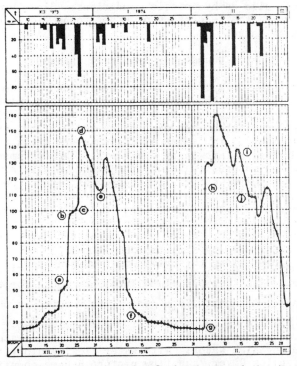

Fig. 6. The Level Hydrograph of the O_3 Borehole (Lower Graph)
         and Precipitation Hydrograph (Upper Graph) in the
         Ombla River Catchment.

Great karstification of the area and a large transmissivity of the aquifer prevent the retention of water at the surface. When precipitation stops, the intensive recharge of the groundwater immediately decreases (Fig. 6).

7. Water Velocities in the Ombla Underground Channels.

Water velocities in the underground were measured by using the tracers. It has been established that velocities were much greater at high levels than at low levels of the groundwater. From the sinkhole Pridvorci it took the tracer, at high waters, 69 hours (average 6.54 cm/sec) to reach the Ombla River, while at the low level of the groundwater it took 137 hours and 50 minutes, that is 3.2 cm/sec. From the sinkhole Mlinice near Poljice (Figs. 1 and 2) the tagged water, at high water flow, had the velocity of 6.7 cm/sec, or 18 km in 75 hours. At low levels of groundwater, the tagged wave passed 11,300 m (Kočela-Ombla Spring) in 190 hours, at a velocity of 1.9 cm/sec.

These results show that velocities of water circulation in karst do not depend only on the gradient and transmissivity but also on hydrologic conditions. Since hydrologic conditions vary, the velocities of underground flow fluctuate within a large range.

8. Recharge of the Groundwater System of Channels.

The main recharge of the Ombla underground channels is from precipitation at the immediate drainage area, plus waters which percolate through numerous sinkholes (see Fig. 2) along the Trebišnjica riverbed between Gorica and Poljice, at a distance of about 30 km. Most of these waters drain towards the Ombla Spring, as proven by dye tests. The Dobromani-Poljice zone is interesting since the water in this area tends to reach the lowest erosion base. As soon as possible, however, the thick dolomite barrier forces water to deviate from its shortest route. Water then follows the circulation direction along the barrier, perpendicular to that of the surface flow direction. Water then passes the narrow passage to the Ombla Spring. By simultaneous hydrologic measurements at several places along this reach of riverbed it was established that about 38 m^3/sec percolate into the ground for the river discharge of about 150 m^3/sec. The result was obtained during the release of 150 m^3/sec from the Gorica daily pondage in the period when the Ombla aquifer had low groundwater levels. During high waters, with water flowing along the whole Trebišnjica River, the flow picture became complicated along the reach between Gorica and Poljice. It was impossible to establish the exact quantity of water percolating from the

riverbed by using the present measuring techniques. It was
proven that these losses to the Ombla aquifer sometimes decrease to only 15 m^3/sec as the result of high groundwater
levels in the aquifer. In dry months the river water flows
down to Dražin Dol, with the flow formed by the biological
minimum released from the Gorica pondage for the town of
Trebinje. This quantity varies from 4.5 to 2.0 m^3/sec. It
then represents the major flow at the Ombla Spring.

The dynamic water reserves of the Ombla aquifer result
mainly from precipitation over the catchment. Discharges at
the spring over 35 m^3/sec result exclusively from precipitation
on the immediate drainage area. This is illustrated in Fig. 7.

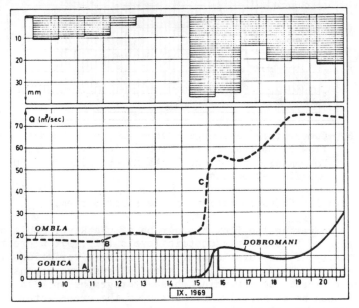

Fig. 7.   Influence of Precipitation on the Ombla River Flows:
          Rainfall Data (Upper Graph), and Flow Discharges of
          the Trebišnjica River at Gorica, Dobromani, and the
          Ombla Spring (Lower Graph).

The overflow of 13 m^3/sec at the Gorica Dam only slightly
influenced the Ombla Spring flow. While the Trebišnjica River
flow varies at Dobromani between 10 and 30 m^3/sec, the flow at
the Ombla Spring increased to 75 m^3/sec in the same period.
Heavy precipitation in wet months may increase the flow at
the Ombla Spring by 60-70 m^3/sec in 24 hours.

Similar conclusions can be drawn from the example in Fig. 8. For a release of 150 m^3/sec over the Gorica Dam in a relatively dry period, the discharge at the Ombla Spring increased only to 35 m^3/sec and stayed constant. It is obvious that the water from the riverbed is limited by the channel percolation capacity and the hydraulic conditions around the riverbed.

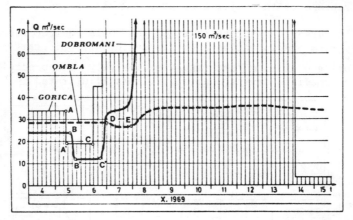

Fig. 8. Comparative Discharge Hydrographs of: The Water Overflow at Gorica, in the Trebišnjica River near Dobromani, and at the Ombla River, with the 150 m^3/sec Overflow at Gorica.

9. Hydraulic Characteristics of the Karst System.

By comparing the flow hydrograph of the River Ombla and the graph of borehole piezometric levels (Fig. 9), a great sensitivity of the karst system to hydrologic variations in the drainage area and the large speed of systems response can be noticed. By comparing these hydrographs on a larger scale, such as in Fig. 10, responses of the groundwater level in the aquifer around the borehole O_6 were almost instantaneously transferred to the Spring 3890 m away.

Hydrogeologic data and hydraulic parameters of the aquifer were obtained by investigating the character of the connection between the discharge of the Ombla Spring and the water levels in boreholes O_3 and O_6. For this purpose, the correlation coefficients were calculated for two samples of data (N = 32 and N = 167). Results are given in Tables 1 and 2.

As seen from Tables 1 and 2, a strong correlation exists between the variables investigated except for precipitation. In some cases it was close to a functional relationship, such as between the borehole O_6 levels and the Ombla Spring flow, with the correlation coefficient of 0.976. Such high correlation coefficients point to a very close hydraulic relationship. Circulation through a system of karst channels and caves of great transmissivity indicates that this system functions under pressure. Such relationships make it possible to predict the discharge at the spring, which is 4 km from the borehole, by measuring water levels in it.

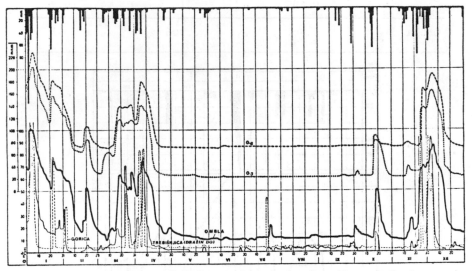

Fig. 9. Comparison of Hydrographs of the Overflow at Gorica, at the Trebišnjica River Near Dražin Dol, at the Ombla River, and the Level Graphs of O_3 and O_6 Boreholes (1971) with the Precipitation Data at the Top of the Graph.

Table 1. Matrix of Correlation Coefficients for N = 32.

	Borehole O_3 Levels	Borehole O_6 Levels	Ombla Spring	Precipitation
O_3	1	0.874	0.868	0.473
O_6	0.874	1	0.976	0.418
Ombla	0.868	0.976	1	0.400
Precipitation	0.473	0.418	0.400	1

Table 2. Matrix of Correlation Coefficients for N = 167.

	O_3	O_6	Ombla Spring
O_3	1	0.896	0.961
O_6	0.895	1	0.906
Ombla	0.961	0.906	1

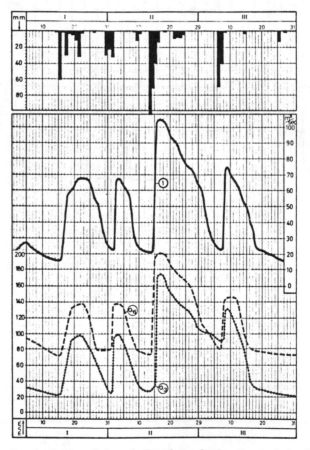

Fig. 10. Comparison of Level Graphs of the O_3 and O_6 Boreholes and the Hydrograph of the Ombla River in the First Three Months of 1973 (Precipitation Data are Given as the Upper Graph).

Analysis of propagation of sudden changes in water flow at the Gorica Dam is the other evidence. The overflow at the Gorica Dam represents the inflow and the Ombla Spring the outflow of the system. After a dry period, which lasted for several months, the Dam spillover release went from 22 to 78 m^3/sec on 19 July, 1971 (Fig. 11). After the release the water flows about 4-5 km to Pridvorci where the intensive percolation starts. Straight-line distance from the beginning of this zone to the Ombla Spring is 16.5 km. The tracer traveled this route in 137 hours under similar hydrologic conditions. However, the response of the system to the sudden change was faster than for the normal circulation. Only 35 hours passed since the release for the sudden change to show at the Ombla Spring (marked as E at the Gorica hydrograph and as F at the Ombla hydrograph in Fig. 11, with t = the travel time). The travel time of a sudden discharge change (or of a surge) is only one fourth (25%) of the tracer travel time under the same hydrologic conditions of inflow and outflow.

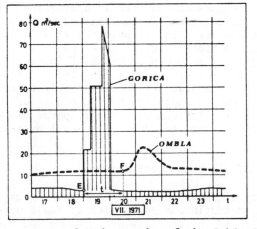

Fig. 11. Comparison of Hydrographs of the Ombla River Flow and the Overflow at the Gorica Dam in the Dry Period of 1971.

The water release at the Gorica Dam in dry period of 1969, for conducting the simultaneous discharge measurement along the Trebišnjica River reach for water percolation, offers a similar evidence. Then 50 m^3/sec of water were released into the dry riverbed of the Trebišnjica River (Fig. 12, point A). It reached Dobromani in about 16 hours as the surface flow. The response at the Ombla Spring, appearing as a sudden increase of discharge, occurred after 24 hours (point C in Fig. 12). Of these 50 m^3/sec released into the riverbed 17-18 m^3/sec were constantly lost downstream to Dobromani (designated as q in Fig. 12).

7-17

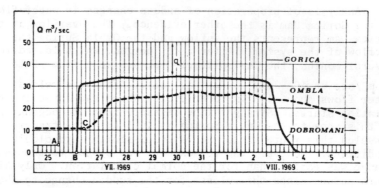

Fig. 12. Comparison of Hydrographs of the Overflow at the
Gorica Dam of the River Trebišnjica Near Dobroman,
and the Ombla River, in the Course of Release of
50 m³/sec from the Gorica Reservoir into the Dry Bed.

Similar responses can be seen in hydrographs of Figs. 8
and 9. Sudden percolation of the large quantities of water
into the Ombla aquifer (Fig. 8, point C) is shown at the Ombla
Spring after 35-37 hours (Fig. 8, point E). Similar travel
time was found for the sudden decrease of inflow into the
aquifer (point A and D of Fig. 8). In Fig. 9 (points A and
B), this response was somewhat faster, namely after about
15 hours. This can be explained by the effect of precipitation,
which was of greater influence on the response of the groundwater than the relative influence of a small overflow at the
Gorica Dam.

11. Analysis of Discharge Coefficient.

Complexity of water regime of the Ombla Spring karst
system is due to continuous variations of basic parameters
such as the size of the drainage area, space and time variations in recharge to and outflow from the groundwater system.
The hydrologic conditions become more complex during the
period of heavy rainfall. The approximate water budget
equation, expressed as the change dV in water dynamic
reserves of the groundwater in time dt, is given by

$$dV = [(Q_p + Q_g + Q_m) - (Q + Q_z + Q_{pp})] \, dt, \qquad (1)$$

where Q_p = the inflow into the groundwater by percolation of
rainfall in the immediate drainage area, Q_g = the release
into the system at the Gorica Dam; Q_m = the inflow into the
system from the Mokro Polje (see Fig. 1); Q = the Ombla

Spring outflow discharge; Q_z = the flow discharges at the springs Zavrelje, Slavljen, etc., through which a part of the Ombla aquifer is discharged at high waters; and Q_{pp} = the flow along the Trebišnjica River bed towards the lower parts of the Popovo Polje. The inflow Q_p represents the difference between the precipitation, P, losses due to evapotranspiration, E_t, and the compensation for the deficiency, D_v, in humidity of the zone above the groundwater, computed as

$$Q_p = P - E_t - D_v \ . \tag{2}$$

In wet months the evaporation is the only factor because the transpiration and the soil humidity deficit are not important.

The most favorable period for the analysis of water regime and the study of water budget was when the Trebišnjica River flowed only as far as Poljice (Fig. 1). In that case Eq. (1) becomes

$$dV = [(Q_p + Q_g) - Q] \ dt \tag{3}$$

or in the period of no recharge by precipitation, $Q_p = 0$,

$$dV = (Q_g - Q) \ dt \ . \tag{4}$$

The Gorica Dam releases are always known and rather constant. In the study period the average release was 4.5 m^3/sec (Fig. 13). Besides this water constitutes some kind of *through-flow* and is not a part of the dynamic reserve. Since Q_g = constant, Eq. (4) is simplified as

$$dV = - Q \ dt \ , \tag{5}$$

or a linear dynamic reserves equation. In such retention conditions the flow at the Ombla Spring at any time may be represented by the simple exponential recession curve

$$Q = Q_o \ e^{-\alpha t} \ , \tag{6}$$

where Q_o = the outflow at the Spring at the chosen moment of outflow studies, α = the discharge coefficient.

The discharge coefficient α characterizes the capacity of the aquifer to supply the water. This is a function of the effective porosity and the transmissivity of the water-bearing

porous media. The Ombla River aquifer is characterized by
three types of porosity, represented by three different slopes
of the hydrograph recession   Q   in the logarithmic scales,
as shown by Fig. 13.

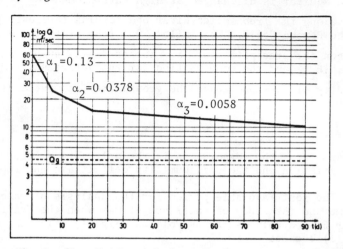

Fig. 13.   The Outflow Regime of the Dynamic Reserves of the
           Ombla Spring Karst Aquifer System.

Discharge coefficients are then α_1 = 0.13, α_2 = 0.038,
and α_3 = 0.0058.

The coefficient α_1 characterizes a rapid outflow from
caves and channels. A large volume of water which had filled
this system empties rapidly. In the Ombla case, this emptying
lasts only about seven days (Fig. 13).

The discharge coefficient α_2 characterizes the outflow
of the system of well-connected and locally karstified joints
and larger fissures. The outflow of this system lasts about
13 days in the above case (Fig. 13). The coefficients α_1
and α_2 characterize the outflow of large-space reserves of
the underground karst system.

The discharge coefficient α_3 characterizes the outflow
from those water reserves which only conditionally are called
the groundwater. These water reserves depend on local hydrogeologic characteristics and are irregularly distributed over
the whole mass of the aquifer. They are stored in the
fissured porosity, in sand-clayed materials deposited in
fossil channels and caverns, local *hanging* groundwaters, and
innumerable siphon parts of the channel system. One part of
these reserves is a result of the condensation of water in

rocks and soils above the groundwater level. The flows up to
several 1/sec were found during investigations of some caves
and channels between the Trebišnjica River and the sea, located
high above the Popovo Polje and above the maximum underground
water levels. The formation of these small flow streams can
only be the consequence of the special hydrogeologic conditions.

The non-karstified dolomite zone, found at the borehole
O_6, forms a kind of the water barrier in the lowest part of the
Ombla karst *corridor*. It considerably retards the outflow
from the lowest parts of the aquifer. This part of karst
groundwater is relatively thin, lying beneath the karstification base. The outflow towards the Ombla Spring is limited
by the low permeability of this barrier, over which then water
flows from the hinterland. Water reserves in this zone are
continuously fed by water reserves of the whole aquifer. A
long dry period would be needed to drain them. By using Eq.
(6) it was established that 470 days would be necessary for
nearly a complete drainage of these reserves, which at the
same time would mean a complete drainage of the aquifer. This
applies then to conditions when any inflow into the aquifer
is excluded.

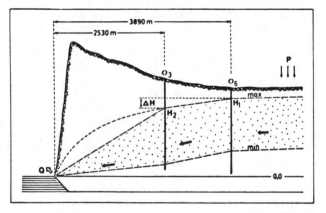

Fig. 14. A Profile Between the Ombla Spring (Q), the Borehole
O_3 and the Borehole O_6, with the Minimum and Maximum Groundwater Levels. (The Horizontal Lines in
the Left Lower Corner Denote the Flysh Barrier).

12. References.

[1] Mijatović, B., Metoda ispitivanja hidrodinamičkog režima
    kraških izdani pomoću analize i fluktuacije nivoa izdani
    u recentnim uslovima (Method of investigating the hydro-
    dynamic regime of karst aquifers by using the analysis
    and fluctuation of aquifer levels under recent conditions):
    Vesnik Geozavoda, Beograd, 1968 (In Serbo-Croatian).

[2] De Wiest, R., Geohydrology: John Wiley and Sons, New York, 1965.

[3] Lebedev, V. A., Proučavanje režima i bilansa podzemnih voda, a u vezi sa vodosnabdijevanjem, navodnjavanjem i odvodnjavanjem (Investigation of the regime and budget of underground waters, in connection with water supply, irrigation and drainage): Publikacija sa seminara *Bilans podzemnih voda* (Publication from the Seminar *Budget of underground waters*), Beograd 1967/68.

[4] Fond stručne dokumentacije, Hidroelektrane na Trebišnjici. (Professional files of the Hydroelectric Power System of the Trebišnjica River).

DISCUSSION

Öziş. In this paper a statement was made that velocities of 1600 m/h are common in karst underground channels. This corresponds to a velocity of 40-50 cm/s. Does this figure represent the actual flow velocity in solution channels or an overall apparent velocity of wave propagation in the karst system? Another question is what can be considered as the most often encountered, apparent velocity in well-developed karst areas? For the Ombla Spring presented in the paper, this was of the order of 2-6 cm/s. In the paper by Arandjelović, et al., it was of the order of 1 cm/s. In my paper I gave results for three case studies in Turkey, where these velocities ranged from 0.1 cm/s to 3.5 cm/s. In the paper by Faulkner on the Silver Springs in Florida, this velocity was much lower, about few per thousand of cm/s. Although the apparent propagation velocity in karst areas vary within a very wide range, could it be possible to generalize about this velocity in well-developed karst areas, even if it appears quite difficult to make such generalizations?

LeGrand. The movement of groundwater from high inland poljes to lower coastward poljes and on to the sea has been established by this paper. The direction of this flow is at a sharp angle to the flow of surface streams in wet seasons. This setting applies to dry-season conditions, but does it apply to the wet season setting?

The point to be made is that the size of a catchment area in a karst region may vary in size. Where adjacent higher valleys have intermittent surface flows, the lower base valley will enlarge to include the area of higher valleys in dry seasons and will be reduced to a smaller area in wet seasons. In terms of the water-table behavior, during the wet season the water table rises appreciably beneath close topographic highs and forms a groundwater divide between the base valley and the adjacent valley. In dry seasons, the water-table divide is lowered and disappears, so that the lower valley with a major stream will draw water from adjacent valleys. A good conceptual model of the physical characteristics of the karst system should consider the variation of size in a catchment system between wet and dry seasons.

Milanović. The velocity of the underground stream was established by experiments in Popovo Polje. Using the radio-active isotope BR-82 as a tracer, the water circulation was investigated at the sinkholes Ponikva and Žira. The arrival of the tracer wave was recorded at two boreholes. Between the sinkhole and the borehole located 1.5 km from it, the wave moved at a velocity of 1600 m/hr, while between the sinkhole and the borehole located at a distance of 3.4 km from it, the velocity was 1200 m/hr. The same velocities were obtained in the repeated measurements. When dyes (Na-fluorescine) were injected in the same sinkholes, underground connections were established with the 18-20 km distant springs. The average velocity for this route ranged between 150 and 300 m/hr. The higher velocity found in the zone of the nearer sinkholes can be explained by a large gradient and extensive system of canals in the sinkhole zones.

By using a dye test at the Biograd sinkhole during a rainy period, similar velocities were obtained. The dye was injected when the inflow into the sinkhole was 60 m^3/s. The dye appeared at the Bunica Spring (located 20 km from the sinkhole) in 13 hours and 30 minutes.

A definite answer on the most frequent velocity of circulation cannot be given since the velocity of underground circulation changes with the levels of underground water and the hydrological situation of the surface.

With dye tests carried out thus far, it was established that the velocity is always higher during a high water period and smaller during the low flow period. It can be, nonetheless, said that velocities range between 1 and 7 cm/sec. This generalization applies to the karst region of Eastern Herzegovina.

Parizek. Is there any evidence of very deep groundwater circulation (1,000 to 3,000 m) within the karst regions of Yugoslavia, which is obtained from oil and gas explorations, deep mines or similar other mineral resource developments? The high relief and structural and stratigraphic complexities of Yugoslav carbonate terrane would suggest such a system of deep circulation must exist on a regional scale.

Knowledge of the depth of cavity and significant permeability and porosity distribution and development is used in hydrologic budget studies, in determining the leakage from and into study areas, when attempting to determine the

sustained yield of carbonate aquifer systems, in defining
regional groundwater flow systems, etc. In the central
Appalachian Mountain area of Pennsylvania the depth of
significant cavity development has been shown to vary with
rock type, topographic setting within central valley areas,
topographic setting with respect to mountain uplands, relief
on the water table, and other factors. In the central valley
upland setting somewhat distant from mountain ridges (3 to 5
km), for example, where streams and rivers may be incised
from 10 to 130 meters, cavities are typically restricted
to the upper 50 to 170 m of land surface. These have been
detected by observing drilling behavior, from drillers logs
and drill cuttings, noting changes in yields of deep water
wells during drilling, inspection of rock conditions in mines
and quarries extending to depths of 300 m and from caliper
surveys conducted on water wells and test holes.

Where intergranular and paleo-secondary permeability
and porosity development are still preserved, deeper active
circulation of groundwater and development of solution features
should be possible in all topographic settings. This condition
is afforded by some orthoquartzites interbedded with dolomites
and sandy dolomites of Cambrian age in central Pennsylvania,
such as Gatesburg Formation (Egus in Fig. 1) and within the
Dale Summit Sandstone Member (Ods in Fig. 1) of the
Ordovician-aged Bellefonte Dolomite. Little is known of
even deeper zones of circulation of little importance as a
major source of groundwater, that may be controlled by thrust
faults and other controls within thick sequences of folded
and faulted carbonate rocks (2,000 to 3,000 m). Petrographic,
topographic and structural settings favor deep circulation
within the folded and faulted Appalachian Mountain region,
but these routes of water movement are ill defined except
where subjected to recent weathering. Solution development
within deep artesian or confined groundwater flow systems
must take place because these same rocks serve as reservoirs
for oil and gas, fault zones to depths of 400 m have been
penetrated during drilling of oil and gas test wells that have
caused considerate drilling difficulties, and potable groundwater is reported in even the deepest of water wells drilled
to depths of 200 to 400 m. Recently a clay filled crevasse
was encountered between a depth of 160 to 178 m in dolomite,
in an upland setting with <30 m of relief indicating that
active groundwater circulation extended below that depth.

Active groundwater circulation and development of
solution features should be possible to considerable depths
where sandstones and carbonate rocks with intergranular permeability are down folded in mountainous regions. These
selected bedrock units should provide avenues for interbasin
flow of groundwater independent of local, shallow groundwater
divides. Water level data obtained within the outcrop area of

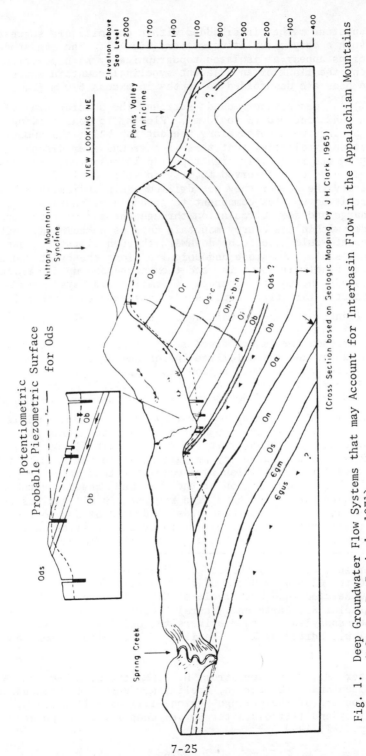

Fig. 1. Deep Groundwater Flow Systems that may Account for Interbasin Flow in the Appalachian Mountains (After R.R. Parizek, 1971).

a sandstone member interbedded within dolomite are suggestive
of such a deep circulation system (Fig. 1). The sandstone
outcrops appear at isolated topographically high positions
beyond the flank of an adjacent synclinal mountain where the
same beds are downfolded to depths in excess 670 m (Parizek,
1971)[1]. Groundwater mounds surround the outcrop area of this
thin sandstone bed (3 to 10 m). Flowing to near flowing wells
and springs were noted along the outcrop belt at a number of
locations indicating that this is a groundwater discharge area
dispite its relatively high topographic position. Water
levels have been observed to rise in wells drilled in this
vicinity the deeper they are drilled again indicating that
there is an up flow component to groundwater in this region.
Recharge and deep circulation through the sedimentary rocks
folded within the nearby mountain core is postulated. Water
movement would have to be downward through siltstone, sandstone, shale, limestone and dolomite along the crest and core
of the synclinal mountain, and then along and up dip through
the sandstone to its outcrop. A similar flow system is
postulated for still deeper sandstones exposed further from
the flanks of this mountain range (Parizek, 1971)[1], (Fig. 1).

Groundwater is exploited from Cambrian and Ordovician
aged sandstones and dolomites in the Chicago, Illinois region.
Carbonate rocks in this region are gently dipping in a
relatively low relief area, and yield potable water to wells
drilled to depths of 300 to 670 m below land surface (Suter
et al, 1959)[2]. Anomalously high well yields and cavities
have been reported in carbonate rocks located below an
Ordovician-aged unconformity in the northern Illinois-southern
Wisconsin area. These may be paleokarst features as have been
reported for Mississipian aged Dolomites that underlie portions
of the high plains region of the U.S. and Canada. Potable
groundwater and voids have been reported in oil and gas test
wells that penetrated these beds at depths of 300 to 1,000 m.
These carbonate rocks are overlain by shale, siltstones and
sandstones that contain brackish to saline groundwater.

---

[1] Parizek, R. R., Hydrogeology and Geochemistry of Folded and
Faulted Carbonate Rocks of the Central Appalachian Type
and Related Land Use Problems: Mineral Conservation Series,
Circular 82, Earth and Mineral Sciences Experiment Station,
The Pennsylvania State University, University Park, Pa.,
181 p., Edited by R. R. Parizek, W. E. White and D. Langmuir,
1971.

[2] Suter, M., R. E. Bergstrom, H. F. Smith, G. H. Emrich, W. C.
Walton and T. E. Larson, Preliminary Report on Groundwater
Resources of the Chicago Region, Illinois: Illinois Geol.
Survey and Illinois Water Survey Cooperative Groundwater
Report 1, 1959.

Still other examples of deep and active groundwater
circulation within carbonate rocks have been documented for
the U.S. nuclear test facility in Nevada (Winograd 1962[3]);
Eakin 1966[4]; Mifflin 1968[5] and Maxey 1968[6]). The catchment for this flow system involves vast areas of mountains
and plays lake basins alike and discharge is concentrated
at several major distant springs in Ash Meadows (Maxey, 1968[6]).

A similar deep flow system containing potable groundwater
has been postulated for cavernous carbonate formations of the
Madison Group of Mississippian age. The water that enters
this formation in outcrops in the Black Hills in the High
Plains region of U.S. and presumably migrates eastward for
more than 375 km while at the same time leaking upward to
recharge the important Dakota Sandstone aquifer over a broad
region in eastern South Dakota.

Some of these and other deep circulation systems appear
to occupy permeability avenues developed and preserved as
paleokarst features.

[3] Winograd, I. H., Interbasin Movement of Groundwater at the
Nevada Test Site, Nevada: U.S. Geol. Survey, Professional
Paper 450-C, p. 108-111, 1962.

[4] Eakin, T. A., A Regional Interbasin Groundwater System in
the White River Area, Southeastern Nevada: Water Resources
Research, vol. 2, p. 251-271, 1966.

[5] Mifflin, M. D., Delineation of Groundwater Flow Systems
in Nevada: Desert Research Institute, Technical Report Series
H.W. no. 4, Reno, Nevada, 1968.

[6] Maxey, G. B., Hydrogeology of Desert Basins: Groundwater,
vol. 6, no. 5, p. 10-22, 1968.

HYDROGEOLOGIC ESTIMATION OF GROUNDWATER STORAGE CONNECTED WITH THE SURFACE WATER STORAGE. CASE OF THE SALAKOVAC RESERVOIR.

by

Tomislav Ivanković, Geologist, Head of Geologic Studies,
Elektroprivreda B.H, Sarajevo

and

Miomir Komatina, Geologist, Director of the Institute
of Hydrogeologic and Geotechnic Studies,
Geozavod, Beograd, Yugoslavia

Synopsis. The construction of storage reservoirs in
the Yugoslav Karst, and in the other karst regions in general,
requires complex, detailed studies of geologic and hydrogeologic conditions of a large area around the storage reservoir. The correct description of hydrogeologic phenomena in
karst regions has been demonstrated to be an essential condition for undertaking the proper measures in securing the
impermeability of storage reservoirs. In most cases, surface
storage reservoirs induce hydrogeologic changes in the underground of the surrounding karst area. First, water accumulates
in the underground, with its regime somewhat changed in
comparison with natural conditions. The study of groundwater
retention and of positive effects of interconnected surface
and groundwater reservoirs has unfortunately not been given
due attention. The objective of this paper is to contribute
to research methodology of hydrogeologic aspects of groundwater
storage reservoirs. Some research results, as applied to the
planned storage reservoir Salakovac, are discussed in the
paper. Among other studies, an analysis of water permeability
tests and recession curves were used to estimate the aquifer
parameters.

The space volume of an underground storage reservoir is
defined in one of these two ways: (1) For the aquifer confined
only within the young formations of Upper Cretaceous, and (2)
For high levels of the storage reservoir the contributing
underground storage area is divided into four subareas with
varying subarea parameters.

The second part of the paper describes the hydrogeologic
properties of the Salakovac Reservoir. It was found that these
properties can be defined by: (a) A highly karstified and
tectonically intensely fractured limestones of Turonian and
Senonian, functioning basically as aquifers; (b) A composition
of dolomites and limestones of Lower Cretaceous, Upper Jurassic
and Triassic, functioning as aquifers only in their immediate
subsurface and considered to be lesser hydrogeologic barriers;

and (c) Sediments of Neogen, such as marls, functioning as full
hydrogeologic barriers.

The analysis of recession curves showed that the exponent
of simple exponential recession of the underground storage is
α = 0.0195, conductivity T = 18 m^2/sec, and the average yield
rate S = 0.025. For the case study, hydrogeologic properties
are such that it will be feasible to retain a considerable
amount of groundwaters in underground storage. The retention
will be smaller if the grouting curtain for decreasing water
losses through permanent or intermittent springs downstream
of the future dam would not be undertaken. These man-made
interventions, by using the grouting curtain between the
dam and the impermeable Tertiary rocks will make feasible the
storage in a large groundwater area.

1. Introduction.

It is not feasible even by making very detailed studies,
to obtain an accurate estimate of karst underground storage
spaces, created by construction of a surface storage reservoir.
Systematic investigations of karst areas must be designed
according to concrete hydrogeologic conditions. Collecting
and processing of data available is the basis for the estimation of underground storage spaces, even if data were not
exclusively or even at all collected with this objective in
sight. The example of this estimation is the study of
the underground storage space to be connected with the future
Salakovac Reservoir on the Neretva River upstream of the city
of Mostar. Investigations contained the following analysis:
(i) water permeability tests; (ii) water recession curves at
karst springs; (iii) hydrogeologic properties under the
natural conditions, such as geologic composition, geomorphologic
and hydrometeorologic characteristics and general hydrogeology
of the catchment area; (iv) hydrogeologic feasibility for
underground storage; and (v) the size of underground storage.

2. Analysis of Results of Water Permeability Tests.

The water permeability tests were mostly carried out in
lithologically and hydrogeologically heterogeneous rocks. The
test region was divided into homogeneously permeable subregions,
with differences in their hydrogeologic characteristics. By
defining the approximate spatial locations of subregions,
with their permeability characteristics, a reliable approach
was created for estimates of underground storage space.

In carrying out the field tests for water permeability,
it was assumed that privileged routes were reflected in the
drainage spring flow hydrographs, with their parameters. The
analysis of a sufficient number of water permeability tests
permitted the separation of the rock massif into homogeneous

permeable subregions. Of the total volume of rock storage spaces only a very small part belongs to large-scale channels.

For the example of the Salakovac Reservoir, the whole area is composed of dolomites and limestones of Jurassic and Cretaceous. For the dam site the left bank is in Cretaceous limestone while the right bank is in Jurassic dolomite and limestone with the rock anisotropy in hydrologic sense being determined by stratigraphic and lithologic differences. The Cretaceous limestone of the left bank are highly fissured and karstified, while the Jurassic dolomite and limestone of the right bank act as partial hydrogeologic barriers. These differences were shown in water permeability tests. Data showed the average permeability of the left bank to be five times greater than the average permeability of the right bank. Figure 1 shows that the left bank rocks below the elevation 70 m a.s.l have a small water permeability. Figure 2 shows that the permeability does not decrease exponentially with the depth, as usual. Starting with the depth of 140 m, water permeability of Cretaceous limestone at the left bank decreased abruptedly. The depths under 140 m are in fact below the elevation of 70 m a.s.l., so that Cretaceous limestone of the left bank is highly permeable only above the Neretva River bed level. Figure 3 shows Jurassic dolomite and limestone of the right bank to be permeable to a depth of 30 m.

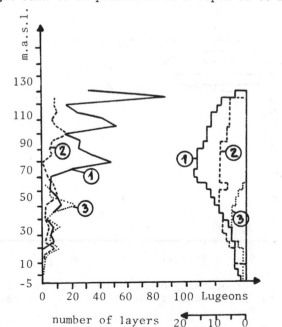

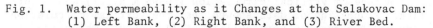

Fig. 1. Water permeability as it Changes at the Salakovac Dam: (1) Left Bank, (2) Right Bank, and (3) River Bed.

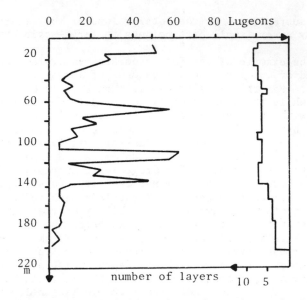

Fig. 2. Water Permeability on the Left Bank at the Dam Site of the Salakovac Reservoir, as it Changes with Elevation.

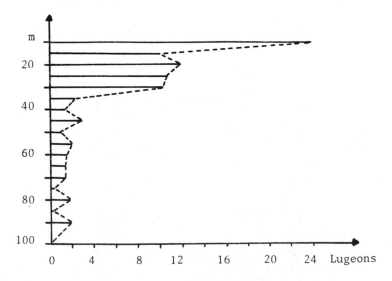

Fig. 3. Water Permeability of Jurassic Dolomite and Limestone at the Right Bank of the Salakovac Dam Site.

A zone of vertical circulation (70-95 m a.s.1) was identified. Processing of data showed that the vertical circulation zone had the average permeability of 34 Lugeons, while the average permeability of 6 Lugeons was found for the horizontal circulation zone. In estimating the volume of underground storage spaces, the estimated effective porosity was slightly increased.

3. Analysis of Recession Curves.

The recession curves were approximated by the exponential function $y = \beta e^{-\alpha t}$. The simplest form is

$$Q_t = Q_o \, e^{-\alpha(t-t_o)}, \tag{1}$$

where Q_t = the flow in m^3/sec in the interval $(t-t_o)$; Q_o = the discharge at the time t_o, α = the exponent rate, and t = the time at the moment of computing Q_t. The exponent rate is then

$$\alpha = \frac{\log Q_o - \log Q_t}{0.4343 \, (t-t_o)} \, . \tag{2}$$

Equation (1) plots in semi-logarithmic scales as a straight line with α its slope. The recession curve for karst aquifers is often very complex, approximated by the form

$$Q_t = Q_{0,1} \, e^{-\alpha_1 t} + Q_{0,2} \, e^{-\alpha_2 t} + \ldots + Q_{0,n} \, e^{-\alpha_n t} \, . \tag{3}$$

The other aquifer characteristics are its permeability $T(m^2/sec)$ and its effective porosity S (in percent). The permeability T was deduced from the Theis'es equation for unsteady conditions in the recession period, namely,

$$T = \frac{0.183 \, Q_a}{C} \tag{4}$$

with

$$C = \frac{\Delta R_2 - \Delta R_1}{\log t_2 - \log t_1} \tag{5}$$

where ΔR = the variation of effective groundwater levels, expressed in water column height in mm, and t = the period during which ΔR was observed. The effective porosity of the rock mass was also calculated from Theis'es equation by

$$S = \frac{2.25 \, T \, t_o}{x^2} \tag{6}$$

8-5

where   x = the distance of the observed piezometer from the karst spring, and t_o corresponds to the instant of $\Delta R = 0$. This rate is also $S = \Delta R / \Delta H$,   with ΔH the absolute difference of groundwater levels.

The effective porosity for some rock mass was calculated from fissure data in test galleries. The relation was established between the drained water for the period without precipitation and the volume of the estimated rock mass from which drainage occurs. The rock mass was a determining factor in using the data on maximum rate of groundwater level changes at times when only the vertical water replenishment was present.

To apply the above equations to the storage reservoir Salakovac, several years of observations of the Neretva River flow at cross sections located exactly at the beginning and the end of the storage reservoir were available, at the gauging stations Salakovac and Grabovica, respectively. Differences in flow correspond to the underground effluent into the river during the periods of negligible infiltration from precipitation. From hydrographs of flow differences for a period of 40 years, the recession part without any significant effects of precipitation was singled out, namely from May 15 to September 1, as shown in Fig. 4. In Fig. 5, the recession curve was plotted in semi-logarithmic scales as a straight line. For the sample exponential recession $Q_t = Q_o$ exp. $[-\alpha (t-t_o]$ with $Q_o = 71.0$ m^3/sec, and the selected $Q_t = 20.0$ m^3/sec, with t = 65 days, $\alpha = 0.0195$, and the recession equation $Q_t = 71.0$ exp. $(-0.0195t)$. Because α is a constant, a simple linear function between the outflow discharge and the underground water storage volume was implied. The average hydrograph obtained was satisfactory in estimating changes in underground water storage.

Table 1 presents the values from the recession curve of hydrograph of flow differences with: (i) ΔR_t = the fictitious height of water column for given time intervals of recession period, with $\Delta R_t = 86,400 Q_t / \alpha A$, and A = the involved area of the rock mass; (ii) $\Delta R = R_o - R_t$; and (iii) the water stored in the underground at the beginning of each time interval of the recession period, $V_r = 86400 Q_t / \alpha$, with $\alpha = 0.0195$. From Table 1 and Fig. 6 it follows that T = 0.183 x 30.0/0.305 = 18 m^2/sec.

Existing piezometer observations were also used on the left side of the Neretva Valley which is in the Upper Cretaceous limestones. The period with no water supply to underground was selected by the study of nearby precipitation gauging

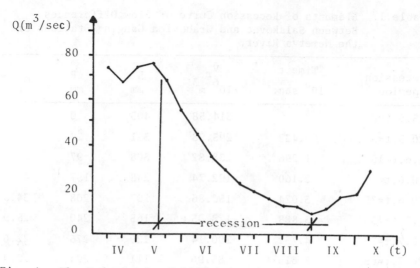

Fig. 4. The Hydrograph of Difference in Flow of the Neretva
River Between Grabovica and Salakovac Gauging Stations
in the Recession Period.

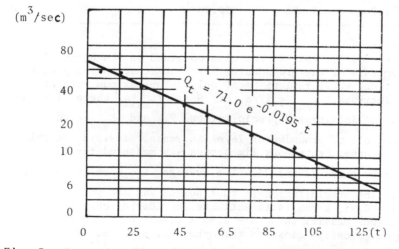

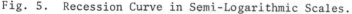

Fig. 5. Recession Curve in Semi-Logarithmic Scales.

stations at Gornje Zijemlje and Bijelo Polje. For the recession period the average difference of groundwater levels was
$\Delta H = 12$ m, so that for the involved rock area $S = 0.354/12 =$
0.03, or the porosity is 3%. This porosity of 0.02 to 0.03
was also obtained by detailed surveys of fissures of all the
underground excavations in the area.

Table 1. Elements of Recession Curve of Flow Differences
          Between Salakovac and Grabovica Gauging Stations of
          the Neretva River.

Recession period	Time t 10^6 sec.	V_r $10^6 m^3$	R mm	ΔR mm	Q_t
15.5, t=0	0	314.58	405	0	71.0
20.5, t=5	0.432	295.98	381	24	66.8
1.6, t=15	1.296	238.82	308	97	53.9
10.6, t=25	2.160	192.74	248	157	43.5
20.6, t=35	3.024	152.86	197	208	34.5
1.7, t=45	3.888	128.05	165	240	28.9
10.7, t=55	4.752	100.14	129	276	22.6
20.7, t=65	5.616	85.96	111	294	19.4
1.8, t=75	6.480	67.79	87	318	15.3
10.8, t=85	7.344	57.60	74	331	13.0
20.8, t=95	8.208	55.38	71	334	12.5
1.9, t=105	9.072	39.88	51	354	9.0

The coefficient S was also obtained on the basis of
maximum rate of the groundwater level increase in the period
of vertical water replenishment only. The maximum rate of
level increase, L_{max} = iP/S, or S = iP/L_{max}, where i = the
percent of infiltrated precipitation P, and L_{max} = the
maximum rate of groundwater level increase. In 1973 the value
L_{max} in Upper Cretaceous limestones was measured for the two
days of December 22 and 23. The average L_{max} value was 1.62
m/day. The precipitation in that period was 400 mm (0.40 m).
For i = 0.95, a realistic estimate considering characteristics
of the rock massif, then S = 0.95 x 0.40/1.62 = 0.023, a
value of porosity close to the other estimates of S.

4. Hydrogeologic Characteristics of the Terrane.

Geologic Structure. The area around the Neretva River
from Grabovica to Salakovac consists of Jurassic and Cretaceous
limestones. The Drežanka River valley and the Prenj Massif
consist of other sedimentary and volcanic formations of Middle
Triassic, and the main dolomites and limestones of Upper
Triassic.

In the narrow area of the cross section of the Salakovac Dam site, the following four lithostratigraphic members are present: thin-stratified dolomites and dolomitic limestones; Neogen sediments of the Mostar Depression, mainly marls of great thickness; and Quaternary sediments, called the Neretva Conglomerates, about 30 meters thick.

The narrow area around the cross section of the dam site belongs to the Neretva-Drežnica fault zone, characterized by a very intensive tectonic activity. The catchment area of the planned surface storage reservoir is characterized by complex tectonic relations. The two main structural units are the tectonic block of Prenj and the dislocated anticline of the Drežanka River.

Geomorphologic Characteristics. The area investigated for the storage reservoir Salakovac is of typical karst. The karstification process was particularly intensive in the Neogen and Pleistocene, after high mountains and intermountain depressions have been formed. Morphologically the area presented a suitable ground for water work. Helped by abundant precipitation over limestones, the karstification developed fast and deep.

Tectonic movements contributed to fluvial and fluvio-glacial erosion which was faster than karstification. The inner karst forms, mainly karst springs, important from the hydrogeologic point of view, are found along the Neretva River.

Hydrometeorologic Conditions. The investigated area is on the border of the Mediterranean climatic zone. The climate is mainly continental, mesothermal, humid with medium dry summers. The average precipitation per year, mostly of orographic origin, is about 2400 mm. The average discharge for the period of 40 years (1926-1965) at the Salakovac gauging station is 183 m^3/sec. The difference in mean flows between Salakovac and Grabovica is about 40 m^3/sec for the same period of 40 years.

Hydrogeologic Conditions. The analysis of the observed groundwaters in the area indicated that their minimum levels go very deep, somewhere even below the river level. It showed that the groundwater circulation is mainly parallel to the river.

Sediments of Neogen (marls) present a typical water barrier. They are found in the Bijelo Polje at the border with Cretaceous limestones of the area of Salakovac Dam site. They force the karst waters to come into the river.

The characteristic of a large part of the storage reservoir area is an intensive tectonic disruption. Because the main faults are parallel to the river, many funnel-shaped depressions are oriented in the same direction. Transversal faults and fissures enable the overflow of the groundwater at higher levels into the river, in the form of intermittent karst springs.

The major hydrogeologic characteristics of the area are: highly karstified, tectonically damaged, composed of limestones of Upper Cretaceous, Turonian and Senonian; a karstified complex of dolomites and limestones of Lower Cretaceous and Upper Jurassic; and sediments of Neogen (marls) of the Bijelo Polje.

5. Hydrogeologic Conditions for Underground Storage and Hydrogeology of Changed Conditions.

Possibilities of Retaining Groundwaters Which Under Normal Conditions Would Flow Outside the Planned Salakovac Reservoir. A large number of permanent and intermittent karst springs occur along the left side of the Neretva River in the Salakovac Dam site region going from the future dam-grouting to the place where the grouting curtain cross section in the Cretaceous limestone joins the Tertiary sediments of the Bijelo Polje. Such a line of springs along the river, more than 1000 m long, was well explained showing that the Tertiary marls of the Bijelo Polje present a hydrogeologic barrier to groundwaters of a larger karst area on the left side of the planned storage reservoir. The depth of marls is more than 800 m, or about 700 m below the sea level. This led to conclusion that the groundwater at this river section has changed its north-south flow direction to the east-west direction. More than 40 karst springs were identified along this section, with their total yield of several hundred lit/sec in dry periods and several m^3/sec in wet periods. By some estimates, the maximum yield is about 30 m^3/sec, and the estimate of average flow is about 5 m^3/sec.

The karst waters of left bank entering river below the dam are of interest for the hydroelectric power plant Salakovac, by eventually directing them into the storage reservoir. The planned construction of a sufficiently long grouting curtain between the dam site and the impermeable barrier of Tertiary sediments of the Bijelo Polje should accomplish this objective. Dye injections into piezometric boreholes proved the connection between a group of springs at the dam site and the downstream springs, especially during the wet periods. This fact indicated a high probability for all the ground water to be directed into the storage reservoirs once the grouting curtain has been constructed. The dye always appeared in the springs. The only difference was

the timing of dye occurrence, proving that there exist privileged ground water routes at the left side of the Neretva
River, and that the large underground water storage is
connected with these springs. Besides, the underground voids
within the future reservoir level oscillations would parti-
cipate in the total storage space. Therefore, not only the
increase of water input into the future reservoir was of
interest, but also the increase of the total storage volume
by the use of underground voids required both the study of
the available underground storage and the grouting curtain to
enable the attainment of both objectives.

Basic Characteristics of Grouting Curtain. The right
side of the Neretva River around the Salakovac Dam site is
composed of dolomites and limestones, shown to be permeable
only to about 30 m in depth. As shown in Fig. 3, these rocks
are identified as the low permeable rocks. On the left side
the danger exist of losing water from both, the underground,
and the surface storage space. Figure 6 shows two cross
sections with pervious and less pervious geologic formations
at the Salakovac Dam sites, looking upstream, for a cross
section width of 1500 m. Due to particular geologic conditions
the left bank grouting curtain will be directed downstream,
which is rather uncommon in practice, to reach the contact of
the Upper Cretaceous limestones and the Neogenic marls.

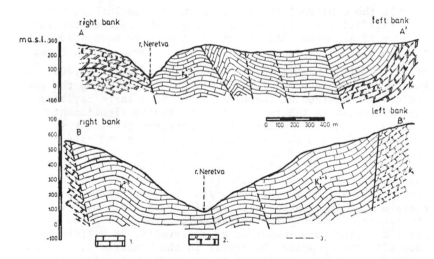

Fig. 6. Hydrogeologic Cross Sections of the Salakovac Reser-
voir: (1) Permeable Rocks, Turonian and Senonian
Limestones; (2) Low Permeable Rocks, Dolomites and
Limestones; and (3) Faults.

DISCUSSION

Yevjevich. The porosity tests of the type presented in
Figs. 1, 2 and 3 do not show the real rock porosity, but a
combination of rock porosity and the hydraulic conditions.
The distance and the character of connections between the
water injection points and the water outflow points determine
the outflow. In this study the water outflows are along the
river, with river level determining the head loss for a given
water pressure at an injection point. The longer the flow
distance, for the same conditions, the smaller the recorded
water losses will be for the same rock porosity. Therefore,
without taking into account the hydraulic flow resistence due
to the length of flow, the effective rock porosity may be
either underestimated or overestimated.

Öziş. Two effects of karst hydrology on surface reservoirs warrant some comments. First, we found out on case
studies in Turkey, that the water effluents of karst springs
significantly decrease the variance of river flows, and both
in the seasonal and inter-annual variations. This implies
that flow regulations require smaller reservoir capacities
than in the case of river flows without karst spring flow
contributions. Second, the additional underground storage,
as treated in this paper, is available as an interconnected
storage to surface storage.

In the construction of the Keban Dam, in Turkey, which
is a rockfill dam with the spillway and the intake structure
in form of a gravity dam, large cavities were encountered at
the dam site. The largest one, named *the crab cavity* because
of its specific shape, was of the volume of over $100,000 \text{ m}^3$.
Extensive groutings and filling of cavities by using the concrete were required at the Keban Dam. Such large cavities
may well exist in the reservoir area, giving significant
underground storage spaces. As it concerns the water imperviousness of the Keban Reservoir, its filling and raising
of the water produced new springs at the left bank downstream
of the dam. Their total discharge is of the order of $5 \text{ m}^3/\text{s}$,
which can be tolerated because it is less than 1% of the
average discharge of over $600 \text{ m}^3/\text{s}$. However, it is not
certain that the leakage will remain around this magnitude in
the future. Another problem, as more severe, is faced when
karstic springs are submerged by reservoirs, as will be the
case with the Oymapinar Reservoir in the Manavgat River basin
in Turkey. It is very useful to exchange such informations
and aspects in details, because the experience gained from
practical examples around the world will enable a more safer
and economical construction of reservoirs in karst regions.

Bagarić. A part of the paper deals with the definition
of the filtration area transmissivity. Because this problem
is a very interesting one, the authors should have said some-

thing more about the conditions under which the Theis'es
equation had been applied in this particular case. To be more
specific, one can wonder whether the observed underground water
flow could have been approximated by a pure radial flow net,
with water coming from all sides. How one can explain the
fissure porosity being treated as homogeneous, and in which
way the assumption of linear resistance law was introduced?
Have the authors used the data of a piezometer to define the
lower value denoted by ΔR? In case the data from piezometers
have not been used, how did they define the area contours when
ΔR was calculated?

Boreli. Yevjevich brought up the question of inter-
dependence between the permeability and certain hydrodynamic
rock characteristics. The permeability is defined not only
by the hydrodynamic rock characteristics (such as, for example,
the Darcy coefficient) but also by the arrangement of permeable
and impermeable zones, and the boundary conditions (such as
the proximity of the contact with the outside water). If the
distance R to water contact from the point where the test
for water permeability is made, the influence is proportional
to log R, with the log R function changing slowly. The distance to this contact is of influence only for areas in the
immediate proximity to the contact. As a whole, this influence
may be very small to explain the changes in permeability with
the depth.

The question of application of Theis equation, raised by
Bagarić, is important, since an impression may be left that
an inadequate method was used. It is necessary to clearly
define the physical conditions for which the applied method
is valid.

Avdagić. The recession curve of the river hydrograph,
given by Eq. (1) in the paper is derived under the assumption
of a linear reservoir, that is $Q = \alpha h$, or $Qdt = -Adh$, with
α in Eq. (1) replaced by α/A, and α = the coefficient of
proportionality of outflow from the reservoir, and A = the
reservoir surface. For A a constant, α is also a constant.
In this paper, as well as in some other papers, a conclusion
was derived that the aquifer transmissibility is proportional
to the coefficient α. It can be demonstrated that this does
not necessarily hold true. For example, in a karst hydrologic
system in which the water table is at the same general elevation as in the channels, this assumption is correct. However,
in a flooded karst polje the situation may be different,
because the reservoir surface has increased. Therefore, the
contention that a large α corresponds to a high transmissibility and the opposite do not hold true in karst. This is
best illustrated by the water level (left) and discharge
(right) curves of the Bregava Spring which is influenced by
a karst polje. (See top of next page).

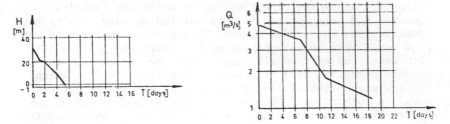

Ivanković, Komatina. In response to the discussion on
selecting the locations for permeability tests with regard to
the place of water outlet at the surface, one should concur with
the idea that the relation of this location to the outlet of an
underground stream to the surface is of a particular significance for a correct interpretation of results. It should be
added, however, that positions of two testing boreholes in relation to the water outflow at the surface should be in different rock permeabilities, so that tests for permeability would
clearly show a difference. A series of pairs of test boreholes
at various distances from the water outlets at the surface
offers an opportunity for better comparison of results and for
their higher accuracy. By using this approach, relative relationships of permeabilities of various rocks have been obtained
for the case of the Salakovac Reservoir.

As to the application of recession curves and the Theis
equation, these analyses have been applied with satisfactory
results to numerous aquifers in France, Lebanon, Yugoslavia,
and in other countries. Several papers deal with this application at this symposium also. If the fulfillment of conditions
for the use of the Theis equation is strictly required, this
equation should not be applied to karst underground flows in
many cases. Taking into account the fact that results sought
represent only the first approximation in the case studied, it
does not matter whether the flow is strictly radial or not.
The opinion was expressed in the introductory remarks of the
paper that it would be desirable to obtain permeability results
by using several methods and by comparing them. For example,
the most important factor in estimating the underground storage
volume, the coefficient of effective porosity, is obtained by
three methods, giving the most likely value of 2-3%, obtained
by averaging the observations from a number of piezometers.
For these piezometers correctly selected, the averages should
be close to actual parameters for a large area.

Concerning the variability of the discharge coefficient,
the method applied in the paper was to define the recession
curve as a straight line in the semi-logarithmic scales. The
discharge coefficient is only of general, informative significance for the estimation of the underground storage volume.
Therefore, only a representative value of this coefficient,
showing its order of magnitude, is given in the paper.

PART 2
KARST HYDROLOGY

ADVANCED APPROACHES TO KARST HYDROLOGY AND WATER RESOURCE SYSTEMS

by

Vujica Yevjevich, Professor of Civil Engineering
Colorado State University, Fort Collins, Colorado, USA

Synopsis. The advanced hydrologic, and particularly geohydrologic, approach to study of karst water problems is the latest newcomer to karstology. Systems approach, with its use of mathematical statistics and optimization in estimation of parameters, has a better promise for new research results than the classical physical modeling of karst aquifers and systems of underground channels. Systems identification needs new approaches because of particular types of information available on inputs, state-of-the system, and outputs of karst formations. Karst has special features, with responses to precipitation being between those of steep impervious surfaces and those of low permeability aquifers, but with complex composition of these responses. The challenge to researchers is the incorporation of information on both the water quantity and quality variables into a new type of systems analysis and identification. Dynamics of erosion and sedimentation, the removal of some of the prevailing myths on the underground properties and responses of karst formations, and the solutions of complex and specific problems of water resources, require a new spiral of advanced research in karst regions.

1.   Investigation of Karst Aquifer and Catchments.

The study of water problems of karst regions has been approached by investigators with both a disciplinary and an interdisciplinary environmental point of view. This was analogous to the approach in other water resource environments, such as hydrometeorology (or hydrology of the atmosphere), surface water hydrology of continental areas, hydrology of snow, ice and glaciers, and similar. Historically, the study of environments were initiated by specialists of some disciplines, in the sense that they first discovered that the karst as an environment was a source of various scientifically interesting research problems. For karstified limestone and dolomite formations, generally and briefly called the karst, geographers and geomorphologists were first to discover them as a special research area, being impressed by the unusual forms of karst surfaces, disappearance and then reappearance of large rivers, and similar karst phenomena. They initiated significant karst investigations. Soon they were joined by geologists, because the karst cannot be studied effectively without geologic descriptions and generalizations. Joined later by biologists, geophysicists, and specialists from the other earth sciences, the karst has been extensively studied in the last hundred years or so. To explain some of the phenomena of water flowing through karst formations, it was necessary to use hydraulics. In the last 30-40 years, this hydraulic component has been added to geophysical methods of inquiry. The hydrologic investigations of the karst have been somewhat neglected, however, being mainly a small appendage to geology and hydraulics in the past.

The hydrogeologic approach, in order to explain some of the geologic aspects of the karst, has been one of the major thrust lines of geologic investigations. However, the other side of hydrology, namely geohydrology, as defined by Meinzer [1,2], has been relatively the latest newcomer to investigations of karst water resource phenomena.

2. Systems Approach to Karst Water Investigation.

The karst aquifers, the systems of large karst underground channels, and karst catchments, can be excellently studied by advanced systems analysis, namely by using the input-response-output approach. Basically, two methods are available in studying the geohydrologic problems of how the karst formations respond to infiltrated water. The classical approach is the physical modeling, by which an environment is studied by using its properties in such a form that the response can be determined, namely, how a given water input must be transformed to produce the water output. Because of insurmountable difficulties in understanding and describing the karst aquifers and systems of underground channels in their entirety, primarily due to inaccessibility of these environments except by very expensive geophysical investigations, and because of necessity for a large number of assumptions to be made about the character of these systems, with some of them rather speculative, the physical modeling of karst systems has shown relatively modest results. It does not promise that it might or would yield significant scientific, practical research results in the future. In turn, systems analysis, particularly by the use of the mathematical statistical approach in systems identification and parameter estimation, has a better outlook for producing the reliable results. It means a determination, in the most general terms, of the character of systems response by using the measured data on input and output variables of karst formations (aquifers, systems of channels, complex catchments, etc.).

Because the input of karst systems is mainly in the form of areal and temporal distributions of precipitation, the effective part of infiltrated precipitation into the karst systems, both as it relates to areal and temporal distributions, is subject to large errors. One does not know completely two out of three factors (input, response, output) in a systems analysis. The input is only partially known. The system which produces this response is poorly known. The output is usually best known, being mostly the concentrated outflows easily

accessible to systematic measurements and observations.
Therefore, the optimization of identified responses must supplement any knowledge on the environment itself by taking into
account various types of errors in input data and the measurement errors in output. Any geophysical exploration which
produces some information on the characteristics of karst
systems should be useful by incorporating it into the identification of the system response in an input-response-output
approach.

The solution of two problems had always preceded, and
should precede, the analysis of karst systems by a systems
approach. First, it was necessary to determine, at least as an
approximation, the catchment area of a given karst system. The
knowledge of geology, hydrogeology and geohydrology of pervious
and impervious geologic formations of karst regions must be
available. Some geophysical investigations should be carried
out in order to determine the underground watersheds, or the
water contributing area to karst systems. The other problem
was an identification of directions of water flows in the underground, and the connections between the concentrated inflows
into the underground at small or large sinkholes and the concentrated outflows in the form of karst springs. The use of
tracers of different kinds are significantly developed for
determining directions and connections.

It was a logical, historical development to start with the
geomorphologic karst investigations, to add the geologic and
hydrogeologic components to investigations, and finally to
apply the hydraulic laws to explain phenomena of water flow in
karst systems. The geohydrologic investigations, however,
required the systems to be explained as unities into which the
portion of precipitation was infiltrated and water was concentrated as large outputs in the form of karst springs. With
this type of basic knowledge on environments from various
disciplines, it was then a logical development that the modern
hydrologic or geohydrologic systems approach, rather than the
physical modeling, became very attractive to use. This input-
response-output approach is likely the most promising method of
hydrologic investigations of karst systems at the present time,
with the two lines of attack: (1) an increase of the knowledge
on precipitation and infiltrated quantities of water; and (2) an
increase of the knowledge on various aspects of karst systems,
in order to supplement the knowledge which is available on inputs and outputs. The positive aspect is that the total (integrated) outflow equals the total (integrated) inflow. Therefore,
the areal and temporal distributions of infiltration could be
checked by integrating them to match the integrated outflow.
Several geologic, geophysic and hydrogeologic investigations are
necessary for supplemental knowledge by obtaining information on
inputs and outputs from a geohydrologic point of view. The
major difficulty arises because of the lack of systems identification methods that are well developed and suited for

treating these types of problems; namely, when the complete
knowledge is not available on inputs, full knowledge is available on outputs, and some knowledge is available on the system
itself, with all these three types of information subject to
different but significant sources of errors. In the writer's
opinion, the development of techniques of systems identification, under the conditions that two out of three factors are
not clearly known, in order to determine the third factor is
necessary. The determination is also subject to conditions that
only one factor is well known, while a partial knowledge is
available on the other two factors, with the partial knowledge
subject to different degrees of errors. These conditions pose
challenging problems for development of geohydrologic methods
for analysis of responses of karst systems. Because of several
specific features of inputs, systems characteristics and outputs of karst aquifers, systems of channels and catchments, it
should be expected that some new systems analysts of karst
aquifers, systems of channels and catchments, in turn, would
contribute to further development of systems analysis in general.

3. Specific Features of Karst Hydrology.

    A logical question to ask is, what makes hydrology and
particularly geohydrology of karst regions specific in comparison with other surface water and groundwater hydrologic environments. A distinction can easily be made, and is made in
practice so often, between the fast-reacting impervious surfaces
to effective rainfall input and a very slow response of low-
porosity aquifers, with prolonged responses to infiltrated
water. The response hydrographs of steep impervious surfaces
to effective rainfall have a sharp, large peak, a relatively
short time-to-peak and a rapid recession. The response hydrographs of classical, low-porosity aquifers have a relatively
very small peak, a long time-to-peak, and long but low recession
outflows. The karst formations, in most cases, have responses
somewhere between these two extremes. Significant differences
in porosity occur, namely from the largest underground channels
to the smallest fissures of rocks and pores of clay depositions.
Also, all types of flow occur in karst formations: capillary,
transient from capillary to laminar, laminar, transient from
laminar to turbulent, and turbulent flow (both subcritical and
supercritical). The karst responses are a combination of
several types of response hydrographs, with all transitions.
One such response is that of large underground channels and enlargements (caverns), through which water flows either free
surface or under pressure, with the response being relatively
rapid but still less rapid than for the steep impervious surfaces. Other responses are those of smaller porosities, such
as of fine materials of deposited sands and silts, rock fissures,
and others with the response being much closer to responses of
common low-permeability aquifers. Last, finest fissures and
silty and clayey deposit materials in underground produce very

slow responses of karst formations. Therefore, whether the
stress is on the rapid, medium rapid, medium slow or very slow
responses in a karst system, the total response hydrograph is
either in between, or close to, surface-area responses or low-
permeability aquifer responses. Figure 1 shows the above concept in general, and Fig. 2 the usual expected composition of
response hydrographs of karst aquifer or systems of underground
channels to infiltrated precipitation. This presentation is
only conceptual, with the intention to show that the karst unit
hydrographs are ordinarily very complex. Often one can find
two-peak or multiple-peak unit hydrograph responses in karst
regions, demonstrating that different areas or parts of the

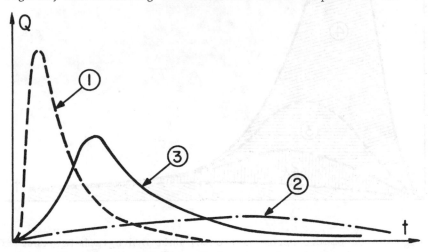

Fig. 1. Distinction of Response of Karst Systems in the Form
of Unit Hydrographs: (1) Rapid Response of Impervious Steep Surfaces; (2) Very Slow Responses of
Common Low-permeability Aquifers; and (3) Medium,
Rapid-to-Slow Responses of Karst Aquifers and Systems
of Underground Channels.

system respond with different time-to-peak and peak, and when
integrated, produce these complex unit hydrographs. This complexity in responses should be used also to explain or supplement the otherwise available information on the system structure
and properties.

     A karst underground system is comprised of a large number
of different subsystems overlapping and intermixing in the same
environment. Therefore, the three major properties of karst
systems are: (a) Medium-size peak and medium-time response of
instantaneous or unit hydrographs; (b) Response hydrographs are
composed of many individual hydrographs of various characteristics, each reflecting the reaction of different types of porosity, permeability and water flow regime; and (c) Subsystems of

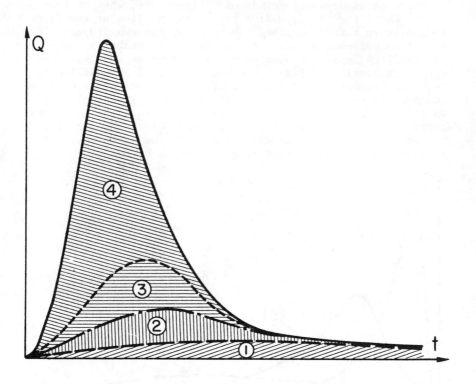

Fig. 2. Schematic Decomposition of Unit Hydrograph Response of
a Karst Aquifer or a System of Underground Channels
and Rock Fissures: (1) Very Slow Response of Finest
Fissures and Clay-silt Deposits; (2) Slow response of
Silt and Sand Deposits and Medium Size Fissures; (3)
Medium, Rapid-to-Slow Response of Sand-to-Gravel Deposits and Medium Size Fissures; and (4) Rapid Response
of Large Channels and Enlargements.

different types of response hydrographs are very much inter-
mixed in space, and their proportions in the total voids may
differ over the system.

Furthermore, the water quality of karst systems has significant differences in comparison with the other geohydrologic
environments, not only in its natural state but also from the
pollution point of view. The fast-flowing portions of karst
waters often carry the organic and other pollutants from the
surface directly to springs. The long-retention portions of
these waters, on the other side, contribute significantly to
the hardness of karst waters, especially in case of limestone
and dolomite formations.

4. Combination of Water Quantity and Quality Variables for a
    Better Response Identification of Karst Systems.

The systems approach, in cases where the water quantities
of inputs and outputs were well known, could be effectively
applied to karst aquifers and systems of underground channels.
However, new knowledge on karst environments can be obtained if
the water quality variables may be combined with the water
quantity inputs and outputs. By combining properly the information on both the water quality and quantity variables of inputs and outputs, and by using systems analysis for identification of responses of karst aquifers, systems of underground
channels and catchments, much more knowledge about these systems can be produced. Not only could the responses be estimated with more accuracy, but also much more may be learned
about the type and structure of hydrogeologic properties of
karst systems. Because it is not simple to combine the information on quantity and quality variables of inputs and outputs
in this analysis, particularly to karst geohydrology and its
complex types of information, new systems identification
approaches need to be developed. It is well known that temperature of outflowing karst waters, their mineral composition,
content of carbon dioxide, the pH-values and other quality
variables of karst waters can always tell something about the
karst environment. Therefore, a systematic search for new
methods for identifying systems response characteristics, by
using both quantity and quality variables of karst water inputs
and outputs, is a worthwhile objective of research in karst
hydrology and geohydrology. The writer of this paper is con-
vinced that the future progress in knowledge on karst geohydrology will highly depend on how well this problem is resolved for a better understanding and description of karst
water systems. Then, the information from classical hydrogeologic investigations, obtained by the geologic, geophysic and
other methods, can be significantly supplemented and/or checked
by the application of quantity-quality, input-response-output,
approach to karst water systems.

The quality variables of karst waters are often measured
at karst outflows, especially if they were in the form of
springs. Information on temperature, pH, chemical analysis
variables, hardness, biological properties, radioactivity, and
several other variables, can thus be available. The selection
of quality variables to be observed, which would also produce
the information on responses and structure of systems, is a
separate problem to solve. Similarly, it is possible to measure the quality of waters which enter the karst environment
immediately below the surface after infiltration.

The interpretation of measurement results on water quality
variables is often only partial and speculative. Namely, it is
hypothesized how the average values and the fluctuation of

temperature, CO_2, pH, chemical compounds, and other indicators of the water quality can be interpreted and related to properties of karst environments. Conclusions about the geohydrologic properties of karst formations from the point of view of water quality variables have been often speculative. A mathematical, systems identification approach, yet to be developed, in which both quantity and quality variables are simultaneously used in determining not only the best information on responses of a karst system, but also in learning about the properties, would represent an objective rather than a subjective method of interpretation.

5. Continuous Processes of Erosion and Sedimentation in Karst Underground Systems.

Combinations of chemical, physical and biological factors make the erosion and sedimentation in limestone and dolomite formations a continuous time process. The water inflow to karst underground systems carries suspended material and bed-load sediment, particularly when water of creeks and rivers enter directly into the large sinkholes. The spring water from a karst system may carry a relatively small amount of sediments; its small turbidity usually does not account for all solid materials carried into the underground. Depositions of gravel, sand, silt, clay and calcium bicarbonate go on all the time in karst systems. They close voids, while the geological and geophysical processes, and chemical or combined physico-chemico-biological erosion processes, continuously create new voids.

Changes in surface erosion and sediment transport into karst systems should make erosion and sedimentation the non-stationary processes. The total volume of voids inside the karst underground systems should increase with time, because of continuous replacement of dissolved solid rocks by loose sediments. The main geohydrologic problem is whether voids filled by fine materials are active participants in water storage and transmission in karst system responses to water inflows. These voids, filled by loose sediments in or over karst systems, have important implications and require proper methods for solving many practical, hydrologic, geohydrologic and water resources problems.

Consequences of various surface and underground sediment deposits over and inside the karst systems on water resources engineering are:

(1) Water storage space inside these deposits may be of significant hydrologic relevance;

(2) Water transmisibility depends on the location and composition of these deposits;

(3) Success in obtaining water by drilled wells in karst
formations depends on whether spaces filled by sufficiently
coarse material and rocks with high degree of fissures are
encountered;

(4) Practical problems are posed whenever tunnels or
other underground excavations encountered voids filled with
loose sediments;

(5) Loss of water from surface storage reservoirs in
karst areas is greatly affected by filled-in voids with these
loose fine sediments, because the water leakage usually increases with time, as this material is easily eroded by water
porous-media flow under a high pressure gradient;

(6) The quality of water is affected by its residence time
in voids of these loose sediments; and similar consequences.

6. Effects of Filled-in Karst Voids and Deposition of Sediment
Over Karst Systems on Sustained Flow.

A current misconception, in explaining the highly sustained
flow from karst formations during long dry periods, is the
assumption that it is the result of large underground karst
channels and enlargements filled with water during wet periods.
This concept is analogous to the system of surface lakes,
reservoirs and streams which sustain low flows. Though these
large-scale voids are not a negligible storage factor, the most
likely explanation for sustained flow is the primary type of
voids, namely rock fissures and deposited fine sediments inside
and over karst systems. During a wet season, high water pressures in karst systems and the flooding over the surface sediment deposits, force large quantities of water to infiltrate
into these voids of deposited fine material and fine rock
fissures. Differences in location, permeability and porosity
require various filling times. Water drains out from voids
slowly during the period of low flows, because of relatively
low piezometric pressures over and inside the system. The finer
the voids, the longer times are necessary for their filling and
emptying. All gradations of voids cause all gradations in water
storage capacity and transmissibility of these rock fissures
and sediment deposits. This concept is schematically presented
in Fig. 3, for the case of karst plain deposits for the cycle
of wet and dry seasons. It is sufficient to calculate the
total storage capacity of deposited sediments, lying over the
karstified rocks in a karst plain, in order to ascertain a large
total volume for potential water storage. Often, this capacity
is equal to, or even exceeds, the total sustained recession
flow, integrated between the time of a low flow discharge and
infinity. Obviously, all of this potential storage space is
not active, in the sense that times of filling and emptying of
voids are not sufficient to make them all effective partici-

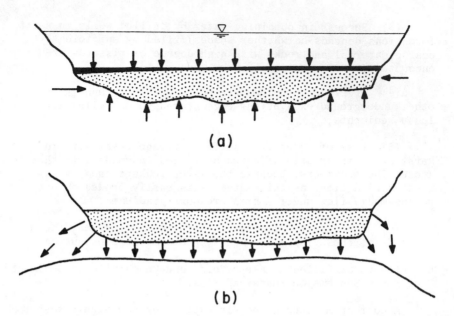

Fig. 3. Effect of Sediment Deposits Over Karst Systems: (a)
Wet Season With the Water Filling the Fine Voids, and
Piezometric Levels Being Approximately at the Level of
Flooded Karst Plains (Poljes); (b) Dry Season With
the Drainage of Stored Water to a Low Position of
Piezometric Levels.

pants in fluctuations of the water storage volume. Besides,
some of them are permanently filled with water.

In the same way as the surface deposits of fine materials,
the filled-in underground voids play a similar water storage
role. Their effective water storage capacity, as the percent
of the total volume of voids, may be greater than for the same
type of surface deposits, because of a larger fluctuation in
piezometric levels between the wet and dry seasons.

7. Water Resources of Karst Regions.

Karst regions have some specific features of water resources
development, conservation and control, when compared with the
other types of regions. To illustrate some of these specific
features of karst water resources, only six aspects are briefly
outlined, namely: (1) Construction of reservoirs in karstified formations; (2) Construction of large dams in karst
terrains; (3) Specific aspects of other structures constructed
over or inside karst formations; (4) Water supply; (5) Pollution control, and (6) Flood control.

Reservoirs. The dominating problem with reservoirs in karst regions is their water imperviousness. Large investigation programs and explorations are usually required in most cases, and large investments in grouting curtains are needed in order to make reservoirs in karst formations sufficiently impervious. As generally known, several large reservoirs built in karst formations in the world, which could not be economically made sufficiently impervious, were never filled and operated. Some are operated with significant water leakage. Therefore, professionals are not surprised to hear from time to time that a large reservoir just built experiences a significant water loss. What is worse, these losses often increase with time.

Dams. The construction of dams in karst formations is not only concerned with the structural aspects of a dam foundation, but particularly with the imperviousness below the dam and around its abutments. More than for any one type of terrain, dams built in limestone and dolomite karstified formations require large investigations and grouting works. The problem is that the rock fissures and old channels in karst areas may be often filled with silt and clay, subject to erosion under a sufficiently high water pressure gradient between the reservoir and the downstream river levels. It is then required to wash out large quantities of fine materials and replace them with more permanent materials. Furthermore, it is often the case in karst regions that the grouting curtains behave only as temporarily impervious cut-offs. The dynamic evolution of these curtains require continuous supervision, observation and survey of various types, and from time to time some additional grouting.

Other Structures. In constructing most of the underground structures to be excavated inside karst formations, such as tunnels, enlargements, underground power and pumping plants, and similar, often large fissures, faults, old voids and channels filled with fine loose materials are encountered. Water intrusion is a most inconvenient occurrence. The construction in karst limestones and dolomites has ideal conditions of sufficient rock resistance, but sufficiently soft rock for easy excavation and shaping of underground spaces. However, the work in these formations with water problems still calls for extreme caution, and occasionally very expensive works.

Water Supply. Water supply in karst regions is subject to several problems of which the most important are where and how to locate water. When it is available or located, the water supply is subject to large fluctuations in cases where precipitation fluctuates with clear wet and dry seasons. The structures for water supply intakes, water treatment plants, transmission lines and water storage, all have features specific to karst areas.

Pollution Control. Pollution control is becoming one of the most recent and important aspects of water resources of karst systems. It is easy to pollute a karst system, permanently or semi-permanently, but difficult to clean it in a relatively short time. Modern industrial communities and urban areas are becoming a threat of permanent or semi-permanent contamination of a multitude of karst systems.

Flood Control. The flooding of larger closed karst plains occurs when the underground connections with lower levels have a smaller flow capacity than the water inflow into these plains. An increase of this flow capacity may mean a relief for floods of an upstream plain, but also a larger flood threat to downstream plains and river valleys. The flood control can be effective in some karst regions using the large and temporary capacities of underground channels and voids for flood water retention.

8. Conclusions.

Because of complex and specific features of hydrologic, particularly of geohydrologic, and water resources problems in karst regions, new investigative approaches are needed. The extension of existing, and the development of new, methods of systems analysis are thus required to fit the specific features of karst regions. The expectation is then that the range of the use of hydrogeologic inferrences based on speculative hypotheses would be further restricted, and replaced or supplemented by the objective conclusions of systems identification and interpretation.

9. References.

Meinzer, O. E., Discussion of Question No. 2 of the International Commission on Subterranean Water: Definitions of the different kinds of subterranean water: Am. Geophs. Union Trans., 1939, Vol. 4, pp. 674-677, 1939.

Meinzer, O. E., Introduction to the book Physics of the Earth - IX, hydrology: Dover Publications, New York, 1942 (Introduction pp. 1-31).

10. Acknowledgement.

The financial support by U. S. National Science Foundation, Grant GK-31529X for the research project "Investigation of Water Resources in Karst Regions" to Colorado State University, with the writer of the paper as the principal investigator, is respectfully acknowledged.

SOME FEATURES OF MATHEMATICAL ANALYSIS OF KARST RUNOFF

by

Ünal Özis, Associate Professor
Faculty of Engineering Sciences,
Ege University, Izmir, Turkey

and

Nejat Keloğlu, Project Engineer
State Hydraulic Works Agency,
Regional Directorate, Izmir, Turkey

Synopsis. Karstified limestone formations are predominant
in Southern Turkey. Due to a large contribution by karst
springs, they significantly affect the streamflow. Certain
features revealed in the mathematical analysis of karst runoff of river basins could be of interest for other areas of
similar karst formations. These features are briefly presented.

Investigations of karst runoff by autocorrelation,
spectral analysis, lag cross correlation were made for three
case studies in Turkey: Manavgat River basin, Esencay River
basin, and Sarikiz Springs, as shown in Fig. 1. The conclusions of investigations are:

(a) Time lags between precipitation and stream- or
spring-flow result in apparent propagation velocities substantially lower than velocities encountered in accessible
underground rivers in karst formations, so that the existence
of very large underground delays and reservoirs were anticipated.

(b) Besides the recharge through well-developed karst
channels, part of the recharge might be in the form of subsurface inflow through alluvial soils or underdeveloped karst
formations.

(c) After the removal of periodicity in parameters, the
dependence function of the stochastic component may be
approximated by the first- or the second-order autoregressive
models. However, because of some significant departures from
this model, the consideration of multi-lag or self-similar
models might be of interest in future analyses.

(d) According to investigations carried out with annual
data series, the normal probability distribution function
satisfactorily fits the independent stochastic component.

(e) Due to scarcity of hydrologic data in Turkey, some
specific approaches are also applied to set-up the mathematical
model of the runoff process.

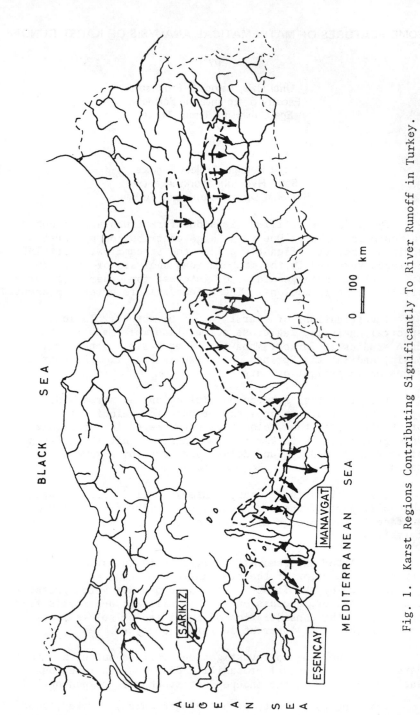

Fig. 1. Karst Regions Contributing Significantly To River Runoff in Turkey.

1. Introduction.

Almost the entire southern coastland and a large part of
the eastern region of Turkey are predominantly covered by
karstified limestone formations. Due to large water contributions of karst springs, these formations affect significantly
the river runoff. These areas in Turkey are shown in Fig. 1.

During recent years, mathematical modeling techniques
have found an increased application in studying hydrologic
processes in Turkey, focusing mainly on two subjects: (a)
streamflows of the Firat (Euphrates) basin, which represents
almost one sixth of the water budget and one third of the
water power potential of Turkey: (b) streamflows of basins
with karstified limestone formations [1].

The mathematical analysis of runoff flows at some of the
river basins in Turkey revealed certain features, with respect
to mathematical simulation models as well as to recharge
systems, which could be of interest for other areas of the
world where karstified limestone formations are predominant.
This paper will breifly present the results of studies and
point to peculiarities of the mathematical analysis of runoff
at the three basins in Turkey. These case studies were
Manavgat [2] and Eşençay [3,4,5,6] in southwest Turkey and
the Sarikiz Springs [7,8] in western Turkey.

These studies were aimed to applying the modern mathematical techniques to hydrologic data in order to achieve a better
appraisal of water resources development plans. The primary
objective of the development of the Manavgat River basin is
water power, of the Esencay River basin both water power and
irrigation, and of the Sarikiz Springs the urban water supply.
Basically, the autocorrelation and spectral analysis techniques
[9,10] and probability distributions [11] were applied to set
up a mathematical simulation model; the lag cross correlation
techniques [10] were applied in the analysis of recharge systems.

2. Mathematical Simulation Models.

Daily flows of the Manavgat River. The Manavgat River
and the adjacent basins are shown in Fig. 2. The characteristics of the three stream gauging stations are given in Table 1.

Because of limited capacity of the computer available,
only daily flows during the years 1965-67 were analyzed, as
a period considered fairly representative of the average
runoff conditions. With respect to cumulative periodograms
and to avoid the negative flows in the deterministic component,
the complex periodicity in daily flows was represented by four
harmonics at Homa and six harmonics at Sinanhoca and Sahapköprü.

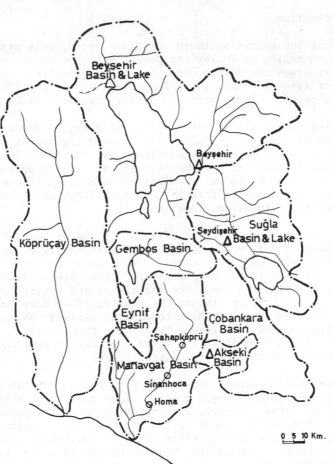

Fig. 2. The Manavgat River Basin and Adjacent Basins.

Table 1. Streamgaging Stations in Manavgat River Basin [2].

Name	Station code Nr.	Elevation (m)	Drainage area (km^2)	Period of record	Mean Flow (m^3/s)	(mm/ year)
Sahapköprü	911	432	438	1964-1970	35.3	2544
Sinanhoca	912	310	626	1964-1970	87.0	4383
Homa	901	35	928	1940-1970	158.1	5371

The part of the variance explained by the periodic component was about 60% at Homa and Sinanhoca, 43% at Sahapköprü.

The stochastic component appears to follow a second-order autoregressive dependence at Homa and Sahapköprü, whereas a first-order dependence was more appropriate at Sinanhoca. An analysis of daily flows at five selected North-American river basins [12] resulted in second-order autoregressive dependence. The analysis of an Alpine river basin [13] used a different rather deterministic approach. For the sake of uniformity, the second-order autoregressive dependence was applied to all three stations in the Manavgat River basin. However, a recent study [14] on Firat flows at Keban, where a relatively minor part of runoff originates from karst springs, showed that the use of a first-order autoregressive scheme would be adequate, thus making unnecessary the use of higher-order models.

On the other hand, the peak values up to $r = 0.25$ for the lags in the range of $k = 20$ to 30 in correlograms appeared to be a persistent departure from the linear first or second-order autoregressive schemes. It would be of interest to investigate the application possibilities of multi-lag [15] or self-similar [16,17] models to these processes. Furthermore, a recent study [18] of dry periods based on runs analysis [10] showed that the critical dry periods are more severe than predicted by autoregressive Markov models.

Based on previous studies [19,20,21], carried out with annual flows, the probability distribution of the random stochastic element is assumed to be normal.

Although the frequency distribution of annual streamflow series usually were best fitted by a gamma or a lognormal distribution [22], which was also confirmed for small Turkish river basins where seasonal rainfall with predominant surface runoff is the principal source of streamflow, the normal distribution proved to be satisfactory in the majority of large basins, where snowmelt and groundwater have a significant contribution to streamflow [20,21]. The standard deviation of residual stochastic components showed a complex periodicity, so that second-order stationarity was not achieved.

Monthly flows of the Esençay River. The characteristics of four streamgaging stations in the Esençay River basin are given in Table 2, and locations shown in Fig. 3.

The autocorrelation and spectral analysis of ten-day average flows at Kemer [3] showed that a sinusoidal simple periodic function would satisfactorily represent the periodic component of the mean. The dependence function can be approximated by a first-order autoregressive scheme, as it is

Table 2. Streamgaging Stations in the Eşençay River Basin.

Name	Station Code Nr.	Elevation (m)	Drainage area (km^2)	Period of record	Mean Flow (m^3/s)	(mm/year)
Kavaklidere	809	1080	547	1957-1971	5.3	306
Örenköy	8-13	190	807	1961-1971	20.6	805
Kemer	802	95	1194	1941-1958 1964-1971	30.3	800
Yapilar	8-28	9	2461	1962-1971	57.0	730

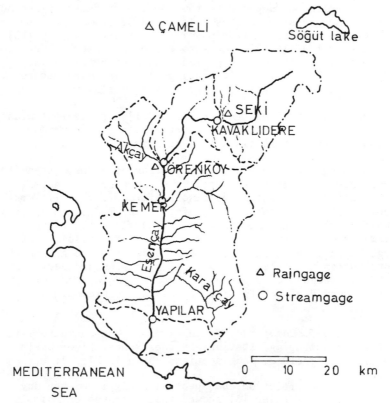

Fig. 3. The Eşençay River Basin.

common for monthly flows [23]. The random element is assumed
to be normally distributed, according to previous studies [20]
on annual flows. The correlogram showed again a peak up to
r = 0.20 for approximately k = 25, and the same discussion as
dealt with respect to the Manavgat River basin applies to the
Esencay River basin. Therefore, a completely new approach [5]
was attempted to set up the mathematical model of monthly flows
at Örenköy, based upon the periodic variation of correlation
parameters [6] between Örenköy flows, where karst springs
contribute almost half of the streamflow, and the upstream
Kavaklidere flows, where such contributions are virtually non-
significant.

Through the introduction of the new concept of reversible
correlation parameters, this model included three components.
The first was the quasi-deterministic monthly spring effluents,
consisting of the reversible intercept plus the mean and the
periodic component of the second-rank residuals. The second
consisted of the conventional mathematical model of Kavaklidere
flows amplified through multiplication by the reversible
regression coefficient. The third was the normally distributed independent stochastic component of the second-rank
residuals, including a complex periodic standard deviation.
Thus the new method provides also a means for the determination of karst springs effluents where they were not readily
measurable as separate flow processes.

Monthly discharges of the Sarikiz Springs. The location
of the Sarikiz Springs, which has a mean discharge of 1.19
m^3/s, is shown in Fig. 4. In contrast to large data of spring
discharge available in the two previous studies, one in
United States [24], the other in Czechoslovakia [25], the
analysis of the Sarikiz Springs discharges had to be carried
out with scarce data of 34 months only. Therefore, two indirect
approaches were attempted to set up a mathematical model.

The first alternative consisted of a combination of the
usual model of precipitation at Akhisar and the multiple
regression equation of the Sarikiz Springs discharges on
Akhisar precipitation [7,8]. The second alternative used the
Sarikiz Springs discharges extended to cover a period of 43
years through the multiple regression on Akhisar [7] in
order to set up their mathematical model [8]. The deterministic
component of the so-obtained discharge data included a complex
periodic component with two harmonics, which represent almost
17% of the variance. However, this component had one distinct annual peak, whereas the data themselves reflect two
distinct peaks per year. This peculiarity will be discussed
later with regard to the recharge system.

The correlogram and the variance density spectrum of
residuals indicated a first-order autoregressive dependence

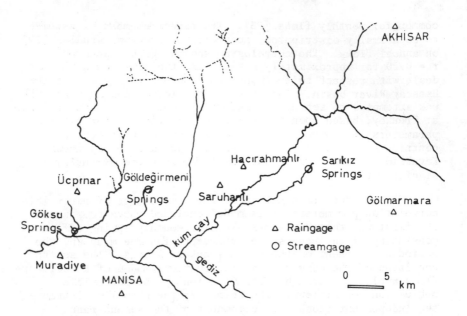

Fig. 4. Sarikiz Springs and the Neighboring Region.

of the stochastic component. For k = 4, the correlogram
showed again a peak up to r = 0.49, which has been encountered in the Manavgat and Eşençay River basins.

The series of monthly standard deviations revealed a
complex periodicity. Based on the analysis of annual discharges, the random stochastic component can be roughly
approximated by a normal probability distribution, whereas
both extremes indicate the probable presence of lower and
upper limits, so that a Beta Type I distribution may appear
more attractive.

3. Recharge Systems.

The Manavgat River Basin. The annual average precipitation over the Manavgat River basin is in the order of 1700 mm
per year [2]. The comparison of this figure and the annual
average discharges given in Table 1 clearly evidences a
contribution of large karst springs. Various studies [26
through 31] carried out previously on the Manavgat River basin
showed that a large part of its flows originate from groundwaters of neighboring basins, particularly from the Beysehir
and Sugla Lake basins. The only exception is the Köprücay
River basin receiving itself the similar contributions. These
basins are shown in Fig. 2.

The complex periodic component of the Manavgat River's
daily flows has a principal peak in January and a secondary

peak in April. The complex periodic component of the precipitation gauging stations Akseki, Seydisehir and Beysehir, has a principal peak in December and a secondary peak in March-April. The time lags between precipitation and streamflow are approximately 30 days for the principal and 20 days for the secondary peak [2].

Additional investigations through the lag cross correlation between precipitation and streamflow confirmed these time lags. Their results are summarized in Table 3, where r_o denotes the correlation coefficient for $k = 0$, r_L the first lowest one, r_H the next highest one and k_H the approximate time lag in days of the occurrence of this next highest correlation coefficient. The location of stations is shown in Fig. 2.

Table 3. Summarized Results of Lag Cross Correlation Between Precipitation and Streamflow in the Manavgat River Basin.

	Beyşehir			Seydişehir			Akseki		
	r_o	r_L	r_H (k_H)	r_o	r_L	r_H (k_H)	r_o	r_L	r_H (k_H)
Sahapköprü	0.39	0.14	0.25 (15-20)	0.56	0.20	0.32 (10-15)	0.52	0.21	0.32 (10-20)
Sinanhoca	0.28	0.16	0.24 (15-20)	0.39	0.21	0.28 (15-20)	0.40	0.20	0.29 (15-30)
Homa	0.31	0.17	0.24 (15-20)	0.43	0.21	0.31 (15-20)	0.46	0.20	0.31 (15-30)

In view of these results and the great distances between Manavgat and anticipated recharge areas, it is assumed that the time lags represent the routing effect through a very large karst reservoir rather than result from snowmelt. In fact, with respect to the amount and variance of the streamflow, the springs near Şahapköprü can be considered as the spillway, those near Sinanhoca and Homa as bottom outlets of this large karst reservoir.

The apparent velocity of propagation through karst formations can be estimated as 3.5 cm/s, taking into account an average distance of 60 km and an average time lag of 20 days. It should be pointed out that this is a too low velocity compared to those encountered in accessible underground rivers in karst formations in Turkey.

The Eşençay River basin. The annual average precipitation over the Upper Esencay River basin is in the order of 650 to 800 mm/year [5]. The comparison of these figures and the annual average discharges given previously in Table 2 clearly evidenced the significant contribution of karst springs down-stream of Kavaklidere.

The lag cross correlations between monthly springs effluents and precipitation at Örenköy, Seki, Gölhisar, Çameli stations, as shown in Fig. 3, revealed a principal lag of two months with correlation coefficients of the order of 0.60 and a secondary lag of four months, for Seki and Gölhisar only, with correlation coefficients of the order of 0.4 [5]. Although snowmelt may have some impact on the principal lag, the recharge system has been assumed to be dual, the first consisting of the contribution by large karst channels, reached readily by infiltrated water, and the second including a substantial water infiltration through alluvium before reaching the karst channels.

The apparent velocity of water propagation through karst formations can be estimated as of 0.60 cm/s, taking into account an average distance of 30 km and an average time lag of two months. This is a slower rate than that of the Manavgat River basin.

The Sarikiz Springs. The investigation of the extended series of the Sarikiz Springs discharges through the multiple correlation on precipitation at Akhisar showed that there were usually two peaks within the year [7]. The comparison of histograms of these peaks with that of precipitation revealed a time lag of approximately 2.5 months for the first and of 7.5 months for the second peak. A lag cross correlation between monthly precipitation at Akhisar and these extended Sarikiz Springs discharges resulted in the respective time lags of 3 to 8 months. With respect to topographical and geological conditions, it was assumed that the first lag was indicative of the water travel through karst formations, the second lag of the flow through alluvium from flooded surface areas.

The apparent velocity of propagation through karst formations was estimated as of 0.13 cm/s, taking into account an average distance of 10 km and an average time lag of 3 months. This was a much slower rate than those of the Manavgat and Eşençay River basins.

4. Conclusions.

Investigations of three different case studies of mixed karst and non-karst hydrologic runoff processes in Turkey led to the following conclusions:

(a) The time lags between precipitation and stream or spring runoff were in the order of a few weeks to a few months and resulted in the apparent propagation velocities in karst formations of the order of cm/s, which are substantially lower than velocities encountered in accessible underground channels. The large time lags were considered as an indication of extremely large underground water retention. The apparent propagation velocities appeared to increase when the ratio of springflow to surface runoff increased.

(b) Besides the distinction between the surface runoff from the immediate drainage area and the springflow from well-developed karst channels, there appeared to be some kind of subsurface flow from alluvial soils or under-developed karst formations.

(c) The discharge series showed a significant periodicity, which is, in many cases, of complex nature, although the fundamental annual harmonic was predominant.

(d) The dependence function of the stochastic component may be expressed by linear autoregressive schemes of first-order for monthly data, and of first- or second-order for daily data. However, the correlograms display for certain time lags in each basin a peak significantly departing from the autoregressive model; which should be further investigated by the multi-lag or self-similar dependence models.

(e) The standard deviations of stochastic residuals usually had an inherent periodicity, which distorted the second-order stationarity. However, this periodicity was weak in some cases and could be neglected with respect to some tests.

(f) According to the investigations carried out with annual flow series, the normal probability distribution fitted satisfactorily the random element of the stochastic component.

(g) Scarcity of data in Turkey in some cases led to the application of special approaches in order to develop the mathematical models of processes.

5. Acknowledgment.

The authors gratefully acknowledge the work previously done by Mr. Atilla Ece, M. Sc. in C.E.; the assistance of Mrs. Nilgün (Bayraktar) Harmancioglu, B. Sc. in C. E., and Mr. Ahmet Alpaslan, M. Sc. in C. E., as well as the support of Dr. Oguz Manas, Associate Professor and Director of the Electronic Computer Center, and his staff in the execution of digital computations.

6. References.

[1] Özis, Ü., Mathematical simulation models of hydrologic processes in Turkey: Wellingford, IASH, Proceedings of the Bratislava International Symposium and Workshops on the Application of Mathematical Models in Hydrology and Water Resource Systems, Publ. No. 115, pp. 185-191, 1975.

[2] Keloğlu, N., Manavgat irmagi günlük akimlarinin matematik modelleri (Mathematical models for the daily flows of Manavgat river): Izmir, Ege Universitesi Muhendislik Bilimleri Fakültesi, Hidroloji ve su Yapilari Yuksek Lisans Tezi (Ege University, Faculty of Engineering Sciences, Thesis for M. Sc. in Hydrology and Hydraulic Structures), n. 3, 71 p., 1974.

[3] Safa, R., Özer, A., Bayraktar, N., et al., Esencay yillik ve aylik akimlarinin matematik modelleri (Mathematical models of annual and monthly flows of Esencay): Izmir, Ege Üniversitesi Mühendislik Bilimleri Fakültesi, Stokastik Hidroloji 1973/74 Yilici Uygulamalari (Ege University, Faculty of Engineering Sciences, 1973/74 Applications in Stochastic Hydrology), (dir.: Ü. Özis), part 3, 8 p., 1974.

[4] Öziş, Ü., Yukari Esençay akimlari korrelasyon parametrelerinin periyodik degisimi (Periodic variation of the correlation parameters of flows in the Upper Eşençay basin). Istanbul, Insaat Mühendisleri Odasi, VI. Teknik Kongresi (Chamber of Civil Engineers, VI. Technical Congress), R.2-11, 28 p., 1974.

[5] Özis, Ü., Stochastic analysis of river flows in karstic regions based upon periodic variations of correlation parameters: Izmir, Ege Üniversitesi Mühendislik Bilimleri Fakültesi Dergisi (Ege University, Faculty of Engineering Sciences Journal), y. 3, sp.n.1, pp. 77-110, 1975.

[6] Öziş, Ü., Keloğlu, N., Pinar katkili akarsularin cevirme santrallarina derlenmesi (Diversion of rivers with springs effluents into hydroelectric schemes). Ankara, DSI Teknik Bülteni (State Hydraulic Works, Technical Bulletin), n. 31., pp. 31-36, 1975.

[7] Ece, A., Sarikiz pinar akimlarinin matematik modeli (Mathematical model for the Sarikiz spring discharges): Izmir, Ege Üniversitesi Mühendislik Bilimleri Fakültesi, Hidroloji ve Su Yapilari Yuksek Lisans Tezi (Ege University, Faculty of Engineering Sciences, Thesis for M.Sc. in Hydrology and Hydraulic Structures), n. 1, 52 p., 1974.

[8] Öziş, Ü., Ece, A., Indirektes mathematisches Abfluss-
     modell der karstischen Sarikizquellen: Izmir, Ege
     Üniversitesi Mühendislik Bilimleri Fakültesi Dergisi
     (Ege University, Faculty of Engineering Sciences Journal),
     y.3, n.2, pp. 1-30, 1975.

[9] Yevjevich, V., Structural analysis of hydrologic time
     series: Fort Collins, Colorado State University, Hydrology
     Paper n. 56, 59 p., 1972.

[10] Yevjevich, V., Stochastic processes in hydrology: Water
     Resources Publications, Fort Collins, 276 p., 1972.

[11] Yevjevich, V., Probability and statistics in hydrology:
     Water Resources Publications, Fort Collins, 302 p., 1972.

[12] Quimpo, R. G., Stochastic analysis of daily river flows:
     A.S.C.E., Journal of Hydraulics Division, HY1, pp. 44-57,
     1968.

[13] Krummenmacher, R., Davaud, E., Modèles journaliers
     d'écoulement dans un bassin karstique: Journal of
     Hydrology, v. 17, n. 4, pp. 375-393, 1972.

[14] Bulu, A., Firat nehri günlük debilerinin yapisal analizi
     (Structural analysis of daily flows of the Euphrates
     river): Istanbul, Insaat Muhendisleri Odasi, VI. Teknik
     Kongresi (Chamber of Civil Engineers, VI. Technical
     Congress), R. 2-7, 17 p., 1974.

[15] Fiering, M. B., Jackson, B. B., Synthetic streamflows:
     Washington, D. C., American Geophysical Union, Water
     Resources Monograph no. 1, 98 p., 1971.

[16] Mandelbrot, B. B., Wallis, J. R., Some long-range proper-
     ties of geophysical records: Water Resources Research
     v. 5, n. 2, pp. 321-340, 1969.

[17] Bayazit, M., Yillik ortalama akis serilerinin istatistik
     analizi (Statistical analysis of annual mean flow
     sequences). Istanbul: T.B.T.A.K. (Scientific and Technical
     Research Council of Turkey), MAG-307, 70 p., 1973.

[18] Bayazit, M., Statistical analysis of dry periods in
     Turkish rivers: Istanbul, Istanbul Teknik Üniversitesi
     Bülteni (Istanbul Technical University Bulletin), v. 27,
     n. 2, pp. 24-35, 1974.

[19] Güripek, H., Öztekin, N., Turkiye akarsularinda ortalama
     akim debilerinin tekerrür analizi (Frequency analysis of
     the mean discharges in Turkish rivers): Insaat Mühendisleri
     Odasi, IV. Teknik Kongresi (Chamber of Civil Engineers,
     IV. Technical Congress), R. 1-14, 8 p., 1968.

[20] Öziş, Ü., Akislilik katsayilari vasitasiyla ortalama
ve düsük akimlarin tayini, güvenilir su kuvveti potansi-
yelinin hesaplanmasi (Determination of average and low
flows through the use of modular hydraulicity coefficients,
computation of firm water power potential): Izmir,
T.B.T.A.K. (Scientific and Technical Research Council of
Turkey), MAG-206, 235 p, 1971.

[21] Bayazit, M., Turkiye akarsularinin yillik ortalama
akislarinin istatistik analizi (Statistical analysis of
the annual mean flows of Turkish rivers): Ankara, Insaat
Mühendisleri Odasi, Teknik Bülten (Chamber of Civil
Engineers, Technical Bulletin), v. 3, n. 10, pp. 115-125,
1972.

[22] Marković, R. D., Probability functions of best fit to
distribution of annual precipitation and runoff: Fort
Collins, Colorado State University, Hydrology paper n. 8,
33 p., 1965.

[23] Roesner, L.N., Yevjevich, V., Mathematical models for
time series of monthly precipitation and monthly runoff:
Fort Collins, Colorado State University, Hydrology Paper
n. 15, 35 p., 1966.

[24] Knisel, W. G., Response of karst aquifers to recharge:
Fort Collins, Colorado State University, Hydrology Paper
n. 60, 48 p., 1972.

[25] Kriz, H., Processing of results of observations of spring
discharge: Ground Water, v. 11, n. 5, pp. 3-14., 1973.

[26] Electricite de France and Etibank, Plan Général d'éléctri-
fication de la Turquie: Paris, Electricité de France
& Ankara, Etibank, 307 p., 1957.

[27] Acatay, T., Beysehir gölü-Manavgat iliskisi (Relation
between Beysehir lake and Manavgat): Ankara, DSI Teknik
Bulteni (State Hydraulic Works, Technical Bulletin), n. 9,
pp. 1-24, 1966.

[28] Aygen, T., Manavgat-Oymapinar (Homa) kemer baraji ile
Beysehir gölü-Manavgat cayi havzasinin jeolojik,
hidrojeolojik ve karstik etüdü (Geological, hydrogeological and karstic study of the Beysehir lake-Manavgat river
basin and the Manavgat - Oymapinar (Homa) arch dam): EIE,
Rapor (Electrical Works Survey Agency Report), 1967.

[29] Bakalowicz, M., Etude du bassin d'alimentation de
Manavgat: Paris, Faculté des Sciences, Hydrodynamique
karstique, Thése du 3. éme cycle., 1970.

235

[30] Çultu, L., Altinbilek, D., Statistical analysis of
Manavgat river basin recharge characteristics: Ankara,
Middle East Technical University, Civil Engineering Department, Water Operations Laboratory, Tech. Publ. n.2, 106 p.,
1971.

[31] Bakalowicz, M. (trans. Akmanaglu, O.), Bati Toroslarda
Manavgat beslenme havzasinin hidrojeolojik etüdü. (Hydrogeological study of the Manavgat recharge basin in
Western Taurus): Ankara, IMO Teknik Bulteni (Chamber
of Civil Engineers, Technical Bulletin), n. 9, pp. 101-
112, 1972.

DISCUSSION

Duckstein. Öziş and Keloğlu in both the paper and presentation, properly define the goals of their study. The
approach may be improved by taking into account prior knowledge
available in addition to the input-output data. In other
words, the same considerations apply as for the paper by
Graupe et al. Perhaps Öziş could consider theoretical ways
to combine results of a daily-event based stochastic model
into a weekly, nonthly, or yearly process. Such a procedure
would make maximum use of available data and provide insight
into acceptable probability distribution functions (PDF) for
both input and output. The authors may thus find a statistical
justification for their empirical result that a normal PDF fits
the random element of the stochastic component of annual
series. Another justification of this result may be sought in
physical terms: Namely, does the annual series result from the
sum of several independent random factors?

Öziş. As I already mentioned during the presentation of
the paper, the first part of our work was devoted to the
structural analysis of runoff data in order to determine their
mathematical model. Then the model will be used to generate
data in order to set up by experimental statistical methods
the long-term operational rules of a water resources system
in karst areas. The second part was concerned with the
relation between input and output, by trying to make the *gray-
box system* less gray. If and when a satisfactory relation
could be established between input and output, it is then
used for predictions in order to make short-term modifications
of the long-term operation rules.

ESTABLISHING KARST UNDERGROUND
CONNECTIONS AND RESPONSES BY USING TRACERS

by

Pavo Ramljak, Civil Engineer
Elektroprivreda BiH, Sarajevo,

Anton Filip, Chemical Engineer,
Institute Mihailo Pupin, Belgrade,

Petar Milanović, Geology Engineer
Elektroprivreda BiH, Trebinje, and

Dušan Arandjelović, Geophysical Engineer,
Geozavod Institute, Belgrade, Yugoslavia.

Synopsis. Results of field investigations of a system of karst sinkholes and of laboratory experiments, made for the purpose of developing of a new tracer to be used in hydrologic karst studies, are presented. Field investigations are carried out in order to establish general directions in groundwater circulation by using dyes and isotopes. Results of dye tracers in establishing underground water connections between the sinkholes and springs of two karst plains are presented.

The objective of laboratory experiments was to develop a radioactive tracer with the following characteristics: low absorption by the ground, half-time decay to be one month or longer, gamma-ray emission, low toxicity, simplicity in the production and low price. Investigations were carried out by means of both static and dynamic methods, in those types of karst formations which are characteristic for karst regions, namely limestone, dolomite, flysch and terra rossa, using the following isotopes: scandium-46, chromium-51, lanthanum-140, bromine-82 and iodine-131. The two last isotopes were used only as references.

It was discovered that scandium-46 in the form of *chelate* with EDTA complex and chromium-51 in the form of chromate-bichromate are the most suitable tracers, satisfying all the required conditions. Scandium EDTA complex is very convenient for subsequent activation experiments, applicable also in cases of tracer investigation in karst systems from which water is used for water supplies.

1. Introduction.

Within the context of complex hydrogeologic investigations for the hydrosystem of the Trebišnjica River, particular attention has been given to investigations of karst underground

water courses. Large explorations have been carried out in
this catchment by using various tracer techniques during
the last twenty years.

The determination of exact underground watersheds and
hydrogeologic functions of individual lithologic members, of
their structures and faults, is essential for ascertaining
both the general and local directions of groundwater circulation, and for predicting the possibility of water leakage
from the surface storage reservoirs. Without it, it would be
very difficult to analyze the water budget of a karst region.
The hydrogeologic method, most frequently used for solving these
and similar problems, consists of tracing the groundwater flows
by using tracer dyes and spores. However, this method is inadequate when it is necessary to locate the exact positions
of pervious zones, specifically of underground karst channels.
The constant presence of this problem during the construction
of structures of hydroelectric power plants required a development of new types of tracers and geophysical methods. The
most significant results in finding the position of a karst
water course in the area of the network of exploration
boreholes has been achieved by using the radioactive tracers
of bromine-82, iodine-131 and chromium-51.

Parallel with the improvement of the tracer technique,
a quite new geophysical method, aimed exclusively for investigations in karst regions, has been developed.

This paper presents basic hypotheses, results of laboratory experiments, procedures in performing the experiments,
analysis of results, as well as the analysis of possible
further development and improvement of the method and technique
developed. Investigations have been carried out also for
the purpose of identifying the position of karst channels
through which water flows after it enters the sinkholes.

2. Hydrogeologic and Hydrologic Characteristics of Field
   Test Cases.

The Fatničko and Popovo Poljes (Fig. 1) represent
exceptionally illustrative examples of typical periodically
flooded karst plains. They are a result of fluvial erosion
in Cretaceous limestones. The bottom of the Popovo Polje is
covered by Quaternary sediments with their thickness increasing
towards the lowest part of the plain. The bottom of the
Fatničko Polje is composed of Eocene flysch sediments with their
thickness partially exceeding 150 m. Sinkholes in the Popovo
and Fatničko Poljes represent the end points of intermittent
surface courses of the Trebišnjica and Oboda Rivers at the
lowest parts of the plains. The entrance capacity of the
Ponikva Sinkhole in the Popovo Polje is about 3 m^3/sec, and
of the entire system of sinkholes 15 m^3/sec. The entrance

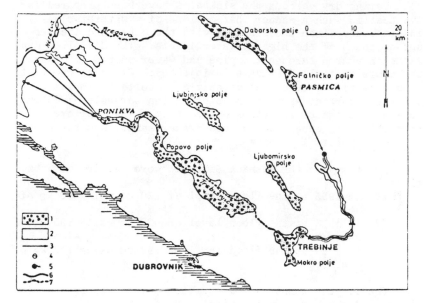

Fig. 1. (1) Karst Poljes (Plains), (2) Karstified Carbonate
Rocks, (3) Established Underground Connections, (4)
Sinkholes, (5) Spring of the Trebišnjica River, (6)
Perennial Surface Streams, and (7) Intermittent
Surface Streams.

capacity of the Pasmica Sinkhole in the Fatničko Polje is
approximately 20 m^3/sec, and of the entire sinkhole zone, of
which Pasmica is the main sinkhole, is above 50 m^3/sec. The
most intensive flow through these sinkholes takes place in
the period of water receding from the plains at the end of
flood periods, when the water table in the flooded plains is
at the highest point above the sinkholes. The maximum recorded
heights of flooding at these sinkholes range from 38 to 40 m.
Being important recipients for drainage of the plains, these
two sinkholes have been the subject of professional interest
from the end of the last century. Very systematic investigations, however, started with the beginning of construction of
hydroelectric power system of the Trebišnjica River.

3. Use of Tracer Dyes.

In order to locate the main directions of groundwater
circulation, both sinkholes have been subjected to dye tracer
investigations during the past sixteen years. Na-fluorescein
($C_{20}H_{10}O_5Na_2$) has been used as a tracer.

During dry periods the sinkholes have been prepared for
dye test in such a manner that one end of a waterpipe was
inserted deep into the sinkhole with the other end located
out of reach of the highest water levels. The dissolved dye
was then poured through the pipe and water pumped afterwards
to insure that all dye has been injected. Prior to dye test,
an observation service was organized to collect samples at
all the important springs and exploration boreholes located
between the tracer injection point and the sea. Before
initiating the experiment a zero-tracer sample was taken at
all these points.

Dye tests of the Pasmica Sinkhole were carried out three
times:
- (1) in 1955 at the flood level of 220 cm using 56 kg of
  dye,
- (2) in 1958 at the flood level of 922 cm using 150 kg of
  dye, and
- (3) in 1959 at the flood level of 956 cm using 117 kg of
  dye.

The largest number of observation points was used during
the second dye test (25 in 1958). The first attempt of dye
test failed because of completely dry conditions in the plain
prevailing on the day following the dye test, so that from
the second day there was no water inflow into the sinkhole.
On the fourth day after dye injection, heavy rains occurred,
yielding a significant discharge increase from 29 to 196 m^3/sec
at the most important monitoring point of the Trebišnjica
River Spring. The spring water was so turbid, that the presence of dye could not be detected for certain, likely also
because of its small quantity injected.

Underground water connection of the Pasmica Sinkhole
with the Trebišnjica Spring and the Kapelica Springs has
been established during the second dye test and confirmed
during the third dye test (results, see Fig. 2).

This fact served as evidence that the Pasmica Sinkhole
does not feed the Bregava Spring, or that water entering this
sinkhole does not drain to the Neretva River, or it drains
exclusively to the Trebišnjica catchment. The distance between the sinkhole and the Trebišnjica Spring is 17.2 km.
Mean velocity of the tracer wave during the second dye test
was 14.1 cm/sec (504 m/hour) and during the third dye test it
was 10.9 cm/sec (396 m/hour). The difference in velocity is
the result of different degrees of water saturation of the
underground, i.e., of various hydrologic conditions prevailing
at the time of tests. The sinkhole inflow capacity depended
on the hydrologic underground conditions rather than on the
water column above it.

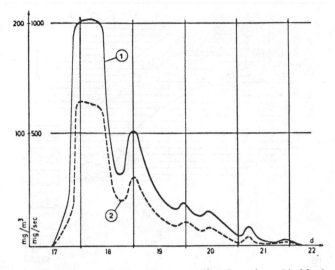

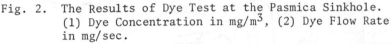

Fig. 2.   The Results of Dye Test at the Pasmica Sinkhole.
(1) Dye Concentration in mg/m³, (2) Dye Flow Rate
in mg/sec.

Dye tests at the Ponikva Sinkhole was carried out two
times:
    (1) in 1962 at the flood level of approximately 1400 cm
        using 105 kg of dye, and
    (2) in 1969 at the flood level of approximately 400 cm
        using 160 kg of dye.

The first dye test covered 32 observational points and
the second 34 points. The water outflow in both dye tests
was established at the same springs in the Neretva Valley. It
is characteristic that the order of first appearance of the
tracer was the same at the individual springs, as shown in
Fig. 3.

The tracer concentration wave always appeared first at
the Spring No. 1 and afterwards at the other springs. Distance from the Ponikva Sinkhole to the Spring No. 1 is 16.5
km and the mean travel velocity of the tracer wave was 720 m/
hour.

A greater average travel velocity of the tracer wave in
the Popovo Polje compared with that of the Fatničko Polje
was the result of a greater energy gradient in the Popovo
Polje and likely wider underground channels, on the average.

A dye test was performed for the purpose of establishing
general directions of circulation of the water sinking at the
lowest part of the Popovo Polje. By analyzing the results

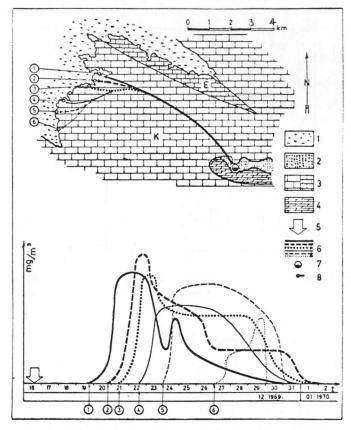

Fig. 3.   The Results of Dye Test of the Ponikva Sinkhole:
(1) Sand and Marsh Sediments, (2) The Popovo Polje,
(3) Limestones, (4) Dolomites, (5) The Beginning of
Dye Test, (6) Established Underground Connections,
(7) Sinkhole, and (8) One or Several Springs.

obtained and using the mapping data collected during the
drilling exploration, the hydrogeologic function of the
dolomite core of the anticline, which extend along the southern rim of the part of the Popovo Polje, and following the
direction of the Dinara Mountain, should be determined. The
assumption that this structure is a barrier with a particular
hydrologic function (hydrogeologic barrier) was established
and later proven in full by dye tests at the other large sinkholes, in this sinkhole system.

4.   Selection and Use of Radioactive Isotopes.

To qualify for use as an underground flow tracer, the
radioactive isotopes should meet the following requirements:

soluble in water, not adsorptant in underground, easily
detectable and measurable in small quantities, having a low
degree of toxicity, and inexpensive and available on the
market.

It is difficult to find an isotope which completely com-
plies with the characteristics required as an *ideal* tracer.
Adsorption and ionic exchange in rocks or with the suspended
particles in water makes narrower the number of radioactive
isotopes to be selected in hydrogeologic tests. However,
anions, ions of alkaline metals, and certain complex cations
are only slightly adsorbed. Therefore, they are most frequently
used as water tracers. By adding isotopic carrier or complexing agents, adsorption may be still more reduced.

Method of detection of a radioisotope and its concentration sensitivity depend on the kind of radiation and its
energy. Significant penetration of gamma-ray radiation in water
makes gamma-rays emitting radioactive isotopes the most frequently used tracers. The use of these isotopes made it possible to trace the travel of tagged water, by immersion of a
detector insulated from either getting into a direct contact
with the labeled water, and attractive in cases when sampling
was difficult or impossible. High concentration sensitivity
enabled the radioactivity of large samples to be measured,
thus reducing the required tracer quantity.

Concentration sensitivity was defined as the lowest
tracer concentration which can be measured with the prescribed
accuracy. For one and the same tracer concentration, sensitivity depended on the measurement method and desired precision.
The same factors influenced also the upper measurable concentration limit.

Concentration sensitivities of radioactive isotopes used
as tracers in the Trebišnjica River catchment are shown in
Table 1. Concentration sensitivity is given as the lowest
concentration of radioactive isotopes in µCi/l which can
be detected with the accuracy of 5 percents by means of a ratemeter with time constant of 30 seconds. The data were given
for two measurement methods, which are most frequently encountered in practice. One type, i.e., comparative position of
the radiation detector and the traced water, was the layout
where the detector is submerged in the mass of traced water,
and the other type was the layout where the detector is in the
cased borehole, which prevented the detector to get in direct
touch with the traced water.

Figures 4 and 5 give the appropriate calibration graphs
and the scheme of the two types of layout.

Table 1. Concentration Sensitivity of Radioactive Tracers.

Isotope	Detector Submerged directly in water		Detector located in cased borehole (not a perforated tube)	
	Concentration sensitivity μCi/l	Dilution	Concentration sensitivity μCi/l	Dilution
bromine-82	0.002	1: 5×10^8	0.04	1: 2.5×10^7
iodine-131	0.007	1: 1.5×10^8	0.08	1: 1.3×10^7
chromium-51	0.070	1: 1.5×10^7	0.70	1: 1.5×10^6

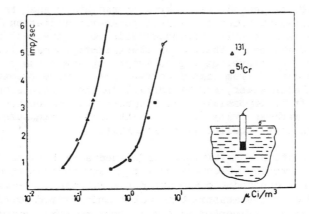

Fig. 4. Calibration Graphs When the Detector is Submerged in The Water.

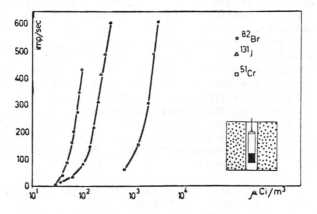

Fig. 5. Calibration Graphs When the Detector is Located in a Cased Borehole.

The efficiency of detection in the cased boreholes is shown in Fig. 5. Detection efficiency of Br-82: I-131: Cr-51 corresponds to 21: 25.5: 1, respectively.

On the basis of already given results, it is possible to calculate that for tracing of one million m^3 of water, 40 kg of fluorescein is needed, or 2 Ci of bromine-82, or 6 Ci of iodine-131, or 60 Ci of chromium-51.

Quantities of these isotopes, expressed in grams which correspond to values of the required ratioactive material for tracing one million m^3 of water, can be evaluated from the data on specific radioactivity of isotopes given in Table 2. It follows that the weight of 2 Ci of bromine-82 is less than 2 gr, and that of chromium-51 is about 25 gr. The weight of iodine-131 is negligible since the iodine is of rather large specific radioactivity (carrier-free). These radioactive isotopes are usually available as water solutions packed in penicillin bottles or in other suitable containers.

The selected radioactive isotope should have the half-time decay of such a duration that the underground is contaminated only for a short period. It then enables experiments to be repeated more frequently. However, the half-time decay should not be too short compared to the duration time of the test itself, because in that case considerably greater initial radioactivity was required and the radiation danger increased.

Table 2. Characteristics of Isotopes Considered and Selected for the Trebišnjica River Tests.

Isotope	Period of half-time decay days	Gamma radiation energy (Megaelectrovolts)	Specific radioactivity* Ci/g (Curie/g)	MPC** µCi/l
Chromium-51	28	0.32	0.26	20.0
Scandium-46	84	1.10	3.8	
Lanthanum-140	1.7	1.60	8.5	
Iodine-131	8.1	0.36	(a)	0.02
Bromine-82	1.5	0.70	2.9	3.0

*Radiation exposure time of one gram of an element; one week in flux 1×10^{13} $n/cm^2/sec$. **Maximum permissible isotope concentration in water. (a) Carrier-free.

Radioactive isotopes have different toxicities, which are expressed as the maximum permissible concentration (MPC) of radioisotopes in water used for drinking purposes. Table 2

contains the values of MPC for those radioisotopes which
have been used as tracers in the Trebišnjica River basin.

5. Cost of Investigations.

Main factors governing the investigation cost are: extent
of laboratory investigations for making selection or checking
of a selected or available tracer under the given field conditions, size of the system subjected to investigations, concentration sensitivity and the required tracer quantity, measurement method and the number of personnel engaged in measuring,
processing and interpretation of results obtained.

Costs related only to the procurement of tracers in the
amounts required for tracing one million m^3 of water are shown
in Fig. 6. They include the fluorescein and certain radioactive isotopes. It could be seen that the duration time of
the test with fluorescein and tritium has no impact on the
purchasing price of the required quantity of a tracer. The
reason is that the quantity of a tracer does not change significantly during the test. As for the radioisotopes with shorter
half-time decay, the purchasing cost depends upon the duration
of experiments. This is particularly true in the case of
bromine-82, whose half-time decay is 36 hours and was, desirable for the experiments lasting several days. It is evident
that chromium-51 is suitable for the experiments with the
duration time of 20 days.

6. Laboratory and Field Investigations.

Radioactive isotopes in hydrogeologic studies in the
catchment under consideration has been applied in two directions.
First, laboratory investigations have been carried out with
the objective of developing the radioactive tracers with
properties most suited to various hydrogeologic characteristics
of the catchment. Second, field investigations have been made
for the purpose of finding out the directions of flow and the
average travel velocity of water by using the radioactive
isotopes already in common use.

7. Laboratory Investigations.

The objective of laboratory investigations was to determine
the behavior of various radioactive isotopes, when they come
into the contact with the materials in karst terrain: limestone,
dolomite, flysch and terra rossa.

The behavior of the following radioactive isotopes was
studied: chromium-51 in the form of $K_2Cr_2O_7$ and Cr (III) -
EDTA; scandium-46 in the form of Sc(III) - EDTA; lanthanum-140
in the form La (III) - EDTA; iodine-131 in the form of KI;

bromine-82 in the form of $BaBr_2$. Essential characteristics
of the investigated radioactive isotopes are given in Table
2. Laboratory investigations have been carried out by static
and dynamic methods.

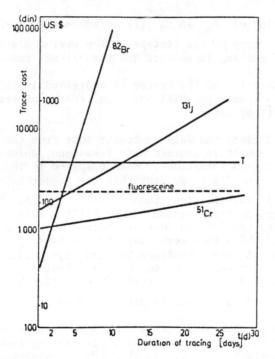

Fig. 6. Cost of Investigation in Function of Duration of
Experiments in Yugoslav Dinars and U.S. Dollars
(1973 year prices).

Static Experiments. Static experiments consist of bringing a sample of the soil or rock into the contact with water
tagged with the radioactive isotope under study. The two media
are kept in contact until the balance distribution of radioactive isotopes is achieved between the sample and the water.
This balance is determined on the basis of termination of
decrease of water radioactivity. This procedure is used to
determine the stability characteristics of the tracer in relation to a given type of the sample.

Loss, G, of the tracer from the solution after the balance
has been achieved can be found by the formula

$$G\% = 100(1 - \frac{A_t}{A_o}) , \qquad (1)$$

where A_o = the radioactivity of the tagged water before getting in contact with the soil, and A_t = the same after the balance distribution of isotope has been achieved (imp/min).

The value of A_o in Eq. (1) is subject to correction for radioactive decay of the isotope in the period elapsed between the time of getting in contact and the balance restoration.

Concentration of the tracer is expressed in this report in ppm units (parts per million), i.e., parts of tracer per million parts of water.

Table 3 gives the data on tracer loss from the water when it is brought in contact with limestone, dolomite, terra rossa, and flysch formations. When compared to the data on loss of chromium, it is evident that the tracer $K_2Cr_2O_7$ is more suitable for limestone than Cr (III) - EDTA. The most desirable tracer for limestone is Sc (III) - EDTA. The table also contains the data on loss of iodine-131 and bromine-82. Examinations which they were subjected to have been carried out in order to make comparison between them, since they are considered to be very close to the *ideal* tracers. As it is seen, $K_2Cr_2O_7$ and Sc (III) - EDTA are by their characteristics very similar to iodine and bromine isotopes.

It was found that Sc (III) - EDTA in contact with dolomite is the best tracer and that among short-lasting isotopes Br-82 is the most similar to it. In this case, iodine-131 had unsteady behavior because the great percentage of it was adsorbed by the dolomite.

When the tracer gets in contact with terra rossa, Sc (III)-EDTA displayed the best characteristics compared with those of other examined tracers. However, it was established that terra rossa had very distinct adsorption power in relation to other types of materials subjected to examination. Iodine-131 and bromine-82 displayed their excellent characteristics when they were brought in contact with terra rossa.

Of all the examined tracers having been brought in contact with flysch, the least loss was shown by Sc (III) - EDTA and $K_2Cr_2O_7$, while iodine-131 and bromine-82 were satisfactory as well.

In order to establish the effect of the present quantity of complexing agent EDTA (aethylene-diamine-tetraacetic acid) on loss of a tracer, experiments were performed with different quantities of EDTA complex or its Na salt, the ratio between

Table 3. Loss of Tracer in Contact with Various Types of Soils and Rocks.

Tracer	Limestone		Dolomite		Terra Rossa		Flysch	
	Concentration of tracer (ppm)	Loss (percentage)	Concentration of tracer (ppm)	Loss (percentage)	Concentration of tracer (ppm)	Loss (percentage)	Concentration of tracer (ppm)	Loss (percentage)
^{51}Cr(VI) as K$_2$Cr$_2$O$_7$	84 12 0.2 0.05 0.02 0.01	1 6 11 12 5 8	90 6 2 1 0.2 0.1 0.02 0.01	2 9 10 7 9 10 10 10	410 84 42 6 2 0.4 0.2 0.02 0.01	9 10 11.5 12 11 11 10.5 5.0 12.0	84 12 5 0.1 0.02 0.01	10 10 10 5 5 7
^{51}Cr(III)-EDTA	84 13 0.5 0.25 0.01 0.002	5.3 8.7 12 8 50.0 60.0	90 10 5 1 0.01 0.002	0 10 14 13 50 50	84 13 5 0.5 0.25 0.01 0.002	13.2 15.5 10.5 21 17.5 50.0 50.0	84 13 0.5 0.25 0.01 0.002	10 9.7 15 7 50 50
^{46}Sc(III)-EDTA	0.07 0.01 0.001	2.0 3.0 1.0	0.07 0.01 0.001	0.5 1.0 0	0.07 0.01 0.001	11.5 24.0 26.0	0.07 0.01 0.001	7.0 111.5 24.0
^{140}La(III)-EDTA	20 2 0.2 0.02	3.0 6.0 30.0 29.0	2 0.2 0.02	55.0 57.0 73.5	2 0.2 0.02	76.0 87.0 88.0	2 0.2 0.02	50.0 54.0 73.5
^{131}I as KI	10 0.1 a	2.2 2.5 2.6	10 0.1 a	4.6 12.1 41	10 0.1 a	2.2 2.0 3.1	10 0.1 a	1.2 2 11.5
^{82}Br as BaBr$_2$	0.1 0.02	7.0 7.0	0.1 0.02	2 2	0.1 0.02	2 2	0.1 0.02	2.0 10.0

a = Carrier-free

Me_2O_3 and $Na_4(EDTA)$ being 1 : 0 and EDTA free up to 1 : 6,000. The results of these experiments are shown in Table 4. It was found that the excess of Na_4 EDTA is required to be at least

a hundred times greater in relation to the tracer converted to oxide.

Table 4. Influence of EDTA Complex Excess on the Stability of Tracer in Contact with Limestone.

Me_2O_3:Na_4(EDTA)	Loss of tracer (in percentage)								
	Scandium			Chromium			Lanthanum		
Weight Ratio	Sc:EDTA mole ratio	(0.2 ppm)	(20 ppm)	Cr:EDTA mole ratio	(0.2 ppm)	(20 ppm)	La:EDTA mole ratio	(0.2 ppm)	(20 ppm)
1 : 0	1:0	95.0	71.0	1:0	64.0	60.0	1:0	83.5	50.0
1 : 1	1:0.17	82.5	62.0	1:0.12	56.0	49.0	1:0.4	80.5	22.0
1 : 2.5	1:0.42	-	9.0	1:0.30	-	43.0	1:1	67.5	-
1 : 10	1:1.7	14.5	-	1:1.2	46.0	-	1:4	53.0	5.0
1 : 100	1:17	11.5	5.0	1:12	58.0	7.0	1:40	30.0	-
1 : 500	1:83	7.0	1.5	1:60	29.0	0	1:100	41.0	3.0
1 : 6000	1:1000	0	-	1:720	-	-	-	-	-

Dynamic Experiments. Dynamic experiments consisted of letting the tagged water with the radioactive isotope pass through a soil or rock layer. The soil sample was within a column height 1 to 2 m, diameter 5 cm. The flow rate was adjusted to correspond to the greatest extent to the water flow under the natural conditions. At one end of the column, a radiation detector was installed, connected to a ratemeter and recorder. The recorder tape registered the passing of a tracer wave. The wave shape and the time of wave passage depended on the characteristics of the tracer. The more *ideal* the tracer, the similar the wave shape to the shape of the injected wave and the time was closer to the nominal residence time t_n, in seconds, namely

$$t_n = \frac{V\,e}{Q}, \tag{2}$$

where V = the volume of the column, e = the layer porosity, and Q = the water flow through the column.

The shape of the tracer wave was defined by the coefficient of axial dispersion D_L, cm^2/s. This parameter is determined from the tracer wave by the following equation

$$D_L = \frac{W^2 V^3}{11.1\ L}, \tag{3}$$

where W = the half-wave width (sec), V = the mean velocity of the tracer wave movement (m/sec) and L = the distance from the injection point to the point of measurement in meters.

Results of dynamic experiments are given in Table 5, of passing of the studied tracers through the column containing limestone, and in Table 6 of passing through the column containing flysch. It can be concluded that there is a trend for an increase of axial dispersion coefficient with a decrease of the tracer concentration. For most of studied tracers, the axial dispersion coefficient was smaller for the limestone than for the flysch. Mean values of axial dispersion coefficients for all the studied tracer concentrations are given in Table 6. Table 7 gives coefficients of axial dispersion for various tracers and their concentrations.

Table 5.   Passing of Tracer Through Limestone Containing Layer Sample (Porosity 52.3 Percents, Height of Layer 126 cm).

Tracer	Applied amount of tracer	$\int cdt$ (imp)	Residence time (in sec) exp.	nom.	Axial dispersion coefficient (cm^2/s)	Mean tracer concentration ppm
$^{51}Cr(VI)$ as $K_2Cr_2O_7$	0.50	5054	97.0	92.0	1.22	1.0
$^{51}Cr(VI)$ as $K_2Cr_2O_7$	0.25	3481	96.6	92.0	1.10	0.5
$^{51}Cr(VI)$ as $K_2Cr_2O_7$	0.10	1920	94.2	92.0	1.71	0.1
$^{51}Cr(III)-EDTA$	1.00	7999	92.0	88.00	1.83	2.0
$^{51}Cr(III)-EDTA$	0.50	4168	92.0	88.0	1.56	1.0
$^{51}Cr(III)-EDTA$	0.25	2441	87.0	88.0	1.76	0.5
$^{51}Cr(III)-EDTA$	0.10	1580	95.5	88.0	2.05	0.2
^{131}I as KI	50.00	-	83.0	83.0	1.68	120
^{131}I as KI	25.00	-	83.0	83.0	1.52	60
^{131}I as KI	2.00	5955	84.0	83.0	1.70	5
^{131}I as KI	1.00	2546	85.0	83.0	1.49	2.5
^{131}I as KI	0.50	1173	85.0	83.0	1.77	1.2
^{131}I as KI	0.25	704	87.0	83.0	1.90	0.6
^{82}Br as KBr	0.50	5160	80.0	77.2	1.74	1.0
^{82}Br as KBr	0.25	2295	81.0	77.2	1.59	0.5
^{82}Br as KBr	0.10	1374	79.0	77.2	1.32	0.2
$^{46}Sc(III)-EDTA$	0.005	233	71.5	72.0	2.81	0.007
	0.01	607	69.5	72.0	3.87	0.014
	0.02	1360	70.6	72.0	2.15	0.028
	0.03	1911	70.0	72.0	1.85	0.043
$^{140}La(III)-EDTA$	0.05	1480	68.5	69.0	2.39	0.1
	0.10	2840	69.0	69.0	2.39	0.2
	0.20	6500	67.5	69.0	2.53	0.4

The shape of the tracer wave after it passes the distance L for the time duration t depends on the total quantity of the tracer injected, i.e., on the concentration C_o and the axial dispersion coefficient after the following relation:

$$C_t = \frac{C_o}{4 D_L t} \exp \left(- \frac{L - Vt}{4 D_L t} \right) , \qquad (4)$$

Table 6.   Passing of Tracer Through Flysch Containing Layer
Sample (Porosity 45 Percent, Height of Layer 126 cm).

Tracer	Applied amount of tracer	∫cdt (imp)	Residence time (in sec) exp.	nom.	Axial dispersion coefficient (cm^2/s)	Mean tracer concentration ppm
$^{51}Cr(VI)$ as $K_2Cr_2O_7$	1.00	109	54.4	50.5	2.38	2.5
$^{51}Cr(VI)$ as $K_2Cr_2O_7$	0.50	56	55.0	50.5	2.65	1.2
$^{51}Cr(VI)$ as $K_2Cr_2O_7$	0.25	30	57.6	50.5	2.83	0.6
$^{51}Cr(III)$-EDTA	2.00	146	59.3	55.0	2.18	4.4
$^{51}Cr(III)$-EDTA	1.50	117	60.6	55.0	2.32	3.3
$^{51}Cr(III)$-EDTA	1.00	68	60.0	55.0	2.22	2.2
$^{51}Cr(III)$-EDTA	0.50	37	61.2	55.0	2.50	1.1
^{131}I as KI	1.00	144	56.0	57.5	2.46	2.0
^{131}I as KI	0.50	59	58.0	57.5	1.94	1.0
^{131}I as KI	0.25	35	59.0	57.5	2.42	0.5
^{131}I as KI	0.10	9	57.8	57.5	3.20	0.2
$^{46}Sc(III)$-EDTA	0.005	125	55.4	56.0	3.80	0.008
	0.01	380	55.4	56.0	2.31	0.02
	0.02	680	56.5	56.0	2.44	0.03
	0.03	1170	53.6	56.0	2.45	0.05
	0.04	1530	56.0	56.0	2.60	0.06
	1.00	24337	54.0	56.0	2.30	1.6
$^{140}La(III)$-EDTA	0.05	851	64.0	57.0	1.68	0.06
$^{140}La(III)$-EDTA	0.10	1650	57.5	57.0	2.74	0.12
$^{140}La(III)$-EDTA	0.20	4190	60.0	57.0	2.55	0.2
$^{140}La(III)$-EDTA	0.30	6760	59.0	57.0	3.17	0.4

Table 7.   Coefficients of Axial Dispersion for Various
Tracers and their Concentrations.

Tracer	Mean tracer concentration - ppm		Coefficient of axial dispersion D_L, cq cm/sec Limestone	Flysch
$^{51}Cr(VI)$ as $K_2Cr_2O_7$	0.1	- 2.5	1.35 ± 0.26	2.62 ± 0.18
$^{51}Cr(III)$-EDTA	0.2	- 4.4	1.80 ± 0.17	2.30 ± 0.12
$^{140}La(III)$-EDTA	0.6	- 0.4	2.40 ± 0.15	2.60 ± 0.58
$^{46}Sc(III)$-EDTA	0.008	- 1.6	2.67 ± 0.46	2.65 ± 0.50
^{131}I as KI	0.2	- 120	1.70 ± 0.14	2.50 ± 0.15
^{82}Br as $BaBr_2$	0.2	- 1.0	1.55 ± 0.17	-

so that on the basis of data given in Table 7 the wave shape
and concentration can be calculated for the distance L passed,
and the time t elapsed from the moment of injection.

It is evident from residence time data in Tables 5 and 6
that with a decrease of the quantity of tracer, the tracer
front became more and more delayed in comparison with the
front of tagged water. This phenomenon of lagging, given as
a difference between the experimental and nominal time of
lagging, is shown in Table 8. It is evident that lagging time
was less in limestone than in flysch.

Table 8. Lagging Time of Tracer Wave in Relation to Water
Front.

Tracer	Retardation or Lagging Time (in percentage)	
	Limestone	Flysch
$^{51}Cr(VI)$ as $K_2Cr_2O_7$	2.4 - 5.4	8 - 14
$^{51}Cr(III)$-EDTA	1 - 8.5	8 - 11
^{131}I as KI	0 - 4.9	0.5 - 2.6
^{82}Br as KBr	2.3 - 4.9	-
$^{46}Sc(III)$-EDTA	0	0 - 1.0
$^{140}La(III)$-EDTA	0	0 -12.0

8. Potentials of Described Methods.

Of all methods and techniques studied for finding directions of karst groundwater flows, the dye test were most
frequently used. In the above case study, about one hundred
experiments with this type of tracer have been carried out.
Radioiosotopes have been used only recently. The results obtained until now point out to an important potential of isotopes for tracing the water flow for purposes of its distribution in time and space.

The main results achieved in applying the methods discussed may be summarized as follows:

(1) Dye tests make it feasible to determine the underground connections between the point of water sinking and the
karst spring, giving the inlet and outlet of the karst groundwater courses, and

(2) In addition,to information obtained by dye tests,
the radioactive isotopes make it possible to follow the
groundwater course in a zone provided by cased borehole network, thus enabling the horizontal position of channels to be
established.

The results of various investigations, as carried out until present by application of all the methods, can be compared by their characteristics and applicability to different case conditions.

Tracing of water circulation by dye or spore tests has the advantage over the other methods of investigations, when carried out on a regional level, because investigations can be made for groundwater courses with completely unknown characteristics. This advantage is based on the stability of dyes under conditions which prevail in karst channels. However, it is not possible to determine the position of these channels by using dyes, so that certain methods with the use of radioactive isotopes had to be developed, which jointly with the use of other techniques and works, give successful solutions.

9. References.

[1] Kaufman, W.J., and G.T. Orlob, An evaluation of groundwater tracers: Trans. Am. Geophysical Union, 37, (3), 1956.

[2] Lacey, W.J., and W. de Laguna, Method of preparing radioactive cations for tracing groundwater: Science, 124, 402, 1956.

[3] Halevy, E. et al, Use of radio-isotopes in studies of groundwater flow: Part 1, Laboratory and field experiments on the suitability of various tracers: Proc. Sec. Conf. Peac. Uses of At. Energy, 20, P/1613, UN Publication, New York, 1958.

[4] Heemstra, R.J. et al, Laboratory evaluation of nine water tracers: Nucleonics, 19, (1), 92, 1961.

[5] Knutsson, G. et al, Radioizotopes in Hydrology: Int. At. En. Agency, Vienna, p. 347, 1936.

[6] Cramer, H., The elements of probability theory and some of its applications: John Wiley and Sons, New York, 1955.

[7] Filip, A., Investigation of dispersion and dilution of suspended species in river flow by radio-tracer techniques: Int. J. Appl. Rad. Isotopes, 22, 331, 1971.

[8] Todorović, Ž. and A. Filip: Proc. Symposia, Isotopes and radiation techniques in Hydrology: IAEA, Vienna, 1967.

[9] Filip, A., Razvoj novog radioaktivnog obilježivača i metoda izotopa iz okoline za hidrološke studije u karstu (Development of a new radioactive tracer and a tracer method for karst hydrologic studies): Izveještaj (Report), Institut za nuklearne nauke (Institute for nuclear sciences) *Boris Kidrič*, Beograd, 1972.

DISCUSSION

Parizek. Reference was made to post activation analysis means of detecting radioactive tracers. The implication was that this method was not found as useful as working directly with radioactive tracers. It would be useful to learn why the post activation method was considered less useful in tracing experiments described in the paper.

In populous areas of the United States and in some states the addition of radioisotopes and most other types of tracers to soil-water, surface-water and groundwater systems is severely restricted or prohibited entirely. In Pennsylvania, for example, the use of radioisotopes as groundwater tracers is prohibited in all areas and the use of all other tracers require a permit from the Department of Environmental Resources, which is the state water quality regulatory and enforcement agency charged with the responsibility of protecting water supplies against pollution. Elsewhere, the total activity of all isotopes must be kept below the limits of 10 CFR 20 as defined by the U.S. Atomic Energy Commission.* These limits arc on the order of 10^{-4} - 10^{-7} νCi/mℓ for cobalt-60, iodine-131, sodium-24, phosphorus-32 and bromine-82 (Schmotzer, Jester and Parizek**). At these low activities it may be necessary to concentrate the samples before counting, but even in these cases the tracers may become so dilute that accurate determinations are not possible. Further, cations are limited as tracers in some field settings where absorption and adsorption processes are extensive as may occur in residual soils, clay rich shales and similar other strata.

It appears that similar restrictions and disadvantages may be eliminated when tracers are detected by post sampling neutron activation because several tracers can be selected and jointly used that are not initially radioactive and can be placed in high concentrations but are still not considered as pollutants. In fact, various tracers can be added at the same time in a number of different possible connecting channel ways and water samples tested to see which discharge points where tied to the flow system under study.

Schmotzer, Jester and Parizek** found that for the most routine groundwater tracing studies the bromide ion best fulfills the requirements set forth for an ideal tracer. It is particularly low in background concentrations in Pennsylvania

---

*U.S. Atomic Energy Commission, Standards for protection against radiation: title 10, part 20, in: Rules and Regulations U.S. Atomic Energy Commission, Washington, D. C., 1969.
**Schmotzer, J.K., W.A. Jester, and R.R. Parizek, Groundwater tracing with post sampling activation analysis: Jour. of Hydrology, vol. 20, p. 217-236, 1973.

area in natural waters, is relatively inexpensive when
purchased as sodium bromide or ammonium bromide and can be
used with a maximum input concentration of 200 p.p.m. within
certain streams not located near municipal water supplies
under Pennsylvania's regulations.

Post activation analysis studies were successfully conducted to determine induced-streambed infiltration to nearby
pumping wells completed in carbonate rocks where organic dyes
were filtered by flood plain sediments, to determine if and
when pump discharge waters were recirculated to unconfined
(water table) aquifers during prolonged pumping tests, to
detect sources of acid mine drainage pollution derived from
coal mining activities that had polluted public water supplies,
and similar other studies.

Admittedly, postactivation methods of analysis require
the availability of special equipment to irradiate water
samples and for detecting the radiation emitted by each sample.
This usually requires bringing water samples to a central
laboratory before the tracer can be detected. However, small
water samples can be used and stored for prolonged periods
without concern for changes in the concentration of the tracer.

Mikulec. It is stated in this paper that, using an isotope, it is possible to establish the position of a channel
if there are boreholes drilled along the route of the channel.
I don't regard this tracer advantageous, because of the
necessity that the channel routes are already established
which is the most difficult task under the conditions and with
the information which are available before the tracer is used.
Furthermore, the same effect can be achieved by using uranium,
given there are several boreholes along the route of channels.
Apart from this major difficulty, the research carried out
with isotopes, and concerning their behavior, have been and
will be of considerable usefulness in karst areas.

With regard to utilization of isotopes, as discussed in
the paper by Bagarić and Kovačina, the method and the conditions, under which the tracer should be introduced into an
underground stream should be well determined, so that the
maximum information would be obtained from each experiment.
This is particularly important if it could help, to any significant extent, to determine the usually unknown characteristics
of an underground stream, and contribute to a better utilization of concentrated underground water resources.

Ramljak. For the question related to establishing the
location of underground streams for the purpose of deciding
where to locate the boreholes, an entire network of boreholes
must be located mainly on the basis of the likely location of
underground stream as established by using the general geologic

information. In Popovo Polje between the Ponikva Sinkhole and
the spring where the tracers have appeared, several boreholes
were drilled. However, when the natrium-fluorescine tracer was
used, it was not detected in these boreholes. It may be the
case with boreholes, which are equipped to serve as piezometers
for observation, the dye may have passed between the borehole
wall and the piezometer pipe. Thus, if water with tracer does
pass the perforated section of the pipe, the tracer cannot be
detected. In such cases, we didn't establish the tracer. However, in cases in which the radio-isotope was used, it has been
recorded, because the measuring equipment was able to detect it
even when it passed between the borehole wall and the pipe, or
even when it passed a few meters away from the borehole. The
results enabled the establishment of the spatial position of
underground streams, which was not possible with the use of
natrium fluorescine.

As to the question concerning whether the isotopes with
the so-called postactivation were used, in the light of examples
used in U.S.A., the answer is that we have also worked with
postactivation isotopes. However, this method had the drawback of not being able to be evaluated, i.e. measured, on the
spot but only when the samples were taken to a laboratory. For
this reason the use of this tracer would require, especially
under the conditions of a yet unknown karst underground system, another tracer which can be measured or readily identified
in the field (or readily visible such as the natrium fluorescine). We worked with the tracer of postactivation type in one
case, and made the mistake of terminating observations precisely
when the tracer wave was arriving. On the basis of an earlier
investigation, we thought that 20 days after the tracer was injected would be adequate for the tracer to appear at the spring.
This estimate proved to be inaccurate.

OPTIMIZATION OF PARAMETERS OF DISCHARGE HYDROGRAPH MODELS UNDER KARST CONDITIONS

by

Božo Knežević, Civil Engineer
Water Resources Board of
Bosnia and Herzegovina, Sarajevo

Synopsis. The conception is developed of a model discharge hydrograph under karst conditions. It is mainly directed towards the solving of two problems: (i) the choice of the mathematical form of the model, and (ii) the solutions for the complexity of the model and the optimization of its parameters. Special attention is given to the technique of nonlinear model parameters optimization in which *independent* variables are not truly independent. The principal component analysis in the orthogonal transformation of the correlation matrix has been applied.

1. Introduction.

Forecasting of flow under karst conditions is complex and yet insufficiently investigated. In addition that karst regions, in comparison with the other regions, are by far more complex in physical-geographical, hydraulic and other characteristics on which the shape of discharge hydrographs depends, one is faced with insufficient information on these characteristics. In the absence of this information and the lack of representative parameters of a karst catchment, the application of models which are based on catchment characteristics must be abandoned, with the karst catchments as dynamic systems considered. Under such circumstances one is compelled to approach the description of the hydrograph shapes by finding the mathematical model of hydrograph formation by considering both, quantitative catchment characteristics and hydrologic data.

A great number of achievements in hydrology are based on the interpretation of hydrologic observations. Such an inductive process is related to the construction of conceptual hydrologic models, often used in hydrologic predictions. The fact that most realistic hydrologic models (especially hydrologic prediction models) are not simple in form, required also a parallel development of corresponding methods for their comprehensive definition, basically consisting of: (i) definition of mathematical and structural forms of a conceptual model; (ii) implementation of the principle of quasi-optimal selection of independent variables; (iii) selection of corresponding optimization methods for an objective identification of model coefficients; (iv) explanation of causes and structure of errors in the conceptual model and the method of their evaluation, and (v) evaluation of practical aspects of the prediction model.

The present methodological approaches to solving the above problems can be classified in the three essential groups:

(1) Physical methods (deterministic, parametric), which give the form and parameter estimation for the physical prediction models basically by using the hydromechanic equations, water budget, etc.;

(2) Statistical methods (probability based methods), which are intended to find out the stochastic dependence between a dependent variable vector and a matrix of independent variables vectors by using the regression analysis; and

(3) Combined methods in which the physical relations of a part of independent variables is used, while the statistical methods are applied to the rest of variables.

This paper mainly treats the latter two groups of methods, in an attempt to present a general concept of prediction models of discharge hydrographs under karst conditions. The particular emphasis is on the selection of optimization techniques for the estimation of parameters of a nonlinear mathematical model.

2. Concept of Discharge Hydrograph Model.

In the quantitative study of a physical system it is necessary to describe the system in terms of mathematical functions. It is obvious that the starting point in the formulation of the appropriate mathematical model must be the conceptual model of the system, which should involve the physical aspects as much as possible. Consequently, the accuracy in the simulation of the system depends on:

(1) Reasonable hypotheses to be used as the unavoidable simplifications;

(2) The size of and the knowledge on the prototype catchment used for deriving the model; and

(3) The reliability of the method for optimization of model parameters.

The usual concept of a hydrologic response model is that the flow hydrograph can be considered as a consequence of excess precipitation transformed by the catchment. This transformation can then be simulated by the conceptual model expressed in mathematical form. In most cases one proceeds from the position that the drainage system transforms the excess

precipitation into direct flow via retention. The retention
effects are seen as a form of delay, adjustment and decrease
of maximum values of input (excess precipitation) in relation
to the output discharge hydrograph. Such an approach has
produced thus far a number of theoretical solutions, essentially
based on the concept of unit hydrograph, the general formulation of which is given in the form.

$$\{u\} = |R' \cdot R|^{-1} \cdot R' \cdot \{Q\} \tag{1}$$

where $\{u\}$ = the column vector of ordinates of T-hour unit
hydrograph; R = the matrix of the corresponding excess (or
effective) precipitation, and $\{Q\}$ = the column vector of the
directly measured ordinates of the discharge hydrograph.

Difficulty arises in applying this approach because of
inaccuracies in estimated losses (evaporation, evapotranspiration, infiltration) as functions of time, or unreliability of
estimated hyetograph of excess precipitation. Because the
water flow in karst, especially in large catchments justifies
the assumption that the system response can be simulated by
a number of reservoirs, the outline of one of the feasible
approaches to the solution of Eq. (1) is given in this paper.

Let us suppose that the response of a system, simulated
by a linear reservoir and a unit of excess precipitation, is
represented by a unit hydrograph in form of a triangle, as shown
in Fig. 1. In this case, two successive ordinates of a unit
hydrograph have the following linear relationships: $u_t = a$
u_{t-1}, for the rising limb, and $u_t = a_1 u_{t-1}$, for the
falling limb, with a and a_1 the proportionality coefficients, or for a number of studied T-hour unit hydrographs, the
linear regression coefficients. It is not difficult to prove
then, provided the linearity principle was applicable, that
in the case of a composite discharge hydrograph, caused by
n blocks of T-hour, its ordinates could be estimated by the
simple scheme

$$Q_t = aQ_{t-1} + u_1 P_{e(t)} \tag{2}$$

for the phase of the hydrograph rising limb, and

$$Q_t = a_1 Q_{t-1} + u_1 P_{e(t)} \tag{3}$$

for the phase of the hydrograph falling limb, where Q_t = the
discharge at the time t, Q_{t-1} = the discharge at the time

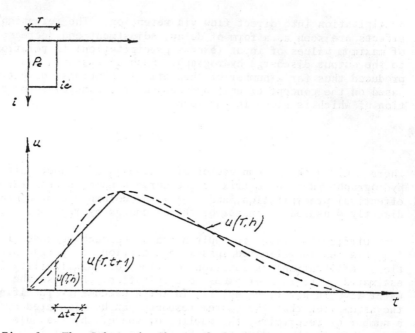

Fig. 1. The Schematic Shape of the Unit Hydrograph.

t-1, $P_{e(t)}$ = the excess precipitation for the interval (t-1,t), u_1 = the first ordinate of the unit hydrograph (generally unknown), and a, a_1 = the coefficients.

Since the unit hydrograph does not have the form of a triangle, the influence of nonlinearity in the above relations must be taken into consideration, so that the

$$Q_t = aQ_{t-1}^b + cP_{e(t)} \qquad (4)$$

and

$$Q_t = a_1Q_{t-1}^{b_1} + c_1P_{e(t)} \qquad (5)$$

for the rising and falling limbs, respectively, where a, b, c, a_1, b_1, c_1 are unknown coefficients of nonlinear relations of Eqs. (4) and (5) to be estimated.

The losses between precipitation P and excess precipitation P_e must be always determined. Taking into account the initial concept that a karst catchment can be simulated by a reservoir of the maximum capacity S_{max}, then the problem of reduction of precipitation into excess precipitation may be represented as in Fig. 2.

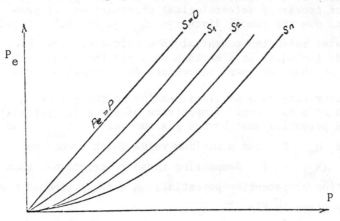

Fig. 2.   The Relation Between Precipitation (P), Excess Precipitation (P$_e$), and the Retention Potential of the Catchment (S).

The mathematical expression for the family of curves in Fig. 2 is

$$P_{e(t)} = P_t - S_{t-1} \cdot \text{tgh} \frac{P_t}{S_{t-1}} , \qquad (6)$$

where S$_{t-1}$ = a function by which the retention potential is defined.

In addition that Eq. (6) has a physical meaning, it also includes the necessary restrictions, namely, it excludes the possibility to obtain in the course of optimization such coefficient values that would, regardless of values P and S, produce the excess precipitation greater than P or even a negative value.

A distinction is made here between the retention potential (S), or the water which a basin can retain from a rainfall, and the retention state (R) or how much of the retention space is occupied by the infiltrated water.

The retention potential function must be defined. As is well known, besides the catchment structure (which can be taken to be fixed), the quantities and distribution of precipitation in a well defined antecedent period (usually measured by the antecedent precipitations index), and the general meteorological conditions that existed in that antecedent period (temperature, moisture, wind, etc.) determine the state of retention at the initiation of the new precipitation. In absence of necessary meteorological observations, it seems logical to use the runoff discharge Q_o as an indirect index of the water retention potential in a catchment area, because it already includes, in a certain way, all the above factors, and more so than the usual antecedent precipitation index.

To attribute some physical meaning to the retention potential of a catchment (importance of space limitations), retention potential must have a maximum value (S_{max}) when the discharge $Q_o = 0$, and a minimum value which cannot be negative $(S_{min} = 0)$. Respecting these restrictions, then the function of retention potential, $S = f(Q_o)$, should have a form as given in Fig. 3.

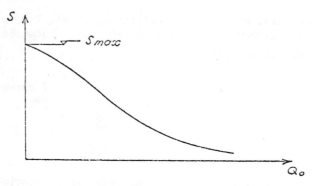

Fig. 3. The Relationship Between the Retention Potential in a Catchment and the Runoff Discharge (Q_o).

The mathematical function of the curve in Fig. 3 can be expressed as

$$S_o = \exp{(dQ_o^2 + eQ_o + f)} \quad , \qquad (7)$$

where d, e and f are coefficients to be estimated by an optimization procedure. The conceptual model of how the retention potential changes with time after the initiation of precipitation must be defined. Based on experience, the retention state R of a karst catchment in case of no precipitation must follow a recession law. One such law is in the form $R_t = e^{-\alpha} R_{t-1}$, given by Fig. 4.

However, due to precipitation in the interval (t-1,t), the retention state R changes for ΔR, which must satisfy the following conditions: $|\Delta R| > 0$ for precipitation P, and $\Delta R = 0$ for $P = 0$.

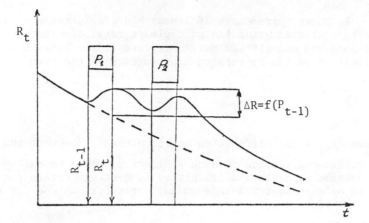
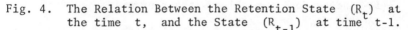

Fig. 4. The Relation Between the Retention State (R_t) at the time t, and the State (R_{t-1}) at time $t-1$.

In addition, the increase ΔR is not always the same for given precipitation P. It depends also, to a certain extent, on the retention state at the time of precipitation. From this assumption and restrictions imposed on ΔR, then $\Delta R = f(R_{t-1}, P_{t-1})$. The function

$$\Delta R = e^{\beta} R_{t-1}^g P_{t-1} \, \text{tgh} \, \frac{R_{t-1}^g}{R_{t-1}^g P_{t-1}} \,, \tag{8}$$

with β and g unknown parameters to be estimated, satisfies these conditions.

Finally, the mathematical form of the general concept of the discharge hydrograph model can be defined as

$$Q_t = cP_t - cR_t \, \text{tgh} \, \frac{P_t}{R_t} + aQ_{t-1}^b \tag{9}$$

and

$$R_t = e^{\alpha} R_{t-1} - e^{\beta} R_{t-1}^g P_{t-1} \, \text{tgh} \, \frac{R_{t-1}}{R_{t-1}^g P_{t-1}} \,. \tag{10}$$

The unknown model parameters a, b, c, d, e, f, g, α, β can be estimated by optimization by using the nonlinear regression analysis based on principal components.

3. Optimization of Parameters of Prediction Model for Discharge Hydrographs.

As known, parameters of linear hydrologic response models can be estimated using the multiple regression, with the standardized correlation matrix representing a basis for definition of the regression hypersurface in the form

$$x_i = - \sum_{i \neq j} \frac{\sigma_i}{\sigma_j} \frac{R_{ij}}{R_{ii}} x_j , \qquad (11)$$

where R_{ij} = the correlation matrix minors. However, the objective application of such a direct approach to multiple regression encounters difficulties in meeting certain requirements by dependent and independent variables, which, for short, consist of:

(1) Independent variables without errors;

(2) Dispersion measure of deviation of dependent variables from the regression equation dependent on independent variables;

(3) Dependent variables not autocorrelated random processes;

(4) Independent variables mutually uncorrelated;

(5) Independent variables approximately normally distributed; and

(6) The sample size considerably greater than the number of independent variables.

Most of hydrologic data used in calibrating the prediction model do not completely meet almost any one of the above six requirements. Hypotheses advanced that these six conditions are satisfied are often without justification. Therefore, the estimated coefficients cannot be considered stable, or they are good only as a selection of the initial values in optimization. It is often said, that they are a satisfactory approximation if the model will be used for prediction in the range of variables of data used. The high correlations between the independent variables particularly decrease the reliability of the developed prediction equations. In fact, it may seem as a better relationship for the range of variables in the used data, but the reliability of prediction outside that range would be considerably decreased. These as well as some other difficulties of the multiple regression analysis could be eliminated to a great extent by using the multivariate, principal components analysis.

The linear methods of estimation of optimized model parameters oriented to principal components analysis offer the possibility of developing a great number of functions by the expansion into a Taylor series, thus producing the basis for a development of nonlinear methods of model parameters optimization. With the only purpose of making this paper more complete, essential principles of well-known optimization method of parameters of nonlinear hydrologic models are given.

In the general case when dealing with a model that needs optimization of parameters related to the corresponding independent variables, the mathematical function is given as $y = f(x_1, x_2, \ldots, x_n; a_1, a_2, \ldots, a_n)$.

Recording the x values and observing the parameters and variables it is possible, after developing the function into the Taylor's series and neglected the residual R_n in the development, display it in the form:

$$y_o - \hat{y} = (h_1 \frac{\partial}{\partial a_1} + h_2 \frac{\partial}{\partial a_2} + \ldots + h_m \frac{\partial}{\partial a_m}) \, g(a_1, \ldots, a_m) \, , \quad (12)$$

i.e.,

$$E = h_1 \frac{\partial \hat{y}}{\partial a_1} + h_2 \frac{\partial \hat{y}}{\partial a_2} + \ldots + h_m \frac{\partial \hat{y}}{\partial a_m} \, . \quad (13)$$

The problem is thus reduced to the linear form in which the unknown coefficients h_j $(j = 1, 2, \ldots, m)$ should be defined. It is obvious that the solution of the problem requires at least m realizations of E_i and the corresponding realizations of $\partial y_i / \partial a_j$. It is then possible to write the given equality in the following matrix form:

$$\Delta \{h\} = \{E\} \text{ with}$$

$$\Delta = \begin{bmatrix} \left(\frac{\Delta \hat{y}}{\Delta a}\right) 11, & \left(\frac{\Delta \hat{y}}{\Delta a}\right) 12, & \cdots, & \left(\frac{\Delta \hat{y}}{\Delta a}\right) 1m \\ \left(\frac{\Delta \hat{y}}{\Delta a}\right) 21, & \left(\frac{\Delta \hat{y}}{\Delta a}\right) 22, & \cdots, & \left(\frac{\Delta \hat{y}}{\Delta a}\right) 2m \\ \cdots\cdots\cdots\cdots\cdots\cdots\cdots\cdots \\ \cdots\cdots\cdots\cdots\cdots\cdots\cdots\cdots \\ \left(\frac{\Delta \hat{y}}{\Delta a}\right) l1, & \left(\frac{\Delta \hat{y}}{\Delta a}\right) l2, & \cdots, & \left(\frac{\Delta \hat{y}}{\Delta a}\right) lm \end{bmatrix} \quad (14)$$

$$
\{h\} = \begin{Bmatrix} h_1 \\ h_2 \\ \cdot \\ \cdot \\ \cdot \\ \cdot \\ h_m \end{Bmatrix} \quad ; \quad \{E\} = \begin{Bmatrix} E_1 \\ E_2 \\ \cdot \\ \cdot \\ \cdot \\ E_\ell \end{Bmatrix} \tag{15}
$$

where Δ = the matrix of the finite derivatives vector (the first index refers to $\hat{y}$, and the second one to a),

$\{h\}$ = the column vector of unknown coefficients h_j used for the evaluation of a_j, and

$\{E\}$ = the column vector of estimated errors.

In order to solve the above problem now the multiple regression technique can be applied by minimizing the sum of squares of E_1, i.e., by solving the matrix equation:

$$
\{h\} = (R^{-1}) \cdot \{E\} \tag{16}
$$

where $R = \Delta'\Delta$ is the correlation matrix, and R^{-1} = the inversive matrix of the R matrix.

It is known that this transformation exists only when the inversive matrix of the R operator matrix exists, and it happens when $|R| \neq 0$, that is when the matrix R is non-singular. If the matrix R were singular, the vector $\{h\}$ to be transferred into the vector $\{E\}$ with fewer dimensions, since due to $|R| \neq 0$ its column vectors are linearly dependent, so the inversive transformation is not defined accurately.

If the matrix of the operator $|R| \neq 0$, but it tends to zero, i.e., if there is an intensive correlation between its column vectors, then it becomes degenerated. For that reason with the inverse matrix R^{-1}, owing to the nonorthogonality of the system, there appears an error, and it cannot be defined accurately in the statistical sense. Therefore, as it has already been mentioned (and here illustrated as well), the direct approach by the regression analysis leads to the instability of calculated regression coefficients.

On the other hand, the fact that the direct approach to the regression analysis means the decomposition of the vector of the dependent variable $\{E\}$ into contra-varianted coordinates in the direction of the vector R_i, which

regularly make (unless the absence of any linear dependence between vector series or R matrix columns is in question) the oblique corner base of the vectorial space R^n, makes the critique of the regression results difficult. Namely, regression coefficients (contravarianted components of the vector {E} towards the vector R_i) cannot be considered as

the incremental value of their corresponding vector, which does not depend on other vectors. By excluding any of R_i

vectors, other regression coefficients will be considerably changed. Just for these reasons the prediction equation form can contradict the physics of the problem. Solution to this problem lies in the use of components regression in which only the orthogonal, truly independent components of the system are used to solve for h_j.

The determination of these components requires the answer to the question whether here in the specified space there are any vectors that can be by the linear transformation, which is defined by the R matrix as a linear operator, transformed into the colinear vectors, so that:

$$R \{x\} = \lambda \{x\}$$

$$(R - \lambda I) \{x\} = \{0\}, \quad \text{where} \quad \lambda \quad \text{is a scalar.}$$

(17)

The R $- \lambda$I matrix is called the characteristic matrix of the R matrix, because it is used to determine the invariant lines of that space in relation to the transformation by the operator R. It is obvious that they will exist only in the case the determinant of the system is zero, that is if

$$f(\lambda) = |B| = |R| - |\lambda I| = \begin{vmatrix} r_{11}-\lambda, & r_{12}, \ldots, & r_{1n} \\ r_{12}, & r_{22}-\lambda, \ldots, r_{2n} \\ \cdots\cdots\cdots\cdots\cdots\cdots \\ \cdots\cdots\cdots\cdots\cdots\cdots \\ r_{n1}, & r_{n2}, \ldots, & r_{nn}-\lambda \end{vmatrix} = 0 . \quad (18)$$

The solution usually gives n real or complex eigenvalues for λ, or the characteristic numbers of the R matrix.

The real or composite vector (x_s) which satisfies the characteristic equation is called the eigenvector of the R matrix,

$$(R - \lambda_s I) \{x_s\} = \{0\} . \tag{19}$$

Each characteristic number λ_s has a corresponding vector x_s, thus they are n in number which for itself represents a sum of n^2 numbers.

These vectors are usually standardized and their module and unit vector must be determined:

$$|\{x_s\}| = \sqrt{(x_s) \{x_s\}} ; \{e_s\} = \{x_s\} : |\{x_s\}| . \tag{20}$$

It is essential to point out that the eigenvalues of a real symmetric matrix (as the matrix of correlation coefficients) are real. Besides, the eigenvectors in such a matrix are linearly independent and for two different characteristics numbers they are orthogonal. In that way it is possible by means of the correlation matrix eigenvalues and eigenvectors, respectively, to examine its interior structure and determine the noncorrelative components of variables, which are usually called the natural components.

The fact that these vectors are orthogonal eliminates now the problems of the decomposition of the vector of the dependent variable into contravariant coordinates of the oblique corner coordinate system, because the eigenvectors are now the basic vectors of the Euclidean vectorial space R^n [3, 4]. They determine new, linear independent variables which are used to obtain the regression equations among initial variables. Namely, with the eigenvectors x which correspond to the characteristic numbers of the correlation matrix R, one is able to transform the initial vectors matrix into new vectors.

$$R \cdot X = T \tag{21}$$

where $R = |\{r_1\}, \{r_2\}, \ldots, \{r_n\}|$ is the correlation coefficients matrix, $X = |\{x_1\}, \{x_2\}, \ldots, \{x_n\}|$ = the eigenvectors matrix, and $T = |\{t_1\}, \ldots, \{t_n\}|$ = the transformed variables matrix, so at last the transformation of the input vector $\{E\}$ can be carried out into the vector $\{b\}$ by means of the T operator, $T \{b\} = \{E\}$, that is, one gets the real regression coefficients h and thereby the required hyperplane equation:

$$\{h\} = X \cdot \{b\} . \tag{22}$$

The eigenvalues in fact describe the size of the variations inside the correlation matrix, and therefore one can conclude

that the size of the eigenvalue is proportional to its partici-
pation in the explanation of these variations. Therefore, very
small values of λ(i.e., their corresponding vectors) will
not essentially influence the explanation of these variations.
On the contrary, in most instances, models designed to explain
a phenomenon will not explain 100 percent of its variations.
Partly errors result from the differences between the model
and the true physical process, and partly errors result from
the random noise in the system [5]. Therefore, these errors
will likely be connected with the small roots. For that
reason they should be reflected and only the highest values
of λ retained.

The number of iterations used for the final optimization
is determined by necessary restrictions that the optimum is
achieved when all the h_j values after the n-th iteration
have become smaller than the values specified beforehand and
expressed as a percentage of a_j.

In that way one has at the disposition an objective
method of optimization of parameters of complex hydrologic
models, which when applied to prediction models require to
be conceived in the way which would reproduce the physics
of the problem as much as feasible.

4. Application to a Case Study.

The methodology presented for the general concept of
discharge hydrograph model and the optimization of model
parameters was applied to a case study in the karst area. It
is a case of the Trebišnjica River, Fig. 5, as a typical karst
catchment for which data on recorded flood hydrographs are
available. It was feasible to separate 18 recorded hydrographs
for which parallel data are available for daily precipitation
on a certain number of precipitation gauging stations in the
catchment.

Since these investigations are still in progress at this
stage of work, no definite generalizations are feasible
(particularly no sufficient number of recorded hydrographs for
both the model calibration and the model testing was available). The results given only in the form of a graphical
relationship between the observed and the estimated, optimized
discharge values, in reference to the line of 45°, give an
overall assessment of the applied method of estimation.

5. Conclusions.

It seems that the application of the multivariate statistical technique, the principal component analysis, is feasible
for the use in the conceptual prediction models of hydrographs

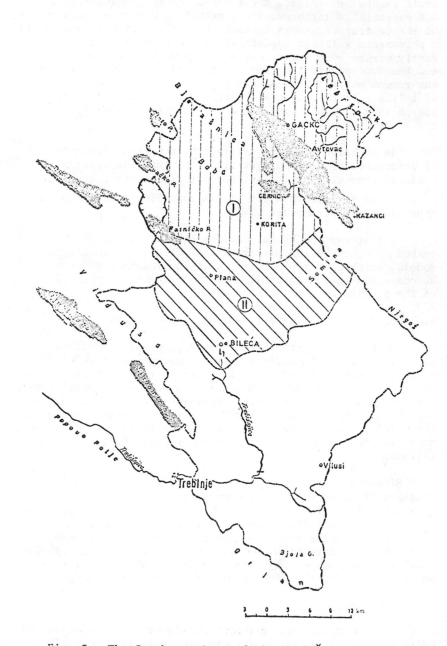

Fig. 5. The Catchment Area of the Trebišnjica River.

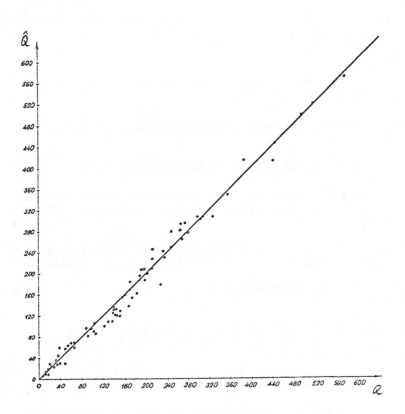

Fig. 6.   The Straight-Line Relationship of the Estimated ($\hat{Q}$)
          and the Measured (Q) Discharges of the Trebišnjica
          River.

under the karst conditions. However, the form of the selected
mathematical function as the simulation model is of no lesser
importance. Thus the conceptual model as for a fictitious
reservoir as the factor of input transformation, gives good
results.

     Since the complexity of the function does not influence
the accuracy of optimization, the further stages in developing
the model will include the piezometric levels of characteristic
boreholes and other points, as a new indicator of the state
of the fictitious reservoir.

274

6. References.

[1] Alexeyev, G.A., Objective statistical methods of computation and generalization of the parameters of maximum rainfall runoff: I.A.S.H. publ., No. 84, 1969, pp. 114-127.

[2] Anis, A.A., Some extensions of two-streams storage model: J. Hydrol., 4, 1970, pp. 363-378.

[3] Andjelić, T., Tenzorski račun (Tensor calculus): Beograd, 1967.

[4] Andjelić, T., Matrice (Matrices): Beograd, 1970.

[5] De Coursey, Donn G., Applications of computer technology to hydrologic model building: I.A.S.H. publ., No. 80, 1968, pp. 233-239.

[6] Dunin, F.X., The infiltration component of a pastoral experimental catchment: J. Hydrol., 2, 1969, pp. 121-157.

[7] Ivanović, B., Teorijska statistika (Theoretical statistics): Beograd, 1973.

[8] Nechaeva, N.S. and Mukhin, V.M., The use of statistical methods for short-range forecasts: I.A.S.H. publ., No. 81, 1968, pp. 405-416.

DISCUSSION

Duckstein. The model choice problem is attacked in the paper, for which many approaches are feasible. In our investigations of this problem at the University of Arizona, it was found that a goal-oriented approach, that is, the development of models with certain engineering and economic problems in mind yields the most satisfying results. Later in his paper, the author mentions the use of the principal component analysis in order to eliminate the multicollinearity, that is, the linear correlation between independent variables. Several difficulties are present in the use of principal components, namely: (a) It may be difficult to interpret the principal components beyond the first or perhaps the second one; (b) How many principal components are to be included into the analysis? (c) As in any statistical model, the linear regression that follows a principal component analysis leans on several hypotheses: what happens to the prediction when one or more of these assumptions are violated?

The principal component analysis eliminates violating the non-multicollinearity assumption. However, it does not eliminate the possibility of violating the assumptions of normal error, of homoscedacity and of serial independence of errors. As a matter of fact, the last slide presented by the author would tend to show that the autocorrelation of errors (residuals) may be present in the data. The author could check such an autocorrelation by using the Dubin-Watson statistical test.

Knežević. The application of empirical orthogonal functions, as well as the interpretation of eigenvectors, is a difficult and complex problem. By agreeing entirely with this point, an additional explanation is warranted.

The purpose of the work presented in the paper was primarily to test, by means of orthogonalization, the internal structure of the correlation matrix and to determine the non-correlative components of variables which are modelled in order to guarantee the convergence in optimization of the model parameters. The search for the physical meaning of characteristic vectors was not the objective of the study, although there have been many such attempts, especially in problems related to dynamics of the atmosphere in analysis of the fall of atmospheric pressure and zonal circulation, except for their geometric explanation as vector bases of n-dimensional vector space.

PREDICTION MODEL FOR RUNOFF FROM KARSTIFIED CATCHMENTS

by

D. Graupe, Professor of Electrical Engineering,
D. Isailović, Ph.D. Graduate Research Assistant, and
V. Yevjevich, Professor of Civil Engineering
Colorado State University, Fort Collins, Colorado, USA,

Synopsis. A mathematical model for predicting the outflow from karstified catchments and karst aquifers using the
precipitation as input is presented. The daily precipitation
and runoff data are used to calibrate this model. The approach
applied is the identification of a linear-optimal prediction
model based on autoregressive-moving average (AR-MA) methods.
The residuals of the rainfall-runoff, input-output, model are
thus whitened in order to obtain linear-optimal prediction.
Subsequently, the use of Kalman filtering of measurement
errors is described for cases where these errors are significant. The problem of removing periodicity in parameters,
as the sources of nonstationarity, is considered along with
the convergence, bias and nonlinearity problems of the model.

1. Introduction.

The prediction of runoff from a drainage area or a
highly pervious aquifer is a practical problem in design,
construction and management of water resources projects. The
problem is complicated by the nature of the dynamic processes
involved. Various approaches that have been used to find
solutions are sometimes divided into two groups: physical
models (using the physical relations) and mathematical statistical prediction models.

Physical models require knowledge of conditions and processes related to each catchment. The reliability of these
models depends on that knowledge. Mathematical statistical
models consider a drainage area or an aquifer as a black
box, which do not require an apriori knowledge of physical
processes inside the box. Furthermore, mathematical models,
in contrast to physical models, can be applied to drainage
basins or aquifers provided sufficient information is
available on inputs and outputs for the purpose of calibrating
models. If convergence and optimality in estimation of
parameters of models can be proven, they are advantageous over
the physical models, since: (1) assumptions on physical
interactions are never unbiased or complete, and (2) proofs
of convergence and optimality in estimating parameters of
physical models are difficult either to prove or to attain.

Concentrating on the mathematical statistical modeling,
a brief review of this approach by using a limited number of

references is as follows. Bidwell [1] considered a nonlinear model of stationary processes and employed a transformation to obtain the linear relation between rainfall and runoff. The prediction results were good, especially for high-flow periods. However, the consistency of estimates was not proven while some assumptions were made on statistical convergence and unbiasedness. Delleur and Rao [2] studied the analysis of linear hydrologic systems by the transform approach, the kernel oscillations, and the effect of noise, and also [3] the characteristics of filtering noise in linear hydrologic systems. Knisel [4] considered the nonstationarity of several karst spring flows in USA in form of periodicities by fitting the Fourier series to the mean and the standard deviation of both rainfall and spring runoff. The convolution was employed to obtain the spring-flow prediction using the observed rainfall. Good prediction results were obtained for medium flows. Assumptions used and the character of karst aquifers and/or watersheds are close to the problem discussed in this paper. The impulse response was obtained by using certain valid approximations, which introduced the bias and affected the prediction. Hino [5] considered a nonlinear prediction model by a rigorous approach, with the system assumed to be of linear dynamics in cascade with a zero-memory nonlinearity and with a gaussian input. Although this assumption is reasonable to assume, the predictions are biased due to omitting a correction term to the estimates [6], with errors claimed, but not proven, to be negligible. Furthermore, although the model was optimal under the assumptions made, the estimation of parameters was complicated and estimates were inconsistent.

In this work an attempt is made to construct a model that is computationally simple but for which the consistency and unbiasedness of estimates can be proven. The model is linear optimal, although it can be extended to a nonlinear structure similar to that of Hino, et al [5], taking into account results given by Graupe in reference [6]. Furthermore, the model can filter the measurement errors by Kalman filtering [7] that is facilitated by the model presented in this paper.

The karstified drainage basins and karst aquifers. The study case in testing the model is that of predicting runoff at a medium-size drainage basin in a karstified limestone area, from data of daily runoff observations at a large karst spring and of daily rainfall at several gauging stations over the area.

Karst regions often must be considered as distinct from other drainage areas [8] in that they respond to rainfall differently than other aquifers, and in such a way that the concentration time of the runoff hydrograph is relatively

much shorter and the discharge peak is relatively much higher
than is the case of classical aquifers. A part of the
precipitation is often stored in large karst underground
storage spaces, which flows out as runoff at springs long
after the rainfall has ceased. Responses of karst aquifers,
or limestone areas with large underground circulation, may be
considered somewhat in between the very fast responses of
impervious steep surfaces and very slow responses of infiltrated water of classical low-permeability aquifers.

The mathematical approach. The mathematical model considered is essentially a mix of a moving-average (MA) scheme
between the discrete observations of input and output combined
with an autoregressive (AR) model between the residuals of
the latter and the discrete uncorrelated noise (orthogonal
stochastic component). It was rigorously shown [9] that
stationary time series obey the AR-MA model regardless of
underlying distributions. Furthermore, once this model is
available, the optimal-linear prediction and filtering are
possible [10,7], which for cases where observations are subject
to measurement errors require transformation into state-space
form [7]. Although the rainfall and runoff considered in
the case study are nonstationary, the nonstationarity is of
a periodic nature. When this periodicity can be removed, the
input, output and the related residuals may be treated as
stationary. The linear-optimal nature of the model of
stationary processes treated is not only rigorous [9] but is
also easy to derive. Due to the non-gaussian nature of the
distributions involved (mixed distributions of daily values)
any fully-optimal prediction is at best extremely difficult.
In practice it is hardly possible, noting the state-of-the-
art of non-linear stochastic estimation theory [11] in contrast
to the parallel case of linear prediction and filtering. Ad-
hoc nonlinear prediction models may still have biased and
inconsistent estimates of parameters. Since bias and inconsistent estimates can be avoided by using the optimal-linear
approach, the investigation of this approach is justified.

2. Mathematical Model.

The input-output relations. The linear AR-MA relations
between the daily runoff y_i and the daily rainfall x_i can
be investigated in one of the two forms:

(1) The MA-model for the y_i to x_i relation is

$$y_i = \sum_{j=0}^{m} \alpha_j x_{i-j} + e_i \tag{1}$$

with α_j = the MA-coefficients (representing the delayed response of the basin or the aquifer), and e_i = the auto-correlated (dependent, colored) residuals with $E[e_i] = 0$, $E(e_i, e_{i+k}) = \gamma_e(k)$ and $E[e_i, x_{i-j}] = 0$, for $j = 0,1,\ldots$. Equation (1) in the backward shift operator form is then

$$y_i = \alpha(B) \cdot x_i + e_i \qquad (2)$$

with α_j being parameters to be identified (estimated from data), B being a delay operator, $B^j x_i \triangleq x_{i-j}$, $\alpha(B)$ being a polynomial in B with coefficients α_j.

The whitening of residuals e_i of Eq. (1) is performed by the following autoregressive (AR) scheme

$$e_i = \sum_{j=1}^{s} \eta_j e_{i-j} + w_i \qquad (3)$$

with w_i being white noise. Substituting for e_i from Eq. (3) into Eq. (1) thus yields

$$y_i = \sum_{j=0}^{m} \alpha_j x_{i-j} + \sum_{j=1}^{s} \eta_j e_{i-j} + w_i \quad . \qquad (4)$$

In the operator form Eqs. (3) and (4) become

$$\eta(B) e_i = w_i \qquad (5)$$

and

$$y_i = \alpha(B) x_i + \eta(B) e_i + w_i \quad , \qquad (6)$$

respectively.

(2) The AR-model for y_i and the MA-model for y_i to x_i relation, with white noise residuals, give

$$\sum_{j=0}^{n} \beta_j y_{i-j} = \sum_{j=0}^{p} \rho_j x_{i-j} + w_i \quad , \qquad (7)$$

with the residuals w_i being the same white noise as in Eq. (4). In the operator form, Eq. (7) becomes

$$\beta(B) y_i = \rho(B) x_i + w_i \quad . \qquad (8)$$

In selecting between the two approaches, namely the MA-AR model of Eq. (4) and the AR-MA model of Eq. (7), the parameters to estimate are α_j and η_j in Eq. (4), and β_j and ρ_j in Eq. (7), with $m+s+2$ and $n+\rho+2$ parameters to be estimated, respectively, beyond those of distributions of w_i white-noise residuals.

One would expect from the hydrologic experience that the MA-parts of the models, $m+1$ values in Eq. (4) and $p+1$ values in Eq. (7), will be relatively long, as representing the response function (unit-type hydrographs) of a basin or an aquifer. On the other side, the AR-parts of models, $s+1$ values in Eq. (4) and $n+1$ values in Eq. (7), are expected to be short (say, first-order to third-order AR-models, in general). Assuming that approximately $m+s = n+p$, as a reasonable hypothesis, the further discussion can be concentrated on the MA-AR model of Eq. (4).

Models of Eqs. (4) and (7) assume the stationarity of the processes involved. Since $\{x_i\}$ and $\{y_i\}$ processes are periodic-stochastic processes in all hydrologic cases, when the Δt-interval is small (say smaller than a year, and definitively for Δt = one day), there are two alternatives of bridging the gap between the assumption of stationarity and the reality of nonstationarity in processes. One approach is to split the period of the year (and in some cases the period of the day) into a sufficient number of large intervals within which one can consider all the parameters to be approximately constants, changing only from interval to interval (the seasons approach). This approach has long dominated the hydrologic practice. It is well exemplified by the twelve monthly variables, each with different parameters.

The second approach is to remove the periodicity in parameters by a structural analysis of series [12], and to investigate the relations between the stationary stochastic components (of a prescribed order of stationarity) of input and output series.

The structures of Eq. (1) and Eq. (7) are not unique, because any structure of the type of Eq. (1) with the auto-correlated residuals cannot directly yield the unbiased estimates of parameters unless w_i are white-noise residuals. Equations (4) and (7) lend themselves to unbiased identification [13] when w_i is proven to be white noise.

The consistent estimates of α_j of Eq. (1) from the measured values of y_i and x_i can be performed recursively, either using the sequential least-squares regression approach or using the stochastic approximations approach [13]. The least-squares estimates $\hat{\alpha}_j$ of α_j are obtained by minimizing

$$\sum_{i=1}^{N} (y_i - y_i^\circ)^2 = \sum_{i=1}^{N} [\sum_{j=0}^{m} \hat{\alpha}_j \, x_{i-j}^\circ + \hat{e}_i - y_i^\circ]^2 \, , \tag{9}$$

with x_{i-j}° and y_i° the sample values of daily rainfall and runoff used for the estimation of $\hat{\alpha}_j$ and the computation of $\hat{e}_i$ as estimates of the e_i process. The classical solution of m linear equations serve to compute $\hat{\alpha}_j$'s.

Since e_i of Eq. (1) is a dependent variable, its auto-correlation structure still contains information. Ignoring this information yields imperfect prediction even when $\hat{\alpha}_j$ converges to the true α_j. To obtain that information, the order m of α_j in Eq. (1) should be selected in such a manner that the sample variance σ_e^2 of e_i is a minimum. At least, no significant decrease of σ_e^2 should result from an increase in m. The use of the number of degrees of freedom in minimizing Eq. (9) and in testing the significance of the term $\hat{\alpha}_{m+1}$ would show a minimum of σ_e^2 for a given m. Although in theory m may be infinite, α_j form a convergent sequence for bounded y_i. Therefore, a choice of a finite m is adequate and can be bounded by an error analysis that is parallel to that of [14], this bound being reducible at will by changing m. This is analoguous to a bounded unit hydrograph for surface runoff of rainfall excess.

Whitening of model residuals. The information contained in e_i of Eq. (1) is obtained through its whitening via Eq. (3), with w_i the discrete white noise, namely with $E[w_i] = 0$ and $E[w_k w_h] = \sigma_w^2 \, \sigma_{k,h}$ ($\sigma_{k,h}$ being Kronecker's delta, i.e., zero for $k \neq h$ and 1 for $k = h$).

At this point a theoretical difficulty is faced with, namely that of determining the order s of the AR-model of Eq. (3) or Eq. (4). In theory, s is infinite. Hydrologic practice, studies [6], and statistical theory [9], show that for bounded $\hat{e}_i$, η_j form a convergent sequence as j increases. Hence, a finite number s of terms of η_j may be identified to provide a good whitening. Furthermore, it is possible to

put an upper bound on the error introduced by considering only
s terms [14]. This bound can be reduced at will by an
appropriate increase of s. In the computations shown in this
paper the sample variance of the prediction error has been
reduced by whitening with s = 1 by a factor of three with
respect to the case where the whitening of e_i of Eq. (1) was
ignored. Further increases of s did not yield significant
improvements. Equation (4) therefore yields the optimal
linear prediction model for the runoff y_i once α_j and η_j

have been estimated, with $\hat{e}_i$ being available from Eq. (1).

Provided that the orders m and s of α_j and of η_j,

respectively, are correct, the estimates $\hat{\alpha}_j$ and $\hat{\eta}_j$ are

consistent and unbiased. Otherwise, a bias is introduced
which is bounded [14] and which can be reduced at will.

Stationarity considerations. Rainfall and runoff variables, with time intervals less than a year, are highly
periodical, and hence nonstationary. However, since the
periodicity of the runoff y_i parallels to a large extent the

periodicity in rainfall, the model relating rainfall x_i

and runoff y_i may be of a less pronounced nonstationary

character. An estimation of $\hat{\alpha}_j$ as stationary parameters may

thus be justified in many practical cases. Consequently,
although the measurable input x_i (rainfall) and output y_i

(runoff) are nonstationary, the residual sequence e_i may

be shown to be less nonstationary. Figure 1, with times
series of y_i, x_i, e_i, and w_i compared, illustrates that
the residuals e_i are less nonstationary than y_i and x_i,

when e_i is obtained from the nonperiodic values $\hat{\alpha}_j$ and

$\hat{\eta}_j$, though e_i is certainly still somewhat nonstationary.

Figure 1 may justify the use of an approximation by dividing
the year (in this case study) into two or more approximately
stationary intervals. In the case of two intervals, one may
be for the high-precipitation season (from mid September to
mid February), and one for the low-precipitation season (from
mid February to mid September), for each of which a separate
approximately stationary model is derived and used.

A justification for the approach of constant-parameter
intervals or seasons is given by data of Table 1. The variance
$E[w_i^2]$ of the w_i residuals, as the measure of prediction

errors, is compared for the model based on using the entire
series of x_i and y_i, unmodified, -- assuming that e_i is

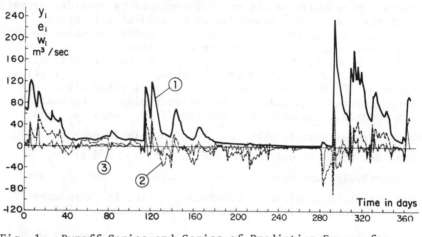

Fig. 1. Runoff Series and Series of Prediction Errors for
Rainfall-Runoff ARMA-Prediction Model, Using the
Observed Rainfall and Runoff Data for the Year 1961
of the Trebišnjica River at the Bileća Spring: (1)
Observed Daily Runoff Series, y_i; (2) Dependent
Residuals, e_i of Eq. (1) for m = 20; and (3) Pre-
diction Error Series, w_i of Eq. (4) for m = 20
and s = 4.

Table 1. Comparison Of Variances For Assessing Prediction
Errors

Period of Data	Model	m	σ^2_y	σ^2_e	ORDERS OF AR MODEL (s)			
					1	2	3	4
					σ^2_w	σ^2_w	σ^2_w	σ^2_w
1961 (365 Points)	Whole Year	10	1507	606	177	161	160	159
		15	1507	523	171	163	161	161
		20	1507	416	158	148	147	145
	Seasons	20	1507	252	98.5	96.4	95.4	94.5
1954 - 1967 (4745 Points)		10	2179	822	195	193	192	192
		15	2179	728	185	183	182	182
		20	2179	663	178	176	175	175

less nonstationary than x_i or y_i --, and for a model which was derived by using the approach of two seasons with approximately constant parameters. For the same value of $m = 20$ and $s = 1$ for the two approaches, values of $\sigma_w^2 = 158$ and $\sigma_w^2 = 98.5$ were obtained, respectively. By using still more seasons, σ_w^2 is further reduced. Therefore, one might expect that by removing periodicities from both x_i and y_i series by proper analyses and tests [12], and using only the stationary stochastic components of x_i and y_i in the model, the prediction errors, measured by σ_w^2, would be minimized.

This latter approach was not attempted, because of difficulties in removing periodicities in a set of stations of daily rainfall. Furthermore, a part of rainfall is in the form of snow accumulation and delayed melting, that would bias the removal of rainfall periodicities.

Treatment of measurement errors in outputs. The rainfall x_i and runoff y_i always contain measurement errors. Because x_i in Eq. (4) are assumed independent variables in a MA linear regression equation, the feasible approach is to consider the model errors e_i of Eq. (1) as a result of input alone. However, one may wish also to separate output measurement errors and to obtain insight into their effect. Two cases occur in practice: (1) errors u_i are linearly related to runoff, or $u_i = by_i + v_i$, with v_i white noise, or (2) errors $u_i = v_i$ are white noises, independent of y_i. If the first case is true, the regression part by_i will be incorporated into the AR part of the model. Therefore, it is sufficient to treat the case of white noise measurement errors, v_i.

Two distinct treatments of v_i errors may be feasible in practice for rainfall-runoff models of Eqs. (4) and (7):

(1) The variance $E[v_i^2]$ of v_i is very small in comparison with the variance $E[w_i^2]$ of w_i, with w_i in this case being the random signal of the process and v_i the measurement noise, so that Eq. (4) can be used for the predictive purposes. In this case the estimates $\hat{a}_j$ and $\hat{\eta}_j$, with $j = 1,2,\ldots,m$ and $j = 1,2,\ldots,s$, respectively for these

coefficients, are sufficient as the unbiased and efficient estimates for a minimum prediction error, σ_w^2 .

(2) The variance $E[v_i^2]$ is not negligible in comparison with the variance $E[w_i^2]$. In that case the model of Eq. (4) is no more linear optimal as far as the true runoff is concerned (though it still is the linear optimal model for the runoff measurements). Hence, filtering of the measurement noise v_i must be performed prior to establishing the final prediction AR-MA model. This can be done via a Kalman filter model, provided v_i is white noise othogonal to the input noise part u_i of w_i.

These two approaches are shown in the further text.

3. Computational Results in Case of Negligible Measurement Errors in Output.

Data preparation. The models are tested on data of a large karst spring (the Bileća Spring of the Trebišnjica River in Yugoslavia) for the period January 1954 through October 1967. Precipitation was measured at 21 gauging stations in the drainage area. However, for most stations data were missing for several months.

The rainfall values x_i of Eq. (4) were obtained from the data of all gauging stations by simple summation

$$x_i = \frac{1}{P_i} \sum_{j=1}^{21} x_{i,j} \, I_j \qquad (10)$$

where

$$P_i = \sum_{j=1}^{21} I_j \qquad (11)$$

with $j = 1,\ldots,21$ referring to 21 rainfall gauging stations, $I_j = 1$ when the observation $x_{i,j}$ was available at the station j on day i, and $I_j = 0$ if that observation was missing. Obviously, weighting according to the area covered by the particular stations and considering its location with respect to the runoff measurement location was important. However, since this information was deficient, it could not be used.

Discussion of computational results. Figure 1 presents the data of runoff y_i of rainfall x_i according to Eq. (10),

of the residual e_i of Eq. (1), and of the white noise
residual w_i of Eq. (4) for the year 1961, when no removal
of periodicities in parameters was performed.

Figure 2 is similar to Fig. 1, except that it considers
the data of the year 1961 to be piece-wise stationary, by
using the high- and low-precipitation seasons, as the two
approximately stationary periods. A comparison of the variance,
$E[w_i^2]$ of the prediction errors of Figs. 1 and 2 indicates
the validity of the assumption used for data of Fig. 2 that
its $E[w_i^2]$ is smaller than that of Fig. 1, noting the plots
of e_i and variance values in Table 1.

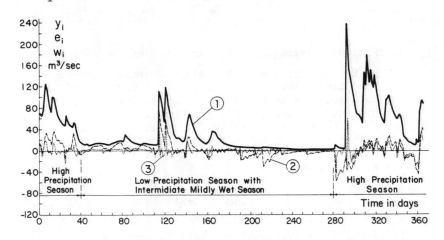

Fig. 2. Runoff Series and Series of Prediction Errors for the
Rainfall-Runoff ARMA-Prediction Model, Using the
Observed Rainfall and Runoff data for the Year 1961
of the Trebišnjica River at the Bileća Spring,
Divided in Separate Seasons: (1) Observed Daily
Runoff Series, y_i; (2) Dependent Residuals, e_i of
Eq. (1) for m = 20; and (3) Prediction Error Series,
w_i of Eq. (4) for m = 20; and s = 4; and for Two
Sets of Estimated Parameters, One for High-Precipita-
tion Season and the Other for Predominately Low-
Precipitation Season.

Figure 3 gives the estimates $\hat{\alpha}_j$ and $\hat{\eta}_j$ of Eq. (4) for
two cases: (1) the use of original data of x_i and y_i for
the year 1961 (365 daily observations) and three values of m,
namely 10, 15 and 20, and four values of s, namely

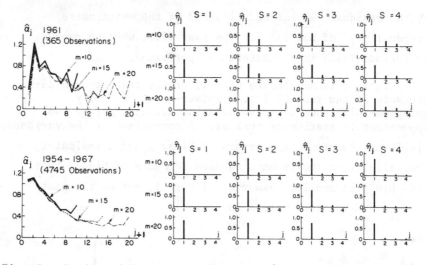

Fig. 3.   Estimated Parameters $\hat{\alpha}_j$ and $\hat{\eta}_j$ of the ARMA-Model
of Eq. (4) for the Negligible Measurement Errors in
The Output, for the Two Cases: (a) For the 365 Daily
Values of the Year 1961 (Without Separating it Into
Distinct Seasons), the Upper Graphs, and (b) For
the Entire Period 1954-1967 of 4745 Daily Values
(Without Separating it Into Distinct Seasons), the
Lower Graphs, for Cases   m = 10, 15 and 20, and
s = 1,2,3 and 4.

s = 1,2,3,4, (upper graphs); and (2) the use of original data
of x_i and y_i for the period January 1954 through October
1967 (4745 daily observations) or about 13 years of data, and
for the same values of   m   and   s   as in the first case,
(lower graphs).   This figure leads to the following basic
results: (a) the estimates of the first 10 values of $\hat{\alpha}_j$
hardly change when   m   increases from 10 to 15 or from 10 to
20;   (b) in order to obtain adequate responses of large karst
aquifers, the recession part requires a very large   m;   (c) If
the measure of prediction is the minimal variance $E[w_i^2]$,   then
it is not necessary to use very long   m   or to consider a
complete reproduction of the long tail of the responses, as
illustrated in Table 1; (d) the smoothness of converging $\hat{\alpha}_j$
coefficients increases when increasing the data considered
from 365 to 4745 daily values, as it should be expected; (e)
the value   s   of terms of AR-part of e_i of the model is very
small with the sample of 4745 values, indicating that   s = 1,
(i.e., the first-order autoregressive model) is sufficient to
whiten the e_i series into the w_i series; and (f) the short

sample of 365 daily values of the year 1961 $\hat{\eta}_j$ to be some-

what higher for up to $s = 4$, which can be explained by this short sample of only one year of data; however, the prediction is not improved significantly with $s = 4$ in comparison with the use of $s = 1$ only.

Figure 4, in turn, demonstrates the results in case that the series are separated in seasons, instead of using the un-interrupted daily values of series x_i and y_i. This figure shows the estimates $\hat{\alpha}_j$ and $\hat{\eta}_j$ for three periods (see Figs. 1 and 2): (a) A very wet season from October 1, 1960 to January 31, 1961; (b) A mix of dry periods with a mildly wet

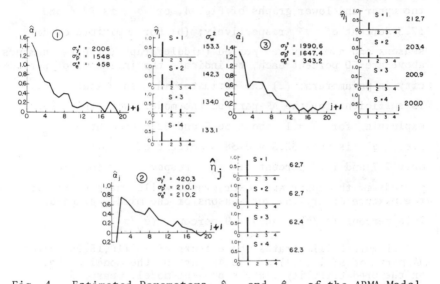

Fig. 4. Estimated Parameters $\hat{\alpha}_j$ and $\hat{\eta}_j$ of the ARMA-Model of Eq. (4) for the Negligible Measurements Errors in the Output, but for the Separation of Input and Output Series in Periods of Wet and Dry Seasons (Fig. 2), for Three Cases: (1) Period October 1, 1960 to January 31, 1961; (2) Period February 1 to October 20, 1961; and (3) Period October 21, 1961 to January 30, 1962, all Three Cases with Variances σ_y^2 of y_i series, σ_p^2 of the MA-Part of Prediction Models of Eq. (4) σ_e^2 of Residuals e_i of Eq. (1), and σ_w^2 of w_i of Eq. (4), for $m = 20$ and $s = 1, 2, 3$ and 4.

season from February 1, to October 20, 1961; and (c) Very wet season from October 21, 1961 to January 30, 1962. For each of the three periods (seasons), $m = 20$, and three variances are given also for three terms in Eq. (1): σ_y^2, the variance of y_i; σ_p^2, the variance of $\sum_{j=0}^{m} \hat{a}_j x_{i-j}$ of the predictive term of MA-model; and σ_e^2, the variance of dependent residuals e_i. The right-hand side graphs of Fig. 4 give the estimates $\hat{\eta}_j$ for $s = 1,2,3$, and 4, as well as the corresponding values of σ_w^2, the variance of white-noise residuals w_i of e_i. The results are: (a) For wet seasons the MA-term of the model explains 77.2 and 82.7 percent of the variance of y_i, for the upper and lower graphs of Fig. 4, or σ_e^2 is 22.8 and 17.3 percent of σ_y^2 respectively; (b) For a mixture of dry seasons and a mildly wet period (middle graph), the two numbers above are 50 percent each, to indicate the influence of periodicity in parameters; (c) the estimates $\hat{\eta}_j$ show that $s = 1$ is sufficient for the AR-part of the model, with this AR-part explaining for $s = 1$ about 66.5 and 62.0 percent of σ_e^2, i.e., σ_w^2 is only 33.5 and 38.0 percent of σ_e^2, or σ_w^2 is only 7.7 and 10.7 percent of σ_y^2, respectively for the wet periods of the upper and lower graph, while these values for the mixture of dry and wet seasons of the middle graph are 29.8 percent (σ_w^2/σ_e^2) and 14.9 percent (σ_w^2/σ_y^2).

Figure 5 illustrates the effects of m (10,15,20) of the MA-part, of $s(1,2,3,4)$ of the AR-part of the model of Eq. (4) on the predictibility via the present model, measured by the ratio σ_w^2/σ_y^2, for two cases: (a) Data for the 365 daily values of the year 1961 (left-side graph), with $\sigma_y^2 = 1507$; and (6) Data for the period 1954-1967 and 4745 daily values (right-side graph), with $\sigma_y^2 = 2179$. The case of $s = 0$ (no whitening of e_i) is also given to indicate the considerable improvement of prediction when the first-order AR-model is used for e_i of Eq. (1).

4. Filtering the Measuring Errors in Output.

The ARMA model and the derivation of a Kalman filter model for filtering of measurement errors. In cases where the values y_i contain the non-negligible measurement errors,

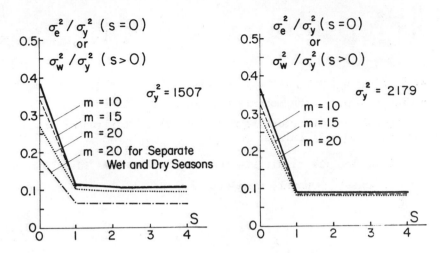

Fig. 5. Comparison of Variances of the ARMA-Prediction Model
in Case of Negligible Measurement Errors in Output
for Various Values of m and s for Two Cases: (a)
The Daily Data for the year 1961 and Two Subcases,
no Separation Into Seasons (m = 10,15,20), and the
Separation into Seasons (m = 20), and s = 0,1,2,3,4,
Left-Side Graph; and (b) The Daily Data for the Period
1954-1967 (4745 Daily Values), and m = 10,15,20 and
s = 0,1,2,3,4, Right-Side Graph.

the prediction model of Eq. (4), as far as the true runoff is
concerned, is no more linear optimal, though it is still
linear optimal regarding the runoff measurements y_i. In
that case, filtering of that error noise should be performed
prior to prediction. If no statistical model of that measurement noise is available, such filtering will first require
the identification of the filter, which is possible only if
that measurement noise v_i is assumed to be white noise and
orthogonal to the input noise part of w_i of Eq. (4). It is
assumed that the runoff observations y_i are given by

$$y_i = z_i + v_i \quad , \tag{12}$$

with z_i being the true values and v_i being the discrete
white measurement noise, hence, Eq. (1) becomes,

$$y_i = \sum_{j=0}^{m} \alpha_j x_{i-j} + e_i' \tag{13}$$

where $e_i' = e_i + v_i$, and by properties of white noise

13-15

$$e_i = \sum_{j=1}^{s} \eta_j \, (e_{i-j} + v_{i-j}) + w_i - v_i = \sum_{j=1}^{q} -\phi_j \, e_{i-j} + \sum_{j=0}^{r} \Theta_j \, u_{i-j}$$

(14)

with $E[u_k \, v_h] = 0$ for all k and h, u_i being white input noise. (Namely, the measurement noise v_i is assumed to be orthogonal to the stochastic components of the runoff process, that are linearly related to u_i).

Equation (14) indicates that e_i is no more identifiable in this case. However, a model given by

$$\sum_{j=0}^{q} \delta_j \, e'_{i-j} = n_i$$

(15)

may be identified, with n_i being discrete white noise. The model of Eq. (15) may yield the relation between e_i and u_i by first identifying an AR-MA model between e'_i and n_i given by

$$\sum_{j=0}^{q} \phi_j \, e'_{i-j} = \sum_{j=0}^{q} \psi_j \, n_{i-j}$$

(16)

with ϕ_j and ψ_j denoting the AR-part and MA-part of that AR-MA model, respectively, the latter equation being a minimum parameter model between e'_i and n_i. Hence the estimates $\hat{\phi}_j$ and $\hat{\psi}_j$ and their orders may be obtained from δ_j of Eq. (15) via properties of polynomial division [15], with $\hat{\delta}_j$, estimated as previously described. For consistent estimates $\hat{\delta}_j$, the estimates $\hat{\phi}_j$ and $\hat{\psi}_j$ are also consistent [16], and they are bounded if $\hat{\delta}_j$ are [14]. It is noted that the orders q of ϕ_j and ψ_j must be equal [17] due to $e'_i = e_i + v_i$. Once ϕ_j and ψ_j are available, the AR-MA model between e_i and w_i is derived as:

$$\sum_{j=0}^{q} \phi_j \, e_{i-j} = \sum_{j=0}^{r} \Theta_j \, u_{i-j} \; .$$

(17)

Substituting $e'_i = e_i + v_i$ and Eq. (17) into Eq. (16) yields,

$$\sum_{j=0}^{q} \phi_i \, e_{i-j} = \sum_{j=0}^{q} \Psi_j \, n_{i-j} - \sum_{j=0}^{q} \phi_j \, v_{i-j} = \sum_{j=0}^{r} \Theta_j \, u_{i-j}, \qquad (18)$$

where, without loss of generality, ϕ_o, ψ_o and Θ_o are assumed to be unities. Consequently, equating covariances yields [17]:

$$\sigma_n^2 \sum_{j=o}^{q-h} \Psi_j \, \Psi_{j+h} = \begin{cases} \sigma_u^2 \sum_{j=0}^{r-h} \Theta_j \, \Theta_{j+h} + \sigma_v^2 \sum_{j=0}^{q-h} \phi_j \, \phi_{j+h}, & o \le h \le r, \\[2em] \sigma_v^2 \sum_{j=0}^{q-h} \phi_j \, \phi_{j+h}, & r < h \le q, \end{cases} \qquad (19)$$

with σ_n^2, σ_u^2 and σ_v^2 denoting the variances of n_i, u_i, and v_i, respectively. Equation (19) thus yields estimates of σ_u^2, σ_v^2 and σ_n^2, which are again consistent [16] and unique [18]. The resulting AR-MA model of Eq. (17) is subsequently transformed into state-space form [17], to yield the Kalman filter for optimal-linear filtering of v_i, that is given in state vector forms as:

$$\underline{e}_{i+1} = \underline{A} \, \underline{e}_i + \underline{u}_i; \quad \underline{e}_i \triangleq [e_{i-1}, \ldots, e_{i-q}]^T \quad ; \qquad (20)$$

$$e_i' = \underline{C} \, \underline{e}_i + v_i; \quad \underline{C} = [1, 0, \ldots, 0] \quad ; \qquad (21)$$

$$\qquad (22)$$

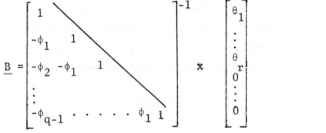

$$\qquad (23)$$

$$E[\underline{u}_k \, \underline{u}_h]^T = \underline{Q}\delta(k,h) = \underline{BB}^T \sigma_u^2 \, \delta(k,h) \qquad (24)$$

$$E[v_k \, v_h] = R\delta(k,h) = \sigma_v^2 \, \delta(k,h) \qquad (25)$$

with e_i of Eq. (17) being e_{i-1} of Eq. (20). The model of Eqs. (20) to (25) finally yields the optimal-linear prediction $\hat{\underline{e}}_{i+1}$ of $\underline{e}_{i+1}$ such that [7]:

$$\hat{\underline{e}}_{i+1|i} = \underline{A} \, \hat{\underline{e}}_{i|i-1} + \underline{D}_i(e_i' - \underline{C} \, \hat{\underline{e}}_{i-1}) \qquad (26)$$

where

$$\underline{D}_i = \underline{P}_i \, \underline{C}^T \, R^{-1} \qquad (27)$$

$$\underline{P}_{i+1} = \underline{A} \, \underline{P}_i + \underline{P}_i \, \underline{A}^T + \underline{Q} + \underline{P}_i \, \underline{C}^T \, R^{-1} \, \underline{C} \, \underline{P}_i \; . \qquad (28)$$

The subscripts $i+1|i$ and $i|i-1$ denote estimates at time $i+1$ given observations up to time i, or similarly at time i given observations up to time $i-1$. Substituting the resulting prediction e_i of above filtering approach into Eq. (1) finally yields the optimal-linear prediction of the runoff y_i.

Application of Kalman filter to the case study. Though the measurement errors v_i in the output y_i are relatively small in comparison with the dependent noise e_i in the case study of karst catchment of the Trebišnjica River, the Kalman filtering is performed to show its application in this hydrologic case. Because the estimates $\hat{\Theta}_j$ were small and they fluctuate in a range as positive and negative values, they have been replaced in Eq. (23) in the last column by $\hat{\psi}_j$.

Table 2 gives the values of σ_v^2, σ_w^2, and σ_e^2 for the AR-MA model between e_i and u_i for cases where measurement noise v_i was assumed to exist in y_i. The relatively low values of $E[v_i^2]$ indicate that the measurement noise is not too significant.

Table 2. Comparison of Variances of Prediction Errors with no
Kalman Filtering and with Kalman Filtering.

Period	Sample	m	s	σ^2_e	σ^2_w with or without Kalman filtering	σ^2_v with Kalman filtering
1954 to 1967	4745	10	2	822	193	25.98
			4	822	192	28.47
		15	2	728	183	26.10
			4	728	182	28.43
		20	2	663	176	25.17
			4	663	175	27.63

5. Conclusions.

The work presented here is a rather rigorous approach to
identifying a prediction model for runoff on the basis of
runoff and rainfall data. The approach outlined yields the
linear-optimal prediction through whitening of residuals of
the input-to-output models considered when any information
contained in the correlation structure of residuals is further
used to increase the goodness of prediction. (For this purpose
compare the variance of the prediction error without whitening
σ^2_e versus that with whitening σ^2_w in Table 1). Convergence
and bias properties have been discussed to demonstrate that
the consistency of the model can be proven, or that, at least,
upper bounds of parameter errors can be established.

Nonstationarities in the form of periodicities in
parameters affect the overall model consistency (this consistency applies only to stationary processes). When nonstationarities in the input-to-output, rainfall-to-rainfall
data are not removed, the model does not have any more
consistency and unbiasedness properties, though it still may
be close to being linear optimal by virtue of whitening of
residuals. Noting this weakness due to need of removing
nonstationarities, and the computational complexity involved
in doing so, it has been shown that an approach based on
dividing the year into periods, over each of which the
stationarity proper parameters can be assumed, is attractive.
This is due to the fact that although the measured time series
of input (rainfall) and of output (runoff) are nonstationary,
the dynamic parameters linking input and output, and the

resultant residuals e_i of Eq. (1) may be relatively
stationary over each of these periods.

Finally, it was shown that the stationarity approximation
facilitates the linear-optimal, recursive (Kalman-type) filtering of measurement errors, when they are significant, since
the previously identified parameters yield the otherwise
unknown Kalman filter parameters.

It is noted that the linearity assumption though leading
to optimal-linear prediction does not permit a fully-optimal
prediction. Since it is not usually possible to obtain consistency or unbiasedness for nonlinear runoff-prediction
models, and considering the state-of-the-art of nonlinear
estimation theory, there appears to be a good justification
for linear but rigorous approach in shaping the AR-MA
prediction models, as has been presented.

6. References.

[1] Bidwell, V. J., Regression Analysis of Nonlinear Catchment Systems: Water Resources Research, Vol. 7, No. 5,
pp. 1118-1125, October 1971.

[2] Delleur, J. W. and Rao, R. A., Linear Systems Analysis
in Hydrology -- The Transform Approach, the Kernel
Oscillations, and the Effect of Noise: Proceedings of
the First US-Japan Seminar in Hydrology, pp. 116-138,
Water Resources Publications, Fort Collins, Colorado, 1971.

[3] Delleur, J. W. and Rao, R. A., Characteristics of Filter-
ing of Noise in Linear Hydrologic Systems: International
Symposium on Mathematical Models in Hydrology, Warsaw,
July 1971 (IAHS Proceedings).

[4] Knisel, W. G., Response of Karst Aquifers to Recharge:
Colorado State University Hydrology Paper No. 60, 1972.

[5] Hino, M., Sukigara T. and Kikkawa 4, Nonlinear Runoff
Kernels of Hydrologic System: Systems Approach to
Hydrology, Proceedings of the 1st Bilateral US-Japan
Seminar in Hydrology, Honolulu 1971, Water Resources
Publications, Fort Collins, Colorado, 1971.

[6] Graupe, D., Identification of Systems: Van Nostrand
Reinhold, New York, 1972.

[7] Kalman, R. E., A New Approach to Linear Filtering and
Prediction Problems: Trans. ASME, J. Basic Engineering,
Vol. 82, pp. 35-43, 1960.

[8] Le Grand, H. E., Hydrological and Ecological Problems of Karst Regions: Science, Volume 179, No. 4076, pp. 859-864, 1973.

[9] Doob, J. L., Stochastic Processes: John Wiley & Sons, New York, 1953.

[10] Wiener, N., Extrapolation, Interpolation and Smoothing of Stationary Time Series: MIT Press, Cambridge, Massachusetts, 1966.

[11] Bucy, R. C., Realization of Nonlinear Filters: Proceedings 2nd Symposium on Nonlinear Estimation Theory, San Diego, pp. 51-58, 1971.

[12] Yevjevich, V., Structural Analysis of Hydrologic Time Series: Colorado State University Hydrology Papers, No. 56, November 1972.

[13] Graupe, D. and Krause, D. J., On the Identification of Input-Output-Noise Models: Int. Journal Sys. Science, Volume 4, pp. 617-621, 1973.

[14] Graupe, D., Estimation of Upper Bounds of Errors in Identifying AR Models: Int. Jour. Sys. Sci., Volume 6, pp. 1-8, 1975.

[15] Graupe, D., Krause, D. J., and Moore, J. B., Identification of Autoregressive Moving-Average Parameters of Time Series: IEEE Trans., Volume AC-20, pp. 104-107, 1975.

[16] Lukacs, E., Stochastic Convergence: D. C. Heath & Co., Lexington, Massachusetts, 1968.

[17] Krause, D. J., and Graupe, D., Identification of Predictor and Filter Parameters by ARMA Methods: International Journal Cont., Volume 17, pp. 1021-1027, 1973.

[18] Wold, H., A Study in the Analysis of Stationary Time Series: Almquist & Wiksell, Stockholm, 1954 (Section III-26).

7. Acknowledgement.

The financial support by the U.S. National Science Foundation, Grant GK-31529x2, through the research project *Investigations of Hydrology and Water Resources in Karst Regions*, with V. Yevjevich as the principal Investigator, is duly acknowledged. This project is the U.S. part of the bilateral U.S. - Yugoslavian research project on hydrology and water resources of karst regions. The data on the Trebišnjica River flows and precipitation were provided by the Yugoslav counterpart of the project, which is duly acknowledged. This paper is a result of this grant and bilateral project.

DISCUSSION

Knežević. The mathematical model used in the paper is composed of the moving average (MA) model part of Eq. (1), relating runoff (y) to rainfall (x), and the autoregressive (AR) model part of Eq. (3), relating dependent residuals (e_i) to white noise residuals (w_i). Furthermore, the x-series is nonstationary; it was implied that it could be used in an autoregressive model.

Because x_i and x_{i-j} are mutually correlated, especially for $j = 1$, and x_{i-j} variables in Eq. (1) are assumed independent while they are not, so that the α_j coefficients will not be uniquely related to the corresponding variables, and will contain a part of information related to the other variables. The fact that the prediction error, e_i, is afterwards filtered by Eq. (3) to obtain the white noise, w_i, does not solve the above problem, because the α_j coefficients -- which have the physical meaning as the delayed responses of the system to a unit input -- remain uncorrected even in the final MA-AR model. This comment is warranted if the first serial correlation coefficient of x_i shows to be significantly greater than zero, especially if the extent of data used in estimating the α_j coefficients did not cover all the variations in x, which can later occur in model application.

As it concerns the applicability of the proposed model, with e_i the difference between the true and by the model predicted y values, does it mean that only one step in advance can be predicted (say, one day in advance for daily flow model), because for the second and following intervals predictions the true values of y, and therefore, e_i, are not known?

Duckstein. This paper provides an excellent method of identifying a karst system. The use of Kalman filters provides a dramatic improvement in the estimation of the output. However, three points may be raised regarding this approach. First, the paper does not clearly state how physical considerations may be imbedded into such an input-output analysis. In other words, using only input-output properties of a karst system neglects a considerable body of information that we may have about the physics of the system. Second, the variance is only one possible measure of system performance. Other possible measures could be of an economic nature, such as the net benefit provided by better model prediction or the expected opportunity loss due to hydrologic uncertainties. The latter point is explained in greater detail in the paper coauthored with Simpson. Finally, a third point is that much data are needed for the type of input-output analysis proposed by the authors, especially if a split sample procedure is used. Such quantities of data are far from being always available.

Yevjevich. The objection to the use of autocorrelated variables x_i, x_{i-j}, $j = 1,2,\ldots$, in Eq. (1), the moving average part of the model, while the variables are assumed to be independent, faces the same problem as in any other application of regression analysis in hydrology, namely when the supposed independent variables are not independent. It is correct that an α_j coefficient of Eq. (1) does not represent the true effect of an x_{i-j} variable, because it may take into account also the effects the other x_{i-j} variables. The only solution then would be to remove from y and x variables periodicities and stochastic dependence (in this latter case by an autoregressive model, facing the same problem as in Eq. 1), and then relate the independent stochastic components of y and x by a linear regression. This would increase significantly the computations, and the prediction of y_i by x_{i-j}'s would involve several transformations. Because x_i is the rainfall in Eq. (1), and since the first serial correlation coefficient of daily rainfall is about 0.15-0.30, the auto-correlation of x_{i-j} variables seems not to be crucial.

It is true that the prediction by the MA-AR model of this paper can be applied only one step at a time. The prediction for two or more steps would then involve much larger errors that for only one step at a time.

Physical considerations and information are not easy to include into an input-output analysis of a karstified catchment. First, what kind of information on the system one has, which is not already integrated in the output? The best way to include the well defined characteristics of a catchment would be through a determination of the mathematical model of catchment response. However, by selecting an MA-AR model, as it is done in the paper, the autoregressive and moving average parts of this model already reflect the physics of the response, so that even that information may be redundant.

It is true that the variance should not be the only measure of performance of a system. The measure should be selected according to the objective of an analysis. When a model is

developed for predictive purposes, namely to forecast the
outflows from a karstified catchment for given precipitation
at a set of gauging stations, the use of variance seems to
be the best measure of the performance of a model.

To calibrate an input-output model data are necessary.
The more reliable the available data, the better is the model,
and the more reliable becomes the split-sample approach in
the testing and final calibration of the model. The question
may be asked whether any physical method can replace the lack
of data. One often wonders how reliable some physical models
of catchment response may be, when there is little data to
check it against, or to improve it. If the transfer of
information from gauged catchments to ungauged catchments is
needed, one may ask whether the transfer of input-output
models and regionalization of model parameters are any worse
than the speculative physical models without data to be
checked on.

WATER REGIME OF FLOODED KARST POLJES

by

Danilo M. Ristić, Civil Engineer and Department Head,
Institute for Water Resources Development, Sarajevo, Yugoslavia

Synopsis. Karst poljes represent hydrologic subsystems
within larger karst systems. Flood dynamics of such poljes is
usually defined by the water budget equation. Poljes can be
classified from the point of view of hydrographic characteristics which have a hydrologic significance. Such poljes are
important for flow regulation in many parts of the Yugoslav
Karst, which is illustrated by many flood recordings. A review
is given of methods used up to the present time for solving
various hydrologic problems of karst poljes. Review of methods
is based on the analysis of individual terms in the overall
water budget equation.

1. Introduction.

    Karst regions of Yugoslavia have a multiple significance
for the country. They have a long history of various investigations, though some of them have not been sufficient to meet
the present-day needs. Amongst others, the karst water resources represent a special importance in the Yugoslav Karst.
Hydrologically, a karst region represents a complex natural
water system. Both in underground and at the surface of karst
systems either a constant or a periodic process of transformation of water input to water outputs goes on. Though such a
process occurs in every hydrologic system, however, it has
several special and particularly unique features in karst.

    The specificity and complexity of Yugoslav karst systems
has attracted attention of investigators with various professional interests. In contrast to earlier, useful but
mainly qualitative approaches to karst, significant results
have been achieved in defining quantitatively as well as
qualitatively the hydrologic processes in the Yugoslav Karst
during the last 30 years.

2. Karst Poljes.

    A hydrologic system in the Yugoslav Karst may be divided
in separate subsystems, which are more or less connected or
interdependent among themselves, as the result of a number of
particular geologic historic influences. Among these subsystems
a significant role is played by the karst poljes[1], as a special

---

1) Reference is to those poljes which have some significant
   surface hydrologic features.

and characteristic phenomenon (both in a general and in a
hydrologic sense) of the Yugoslav Karst.

The earlier practice of investigating the karst poljes
as separate hydrologic systems resulted mainly from the difficulties of investigating them as subsystems of a large karst
system, with this latter approach being a correct approach[2]. It
is now almost generally accepted that hydrologic phenomena
in a karst polje are part of certain processes within the
total hydrologic karst system of a given catchment. When
the underground subsystems of a karst system cannot adequately
convey the infiltrated water from rainfall or snow melt to
the sea (or to some other water recipient), the karst poljes
become temporary and supplementary storage spaces performing
practically the same function as the underground storage,
namely as water recipients and conveyances, but with somewhat
different water movement conditions. Allowing for the local
specific aspects of the usual hydrologic phenemena, the subsystem in the form of a karst polje behaves according to the
changeable contour conditions imposed by a large hydrologic
system. These conditions are determined by the space surface
of underground and surface water levels defined at certain
points over the large system area.

The karst poljes of the large karst region of Yugoslavia
represent practically the cases of flat land in the midst of
a hilly and mountainous area. Frequently, they are located
in a cascade type sequence of various elevations. Their
total area occupies a relatively small part of the total karst
region[3]. However, often the karst poljes are almost the only
zones with some either intermittent or permanent hydrologic
phenomena, though some karst poljes are without water almost
all the time. By using the geomorphologic or hydrographic
criteria (which are of significance to hydrologic problems),
it is feasible, only to a certain extent, to classify karst
poljes in the following four ways: *(i) Enclosed karst poljes.*
Morphologically these poljes are surrounded by high ground
along their entire boundaries. Water enters poljes through
springs and estavellas (which are occasionally flooded) or
directly by rainfall and snowmelt. Water leaves poljes
through sinkholes. Examples are: the Fatničko, Dabarsko,
Glamočko, Livanjsko Poljes, Buško Blato, Konavosko and Nikšičko
Poljes, and others. *(ii) Karst poljes open upstream.* In

---

2) Future hydrologic investigations of water regimes in karst
   poljes in the Yugoslav Karst may likely proceed only by
   using the approach of a karst polje as subsystem of a large
   karst system (region, area, basin).
3) To support this statement, the karst poljes in the Trebišnjica
   River basin cover about 6%, while in the Cetina River basin
   they cover about 23% of the total surface.

contrast to the first group, this type of poljes has a predominant or a significant water inflow, apart from the inflow
through springs and from rainfall, by open water courses.
Examples are the Duvanjsko, Gatačko and Popovo Poljes. *(iii)*
Karst poljes open downstream. In contrast to enclosed poljes,
the water leaves the poljes of this group by a surface stream,
with or without outflows through estavellas and sinkholes. The
example is the Svitavsko-Deransko Blato. *(iv) Karst poljes
open both upstream and downstream.* This group represents a
combination of the group *(ii)* and *(iii).* Examples are the
Sinjsko and Šujičko Poljes.

Regardless of the group to which a polje belongs, the
definition of water regime in karst poljes represents often
one of the most important hydrologic problems in a karst
catchment. Namely, since hydrologic underground phenomena of
karst streams are, as a rule, almost unknown, at least quantitatively, it is understandable that the most attention has
been given until recently to those karst areas at which surface
water observations have been feasible. These areas in the
Yugoslav Karst are most frequently the karst poljes. Karst
poljes of this type of hydrologic significance are mostly
located in the Adriatic Sea drainage area, though some of them
are located also in the Sava River (Black Sea) drainage basin.

Karst poljes are flooded during the winter rainy period,
from time to time, from a few days up to six months duration.
These seasonal and intermittent floodings are subject of
special attention. Flooding usually covers the most important
parts of a polje, including areas of sinkholes, estavellas, and
springs. The fact that inflow and outflow points are flooded
complicates the identification or measurement of individual
terms in the water budget equation of this type of hydrologic
subsystem, especially their reliable, quantitative determination. In this respect the so-called enclosed karst poljes
represent subsystems of practical interest.

The modes in which the floodings occur in karst poljes
of Yugoslavia have been well described in Yugoslav technical
literature and can be also found in various professional
reports and documents. When the total inflow (Q_d) into a
karst polje exceeds the current capacity of all sinkholes, or
the outflow (Q_o), the water surplus $(+\Delta V)$ for a time interval (ΔT) is then stored in the polje as the water retention,
usually called flooding, flood or inundation. In the opposite
case, when $Q_d < Q_o$, the water budget of the polje becomes
negative $(-\Delta V)$ and flooding recedes or ceases. This process
is defined by the simple water budget equation

$$Q_d - Q_o = \pm \frac{\Delta V}{\Delta T}, \qquad (1)$$

with the storage change ΔV of the right side of Eq. (1) representing the net inflow or outflow of the retention in the interval ΔT, or

$$\pm \frac{\Delta V}{\Delta T} = \pm Q_r \; . \tag{2}$$

Figures 1 and 2 present the schematic hydrologic graphs illustrating the flood process in a karst polje, for very simplified conditions of inflows and outflows. Figure 2 gives three level hydrographs for three characteristic piezometric boreholes around the Fatničko Polje in the Trebišnjica River basin, and the water hydrograph in the flooded polje, for the winter period of two and a half months of the flood season.

From a hydrologic point of view the problem is in determining the individual terms of Eq. (1) during the corresponding time intervals, as discussed in the further text. Stored water in the poljes during floods vary significantly, depending on the magnitude of terms in Eq. (1) as well as on particular hydrologic conditions of each polje, flood and time interval.

By natural water retention in flooded karst poljes the available total space may not be considered as being used very effectively. For example, in extreme cases 1 m^2 of the polje area retains most frequently only 1.0 to 10.0 m^3 of water, this proportion rarely exceeding 15.0 m^3/m^2. For storage reservoirs recently constructed in the same karst area the values are 14.1-65.0 m^3/m^2. However, the total stored water in karst polje retentions may be relatively large. In the Popovo Polje before the construction of the Bileća Reservoir, the total volume used to reach even as much as 980×10^6 m^3. As an illustration, data are given in Table 1 for some of the largest natural retentions in the Cetina, Trebišnjica and Neretva River basins. Among the other data, the ratios between the maximum volume recorded for a retention and the average annual water inflow are given, as max V/W_a. These

ratios and the other data show that flow retardations of these natural, temporary karst lakes may be very large. Although seasonal floodings represent an inconvenience from the point of view of utilizing the karst polje areas, they are in fact a useful natural phenomenon in regulating karst waters. Without these karst poljes retentions the variations in runoff from karst hydrologic systems would be much greater than they are at present. Besides the periodically flooded karst poljes, the underground karst subsystems of the total drainage area have the same natural role in regulating the runoff from karst systems.

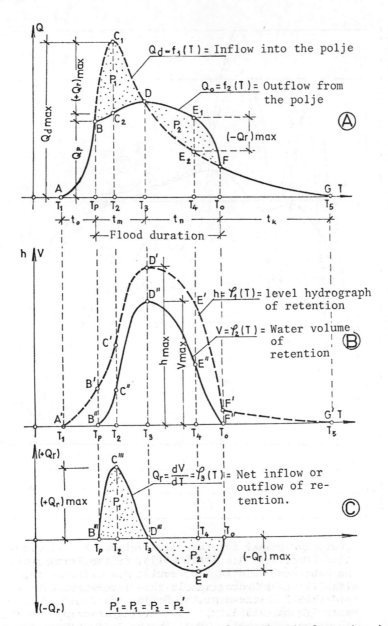

Fig. 1.   Schematic Representation of Flood Transformation in a
Flooded Karst Polje for a Simplified Case of Inflows
and Outflows: (A) Inflow and Outflow Discharge Hydro-
graphs; (B) Level Hydrograph and Volume Hydrograph of
Flooded Polje; and (C) Hydrograph of Difference of
Inflow and Outflow of a Flooded Karst Polje, or the
Net Input or Net Output of the Polje.

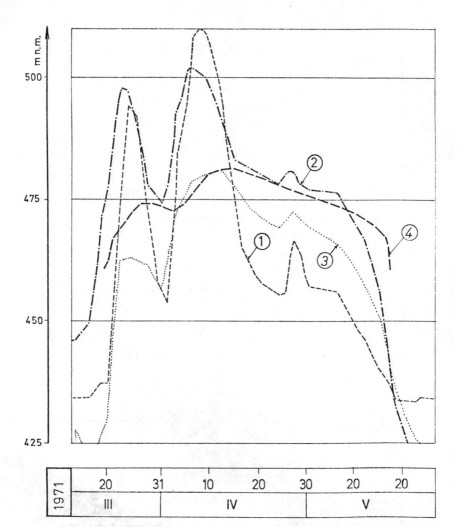

Fig. 2. Level hydrographs for the Illustration of Characteristic Processes in a Karst Polje, on the Example of
the Fatničko Polje in the Trebišnjica River Basin,
with:(1) Level Hydrograph in the Piezometric Borehole (PB-1) Upstream of the Polje in a Zone of High
Water Transmissibility; (2) Level Hydrograph in the
Piezometric Borehole (OK-2) in the Zone of Estavellas
of the Polje; (3) Level Hydrograph in the Piezometric
Borehole (F-5) in the Zone of the Sinkholes of the
Polje; and (4) Level Hydrograph of the Flooded Polje,
all During the 2-5 Month Winter Period (Mid-March
Through May, 1971).

Table 1.   Basic Data for Some Karst Polje Retensions in the Cetina, Trebišnjica, and Neretva River Catchments for the Conditions Existed Before Large Water Resources Developments.

No.	Watershed of the River	Retension on the Karst Polje of	Maximum Flood Level, H_{max} m.a.s.l.	Maximum Flood Volume, V_{max} 10^6 m^3	Maximum Surface, A_{max} K^2 m	$\frac{V_{max}}{A_{max}}$	Average Annual Flow W_a 10^6 m^3	$\frac{V_{max}}{W_a}$	Remarks *
1.		Livno	706.70 708.50	135.0 70.0	108.0 70.0	1.25 1.00	688.8	0.30	Two retensions
2.	Cetina	Buško Blato	705.50	223.0	48.5	4.60	368.8	0.61	
3.		Duvno	864.34	44.0	23.5	1.87	312.0	0.14	
4.		Glamoč	890.54	89.0	29.0	3.06	116.0	0.77	
5.		Sinj		31.0*	39.0	0.80			Estimate
		Total:		592.0			3600.0*	(0.17)	At Trilj
6.		Gacko	933.43	14.1	7.0	2.01	276.0	0.05	
7.	Trebišnjica	Fatnica	500.77	225.8	8.7	25.95	300.0	0.75	
8.		Popovo	260.76	980.0	65.0	15.08	3790.0*	0.26	(Upper limit)
		Total:		1219.9*			3790.0	(0.32)	(Incomplete)
9.		Nevesinje	837.36	94.5	10.7	8.8	431.0	0.22	
10.	Neretva	Mostarsko Blato	234.01	201.0	27.7	7.3			
11.		Dabar	486.42	117.9	13.8	8.5	236.0	0.49	
12.		Prološko Blato	274.07	14.5	2.8	5.1			
13.		Bekija	261.88	225.0	55.0	4.1			
		Total:		652.9			12,100*	(0.05)	At Gabela

From the given information and conclusions it follows, when flood control is implemented by decreasing the flooding of karst poljes, that an attention should be paid not to undertake those flood control measures which will substantially decrease the flow regulation and increase the runoff variability. Flood control should predominately rely on construction of storage reservoirs, which, apart from the other beneficial effects, would replace the hydrologic role of natural retentions of karst poljes. As an example, the three river basins, for which data are given in Table 1, a total storage capacity of 3,440 x 10^6 m^3 has been constructed.

3.   A Survey of Past Hydrologic Methods.

In previous analyses of hydrologic problems in the Yugoslav Karst in general, and of karst poljes in particular, various hydrologic methods were used, however, more or less successfully. The results obtained were often approximate inevitably due to some pertinent difficulties. The projects already realized for the development of karst water resources have

shown that there was no justification in using the approximate
results obtained by such methods, regardless of scepticism expressed by experts both in and outside Yugoslavia in the past
concerning the potential success or failure of engineering
projects in the Yugoslav Karst. On the contrary, the experience
with the operation of the existing large karst systems shows
that they have been built within the limits of customary, or
even smaller risks than usually acceptable, due primarily to
some very flexible, good technical concepts developed by
Yugoslav specialists. The construction of these karst systems
in stages made it feasible to successively improve them as the
accuracy of respective hydrologic data increased, to introduce
new methods of investigations, and to undertake the complex and
versatile investigations.

A development and/or an application of feasible hydrologic
methods occurred within these activities. A more detailed
description of the methods used in the past would require, but
also deserve, a more elaborate approach, not feasible in the
limits of this paper. To be comprehensive in a simple way,
without following either a historic order or entering into
details, the hydrologic methods applied in the past in studying
the Yugoslav Karst can be systematized in five groups:

I. The first group of investigation methods consisted of
various hydrographic, geologic, hydrogeologic, engineering-
geology and other investigations, mainly orientated to acquir-
ing the basic knowledge, with a more or less descriptive interpretation of karst phenomena. This group included also the
methods of using the various tracers for identification of
underground water connections. A significant progress was
achieved in these investigations, and these methods are still
used as necessary or even irreplaceable at present.

II. This group of methods consisted of hydrologic investigations of permanent or intermittent karst streams, which represent entirely or partly the regional water resources, however, without the special hydrologic karst features. Most of
these hydrologic methods are similar to classical, or standard
hydrologic methods used for surface water courses of non-karst
regions. Without neglecting the respective difficulties in
developing the karst water resources, such as obtaining the
proper and reliable information by observations and measurements, these methods used in the past were simple from a
hydrologic point of view, regardless that they have been applied
to the development of water resources in the Yugoslav Karst,
considered more attractive economically, such as the construction of the hydroelectric power plants Perućica and Trebinje.
This historic phase of developing methods in treating karst
water problems has a particular hydrologic significance. They
represented first approach to various complex investigations
of various kinds of water resources in karst catchments. This

included the karst poljes with the first attempts at approxi-
mating all the individual terms in their water budget equations.

III. This group of historic hydrologic methods are
applied to karst poljes, particularly to poljes with a significant seasonal flooding and water retardation. Though the
hydrologic problems may be defined by Eq. (1), the real difficulties occur when determining its terms. A review of problems
and of likely solutions was done by Yevjevich [2] as early as
1955. His paper investigated the general principles in determining the individual terms of water budget equation for enclosed and flooded karst poljes. It is important to emphasize,
in connection with the methods used of determining the terms in
the water budget equation, that almost always and as a rule,
the methods used were mostly oriented to determining those
terms which could be, at that time and in any given case,
easily quantified. The total accounting of the water budget,
at least during floods and for the time being, most often was
not feasible or it was done indirectly by using some regional,
easier to quantify, hydrologic terms. Some examples are presented in the following text.

Determination of inflows into a polje. The inflow, Q_d,
is in principle the most convenient term to determine in an
accurate way, especially in case of an upstream open poljes
type, with an approximate estimate of the remaining, but small
parts of inflow. No progress has been made in measuring
the flow capacity of flooded springs and estavellas. It is
technically difficult and economically unfeasible to measure
a dispersed type of inflows into the polje under the conditions
of these springs and estavellas being covered by water of
flooded poljes, and over a whole chain of either identified
or unidentified, flooded or unflooded, water inlets into a
polje.

Substantial results have been obtained by Srebrenović [6,
7] in defining the stochastic relationships between the flows
of neighboring karst water streams and the inflow into a karst
polje, by using the data obtained during the period when it
was possible to measure all these flows. By using these
correlative relationships, with a certain approximation, in
periods of floods with short durations, satisfactory estimates
of inlfows have been obtained, such as the average values of
the water inflow into a polje over several time intervals.

With some logical assumptions, Srebrenović [6] and some
other authors investigated the rainfall-to-runoff relationships
in karst areas, as well as differentiating between the underground and surface contributions to runoff in karst. Without
an intention to pretentiously evaluate the merits of all
methods of these groups in this paper, it should nevertheless

be emphasized that by using the method given by Srebrenović
represents a valuable contribution to methodology of solving
karst hydrologic problems, as well as pointing out to certain
specific and important aspects of karst hydrology.

Determination of outflow (Q_o) from a polje. The evaluation
of water outflows from flooded karst poljes has been the
subject of special studies and field investigations for a long
time for the following two reasons:

(i) The water inflows into a polje, especially during
the rainy season, are most frequently and highly dispersed
over many locations, impossible to be observed and measured
completely, with significant difficulties to quantify them
to a satisfactory degree of accuracy.

(ii) The great economic interest in developing water
resources of the Yugoslav karst poljes during the past thirty
years has made available a fund of valuable hydrologic information, predominately consisting of observations of outflows
of the zones of most frequent and large sinkholes, i.e. at the
zones of large concentrations of swallowholes with entire
streams entering the sinkholes.

Along with some other field conditions, the above factors
were the main reasons that often the identification of karst
polje hydrology was orientated to investigations nearly exclusively to establish the capacity rating curves of sinkholes.
Since this task is often difficult to achieve in a simple way,
considerable efforts were devoted to this problem but with
modest results, in some way moving in a vicious circle. Most
investigations undertaken during this historic period (and
such types of investigations are still being actively pursued
at present) have been directed to compromising decisions by
unwarranted simplifications in obtaining the shape of capacity
rating curves of sinkholes. Frequently, the assumption was
a constant, unique rating curve as the relationship between
the water level of the flooded polje and the sinkhole outflow
capacity, or the capacity of an entire sinkhole zone. These
attempts to determine the capacity rating curves of sinkholes
in this way remained more or less without significant results,
becoming a subject of controversy and criticism [1].

With some simplifications necessary at that time the
writer of this paper attempted [4] almost 15 years ago to
demonstrate the occurrence of various hydraulic types of
underground karst systems, which make the capacities rating
curves of sinkholes to be nonstationary relationships. The
proposal was then made, and later carried out, to install the
special measuring instruments at one of sinkholes [3] in order
to continuously register the water discharge through the sinkhole, and determine how the rating curve changes with various
factors. The results of these and subsequent investigations

have indirectly shown that the classical hydrogeologic sorting
of sinkholes and estavellas into zones is not acceptable, and
that the flow through the underground channels around and
beneath the karst poljes depends in a small or large measure
on water piezometric states both in the surrounding rock massif
and in the polje itself, and that these channels may serve
both for water inflows and water outflows of karst poljes.

In summary, various efforts to develop methods for the
simple evaluation of sinkhole capacity rating curves in karst
poljes have not yielded a clue, as was believed one time they
would, in solving the major hydrologic problems of karst poljes.
However, the past investigations of this phenomenon have
nevertheless been fruitful. Besides a feasible advancement
of logical hypotheses, with certain approximations, they have
had another byside result, which was not originally expected
but came out to be of a great importance. The effect was,
along with obtaining the better results of hydrogeologic
investigations, in taking a new approach to investigations for
understanding the hydrologic role of karst poljes, and in
better concepts for observation and measurement of certain
hydraulic phenomena which determine the hydrologic processes in
karst poljes.

The investigations of the past to accurately evaluate
the terms of water budget equation of flooded karst poljes
produced the idea that the expected, best future method of
analysis should not be any *packaged* one-sided approach, but a
multidisciplinary approach consisting of investigating the
subsystem multiple characteristics and the use of piezometric
boreholes information, with these piezometric boreholes located
around a karst polje to define its hydrologic boundary conditions.

IV. The use of piezometric borehole observations, as an
additional information for the analysis of hydrology of karst
poljes, represents a new group of methods to be used in
increasing the potential of quantitative and qualitative description of their hydrology.

The exploration boreholes were originally introduced for
several engineering reasons such as the study of the water
imperviousness of karst reservoirs, determination of water
catchment boundaries, potential bifurcation of underground
channels, design of grouting curtains for karst reservoirs,
and similar objectives. A large number of deep piezometric
boreholes have been drilled in the important karst water
catchments in Yugoslavia, mainly as a preconditions for various
decisions in developing the karst water resources. Without
entering into the discussion of techniques used in drilling
these boreholes and in observing the piezometer levels, with
such aspects as the reliability of obtained information,

continuity and frequency of observations of underground water
levels, and similar aspects, some general results of these
piezometric observations will be discussed in this paper only,
though the drilling of boreholes was not the major original
objective in studying the water regime of karst poljes. Careful and accurate observations in piezometers of karst catchments, especially by measuring the oscillations of underground
water levels in piezometers located at the rims of karst
poljes, and a comparison of these observations with the simultaneous observations of water levels in karst polje retentions,
have shown the following results:

(i) Some areas at the rim formations of a karst polje
may show water levels to be independent of water level fluctuations in the flooded karst poljes;

(ii) If the position of piezometer boreholes were
selected at the polje rims, both deliberately and conveniently
within the zones of intensive underground water flows by using
hydrogeologic studies, the piezometer levels may well give
the water level boundary conditions for inflows and outflows
of karst poljes;

(iii) Piezometers with observed level fluctuations
often show some mixed characteristics, namely those combining
the previous two cases, making their interpretation somewhat
difficult. Figure 2 illustrates this case.

The role of piezometers as a means of hydrologic investigations in karst poljes has not yet been sufficiently explored,
and less so applied, because their use started relatively
recently. When they are economically justified and conveniently
combined with the other hydrologic and hydrogeologic objectives
of investigations, piezometers are excellently suited for
quantification of hydraulic characteristics of the flow medium
in the mid of which a karst polje is located, provided the
piezometric observations are properly carried out and interpreted.

This approach by using the piezometric observations in
studying hydrologic problems of enclosed karst poljes was
applied by Avdagić recently (see his paper in this proceedings
book). It can be expected that the methodology introduced
by his paper will, with further improvements, make a substantial
contribution to solution of hydrologic problems related to the
water budget equation of karst poljes. One of the conditions
for the application of the method based on piezometric observations in boreholes is that piezometers, or some other technique
for the observation of underground water levels, to be well
located, based upon prior extensive hydrogeologic and hydrologic
investigations.

V. The computed water budget of karst poljes, until
recently and except in investigation by Srebrenović in the
Cetina River basin, included mainly or only the contributions

by surface inflows. It has been established in several cases
that a significant part of the total water runoff consists of
underground water, flowing intermittently or permanently
under a karst polje, without appearing on the surface at any
time. For example, the runoff coefficient of the water budget
of about 0.75 was obtained in a part of the area of the
Livanjsko Polje. But in another part of it, under the identical
climatic and general geologic conditions, the runoff coefficient of only 0.27 was obtained by using only the surface
inflows. Obviously, a significant part of karst underground
waters was not taking part in the water budget. In using
various water budget methods, a relatively small attention
has been given to identification, location and measurement
of these water flows immediately below the karst poljes. From
a point of view of a long-range karst water resources development, neglecting these underground water resources close to
karst polje surfaces cannot be justified.

4. Analysis of Water Budget Equation.

In the future, the hydrologic investigations of karst
phenomena in Yugoslavia in general, and of karst poljes in
particular should consist, in the writer's opinion, of:

(i) A development of methods specific to karst hydrology
with their testing in various karst areas for a better investigation of complete karst water drainage systems, by which the
rainfall and snowmelt are transformed into the particular water
outflow regimes; and

(ii) An improvement of many existing, and a discovery
of new, methods of investigation of hydrologic problems of
flood-prone karst poljes as subsystems of large karst drainage
areas.

The first direction of developing and improving investigation methods is warranted to pursue, because the results
obtained so far confirm many useful payoffs. However, either
by new methods, by a partial development of new methods, or
by the use of classical methods, the advancement in karst
hydrology can be accomplished only by treating hydrologic
processes as a whole namely by simultaneously analyzing the
surface and underground waters. This need requires a development of new methods by specially designed research projects.

The second direction of developing and improving the
investigation methods for the use in the Yugoslav Karst is
justified by the fact that water resources of the lower karst
regions in Yugoslavia have already been more or less developed;
these developments have not been affected by a lack of hydrologic information. This is not true for the higher located karst
regions. A large group of circumstances indicate that, without

entering into the problems of submarine karst springs, the
forthcoming economic interest in development of karst water
resources, such as the proper use of the space in karst regions,
the development of agriculture, the production of energy, will
be more or less centered in or around the karst poljes. This
means there is already a need for continuing the present and
starting the new research endeavors related to hydrology of
karst poljes. Justifications for such future hydrologic
studies include among others:

(i) Present and expected needs to investigate and
discriminate the eventual influences of engineering structures
in karst areas on the water regime of karst poljes; and

(ii) Expected demands for future development of underground water reserves and storage spaces in karst formations.

If the information on characteristics of the water regime
of karst poljes has been relatively sufficient in the past,
requiring estimates of a small number of hydrologic parameters
(such as the mean, the minimum water flow parameters, the
parameters of water levels in natural retentions), the future
development objectives will definitely require a much greater
information (such as the various properties of daily flows,
maximum flows, a more precise information on weather conditions,
the distributions in space of certain hydrologic characteristics, and similar information). In that case, hydrologic information will be required for both the entire karst polje
and its parts. In summary, a need already exists for a
detailed information on more or less all the terms of the
water budget equation of a karst polje. For the above objectives and not only formally, it makes sense to apply the water
budget equation, Eq. (1), of the karst poljes much more broadly
than has been the case in the past. For such an approach and
for the entire karst polje subsystem, the general form of the
water budget equation becomes:

$$
\left(\sum_1^k Q_{dn} + \sum_1^\alpha Q_{dp} \right) - \left(\sum_1^m Q_{on} + \sum_1^\beta Q_{op} \right) = \left(\pm \sum_1^e \frac{\Delta V}{\Delta T} \right)_n + \left(\pm \sum_1^\gamma \frac{\Delta V}{\Delta T} \right)_p \cdots
$$

(3)

with d and o the indices for inflow and outflow, respectively, and n or p standing for surface or underground terms
of the budget equation. The upper limits of sums (k, α, β,...)
correspond to the number of subterms in each term. This interpretation of the water budget equation might, at the first
glance, appear to be too general or too ambitious. However,
the required hydrologic studies of karst poljes must necessarily
move in the direction of the more complete and generalized
forms. If such a generalized approach is applicable for the
non-karst areas and aquifers, one should pose the question why
it would not be applicable for karst areas and aquifers?

A basic discussion is pertinent for the individual terms of Eq. (3), namely:

(i) The term $\sum Q_{dn}$ covers the entire surface inflow, such as inflow by open streams, karst springs, estavellas, rainfall (with its influence often non-negligible), but it also includes inflow made by the man-made diversions (such cases already exist in the Neretva River drainage basin);

(ii) The term $\sum Q_{on}$, by analogy with inflows, represents all water outflows from the polje, including the man-made diversions (such as in the Livanjsko Polje), and partly or fully unrecoverable water consumption in the polje (such as the irrigation);

(iii) The term $\pm \sum \frac{\Delta V}{\Delta T}$ deserves more than a customary attention, since errors made in its determination (either due to unchecked or imprecise basic information, or due to bad maps) have a significant influence on the results of computations. On the other hand, some karst poljes may possess several water retentions with changing interrelationships (such cases are the karst poljes of the Cetina and Neretva River basins).

The information provided by the graph of the rate-of-change of retention volume with time can be of a greater use than presently used. For example, it follows from the graphs (A, B, C) of Fig. 1 that even in the case of a very simple hydrograph there are five particular (or control) points of varying significance, namely the points (1), (2), and (3) for $T = T_p$, $T = T_3$, and $T = T_o$, that means $Q_d = Q_o$; and points (4) and (5) for $T = T_2$, and $T = T_4$, that correspond to extreme values of Q_r. A more complex graph has a larger number of this type of control points, which can be correspondingly used.

As for the terms concerning the underground waters, unfortunately and apart from what has been said here earlier [6], no details similar to above points can be suggested. It is necessary to find some new techniques for better identifying the underground water terms of a water system and its hydrologic characteristics.

5. Conclusions.

Hydrologic studies of karst poljes in Yugoslavia are expected to receive a full attention in the near future. When based on a better and more detailed knowledge of hydrogeologic and hydrologic characteristics of the surrounded areas of a polje, the expected study results should be much greater than they are at present. In that respect, the more detailed geologic and hydrogeologic investigations may include a more intensive and better use of presently available hydrologic methods, and a development of new methods, for the identification of boundary conditions under which the subsystem of a karst polje operates.

Regarding the detailed but general decomposition of the water budget equation, such as Eq. (3), the economic feasibility of a detailed analysis and of field investigations of its individual terms plays an important influence in decision making. Besides this constraint, difficulties with which (at least at present) an investigator is faced in studying each term in the budget equation, which is related to karst groundwater environment, restrict the optimism for some rapid future progress in developing methods able to treat an entire group of hydrologic problems in karst poljes.

It seems a realistic approach to define the objectives of investigations of karst poljes, in introducing and applied the advanced hydrologic methods, to reinforce the present trends (at least in Yugoslavia), of a gradual decrease of errors in method approximations and of an increase in the quantity of data on water regimes of karst poljes.

6. References.

[1] Djurović, M., Hidrološka studija i melioracija Mostarskog blata (The hydrologic study and reclamation of the Mostarsko Blato): Gradjevinar, 2, 48-58, Zagreb, 1964.

[2] Jevdjević, V., Metode za odredjivanje približnog bilansa voda zatvorenih i plavljenih kraških polja (Yevjevich, V., Methods of determination of approximate water budget of enclosed and flooded karst poljes): Zbornik radova Hidrotehničkog inst. *Jaroslav Černi*, (Transactions of Water Resources Research Institute, *Jaroslav Černi*), 3, 141-154, Beograd, 1955.

[3] Mikulec, S., Bagarić, I., Izbor najpogodnije metode mjerenja kapaciteta ponora (Selection of the most convenient method for measuring the flow capacity of sink-holes): Radovi i saopštenja Zavoda za hidrotehniku (Transactions of Hydrotechnical Institute), 7, 119-130, Sarajevo, 1966.

[4] Ristić, D., Problemi odredjivanja kapaciteta ponora (Problems of determining the sinkhole capacities): III savjet. jug. stručnj. za hidraulička istraž. (Third Conference of Yugoslav specialists for hydraulic investigation), 65-73, Opatija 1962.

[5] Ristić, D., Odbrana od poplava kraških polja - metoda dopunskog kapaciteta (Flood control of karst poljes - the supplimental capacity method): Gradjevinar 23/4, 100-103, Zagreb, 1971.

[6] Srebrenović, D., Problemi velikih voda (Flood problems): Tehnička knjiga, 1-277, Zagreb, 1970.

[7] Srebrenović, D., Kraški ponori i njihova propustna moć (Karst sinkholes and their discharge capacities): Gradjevinar, 16/12, 425-436, Zagreb, 1964.

[8] Srebrenović, D., Još nešto o kraškim ponorima (More on karst sinkholes): Gradjevinar, 3, 114-116, Zagreb, 1965.

[9] Šunjić, J., Poljoprivredne melioracije na kršu Bosne i Hercegovine (Agricultural reclamation in the karst areas of Bosnia and Hercegovina): Krš Bosne i Hercegovine, Savezno savjetovanje o kršu (Federal Conference on Karst), 3, 11-23, Split, 1957.

Apart from the above mentioned literature, various documents at the Institute of Water Resources Engineering, Sarajevo, at the Institute of Water Resources Development, Sarajevo, at the Energoinvest, Sarajevo, and at the Projekt, Zagreb, were used.

DISCUSSION

Yevjevich. Could the author explain, by using examples, why he considers that until now the water regime of karst poljes was studied in Yugoslavia only partially or inadequately, and that the study of the entire river basin would produce much better results? What does he expect that the larger area studies would contribute to the understanding of water regimes of karst poljes in comparison with the study of inputs, states of the water regime in the polje and outputs only.

Ristić. Taking into account the versatile results of studies obtained in karst regions by the Yugoslav engineers and experts of other specialties, I hope it will not be considered as a lack of modesty to point out that those who gained this experience are entitled to make also critical observations, or even that such critical observations are necessary.

Starting from several premises as outlined in the paper, and from the criteria for necessary hydrologic information for various projects and decision making, it seems appropriate to consider the past studies of water regime in karst poljes in Yugoslavia were inadequate in the sense of modern hydrologic concepts and complexity of karst phenomena.

The approach to the water budget equation of flooded karst poljes inevitably has a character of an approximation. Often, one is faced with the problem of solving an equation with two unknowns. If some approximations in determination of budget equation terms were acceptable so far, there are several reasons for searching a higher order approximation of these terms. To enable these better approximations, the karst hydrology problems of karst poljes should be studied in the frame of a much larger system to which this polje belongs. The reasons are: (i) The information from a set of piezometric boreholes at the karst polje boundaries may not be sufficient; and (ii) If a karst polje is a subsystem of a larger karst water system, it should be expected that information obtained from the entire, large system may bear on the inference on the hydrologic regime of a karst polje.

A RAPID METHOD FOR DETERMINING WATER BUDGET
OF ENCLOSED AND FLOODED KARST PLAINS

by

Željko Žibret, Civil Engineer,

and

Zdravko Šimunić, Civil Engineer,
Hidro-biro, Energoinvest, Sarajevo, Yugoslavia

Synopsis. During floods difficulties arise on occasion in estimating water budget of enclosed karst plains. When karst plains were flooded, it was practically impossible to measure water inflows, since the gauging stations were under the high waters of these flooded plains. Besides a number of periodical springs contributed inflows, which often entered the plains below the flood levels.

This paper aims at developing a method for determining water budget using the usually available data, without the cost of special investigations. In such cases it is possible to approximately estimate the inflow by using a simplified budget equation for flooded and enclosed karst plains. In this equation, however, both inflow and outflow are unknown quantities. The change in the water volume stored in the plain can be obtained from the registered water levels during the floods and the volume-to-level relationship of the plain.

To estimate the inflow into the plain during floods, it was first necessary to determine the outflow through sinkholes, which was basically the subject of this paper. The starting assumption was that the outflow, Q_o, from the plain depended on preceding precipitations, I_{pp}, water height in the plain, H, and the month of the year, M. This relationship was developed as a model in the form of the multiple linear regression.

Results obtained for several karst plains of different hydrologic characteristics showed that the method was applicable to enclosed karst plains, for which the precipitation simultaneously and predominantly affected both the inflow and outflow. The method was less applicable to karst plains with flood waters brought in by larger water-courses from larger catchments, since the errors in estimating the inputs by the mathematical model were much greater than in the case of measuring inflows of these streams. It has also been found that the figures computed were somewhat smaller than the actual inflows; thus it was acceptable in case of estimating the hydroelectric potential of the total water

budget of these plains, since the estimates were on the conservative side.

1. Introduction.

The water outflows through sinkholes and percolation
zones of karst plains are limited by their maximum capacity.
Because inflows may be much greater than the outflow capacities
put together, the difference is then stored by flooding the
karst plains. This flooding often brings springs as well as
gauging stations under water. The measurement of inflows
and the estimation of water budget become difficult if not
impossible. The periods in which karst plains were flooded
last for several months per year. Besides, a number of
temporary water springs appear on the karst plain rims during
floods, for which it was difficult, even when there were not
floods, to assess the inflows into the plain. For the estimate of water inflow into the enclosed karst plains during
the flood periods, the water budget of these flooded plains
can be determined by

$$Q_d = Q_o \pm \frac{\Delta V}{\Delta t} , \tag{1}$$

where Q_d = the inflow into the plain in m^3/sec, Q_o = the
discharge out of the plain in m^3/sec and $\pm \Delta V/\Delta t$ is the
rate of change of water volume in the plain, or the change
per time unit. This change of water volume ΔV can always
be obtained from the volume to height relationship for each
plain. To apply the simple budget equation, Eq. (1), of
flooded plains, it is necessary first to determine the outflow
Q_o from the plain. Figure 1 shows schematically the simplified conditions of inflow and outflow hydrographs of flooded,
enclosed karst plains.

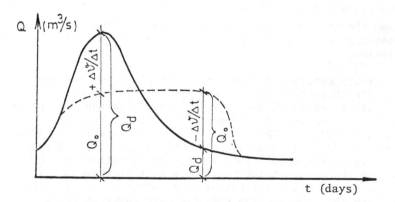

Fig. 1. Inflow and Outflow Hydrographs of Flooded, Closed
Karst Plains.

2.   Problem to be Solved.

For the application of Eq. (1), it is necessary to find either the inflow Q_d or the outflow Q_o of the plain. Solution to the problem was found by processing hydrologic data for a long time period. Data to be used must be reduced to precipitation and water levels in karst plains, because only these data were available in most cases. If the water outflow from karst plains was determined as the flow through a system of channels under pressure, analogous to the water flow through a system of water networks under pressure, it was evident that some indicators that defined the state of piezometric levels in this system must be found. The geometric factors of underground system of channels, such as their lengths, cross sections and roughness, practically do not change during full capacity flow. The state of underground water levels in the area between the sinkholes in the plain and downstream springs were defined only on the basis of precipitation data, because they determine the regime of underground waters between the sinkholes and springs. It was then assumed that the capacity of all sinkholes in the enclosed karst plains depended on the index of previous precipitation in the area that directly fed the drainage channels between the plain and the downstream springs, the water level of the flooded plain and the season (measuring the evaporation and evapotranspiration part of precipitation), that is:

$$Q_o = f(I_{pp}, H, M) \quad , \tag{2}$$

where Q_o = the total outflow capacity in m^3/sec, I_{pp} = the index of previous precipitations in mm, and M = the season of the year, determined by the sequence of months. For this hypothetical relationship, the most appropriate mathematical model should be found.

3.   Input Data.

In selecting the mathematical model for the hypothesized relationship of Eq. (2), the input values on Q_o, I_{pp}, H and M for a sufficiently long time period are necessary.

Determination of Q_o. The determination of input Q_o was the most difficult task. The total outflow capacity could be approximately determined in the final stage of the outflow, when the flooded plain was being emptied [1,2,3,4].

Immediately before the karst plain was emptied, it was possible to extrapolate backwards the inflow hydrograph to past inflows, or which may be simpler but less accurate, to

assume that the inflow into the plain was approximately the
same at the time of its emptying and immediately before that.
When Q_d, the inflow into the plain selected in this way, was
added to the rate $\Delta Q = \Delta V/\Delta t$, the change in the volume V
at that time and time interval Δt, the total capacity Q_o
of all sinkholes that were active at that moment, was obtained.
In some cases, it was possible to neglect Q_d and take only
$\Delta Q = \Delta V/\Delta t$ as the outflow Q_o. This is ordinarily the case
with enclosed karst plains with a small direct catchment area.
Figure 2 shows a scheme of how to determine the input Q_o.
Then approximately

$$Q_o \simeq Q_d' + \Delta Q \tag{3}$$

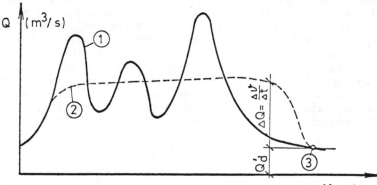

Fig. 2.   A Scheme for Determining the Input Q_o of Enclosed
          Karst Plains: (1) Inflow Hydrograph; (2) Outflow
          Hydrograph; and (3) The Moment of Final Emptying of
          Karst Plain.

The analysis of a number of floods under different weather
conditions gave sufficient data for the calibration of the
mathematical model. The input Q_o obtained in this way
related mainly to dry periods while the plain was still
flooded, because these periods correspond to final time of
emptying of plains.

Determination of I_{pp}. The discharge capacity of sinkholes depends on the underground piezometric pressures. When
no piezometric observations exist, or they exist only for
shorter periods of time not sufficient for calibration of
hydrologic models, an indicator of water flow conditions in
the underground may be   found in an indirect way.   The index

of previous precipitation, I_{pp}, can serve this objective.
It is obvious that previous precipitation affect most the
regime of underground waters, with their total effect changing
with time. These effects do not exist only if the underground
channels were always under a free-surface flow, which may not
be common. The effect of precipitation on the state of
piezometric pressures decreases with the time elapsed. Therefore, this time factor was taken as K_t = exp $(-\alpha t)$, where
e = the basis of the natural logarithm, α = the coefficient
determined experimentally, and t = usually the number of
days between the rainfall and the moment of computing the
outflow. Antecedent precipitation, I_{pp}, was extended in
this analysis to past 60 days as:

$$I_{pp} = \sum_{t=1}^{60} K_t P_t = \sum_{t=1}^{60} e^{-\alpha t} P_t , \qquad (4)$$

where P_t = the average daily precipitation of the catchment
of the t-th day before estimating the outflow by taking precipitation of the past 60 days. All the antecedent large
precipitation events of effect on the state of piezometric
pressures in the underground should be taken into account.
Usually, this period can be shorter than 60 days.

Determination of H. Water flood levels in enclosed
karst plains were usually observed once every 24 hours. By
using the volume-to-level relationship the total water volume
stored in the plain could be determined. Consequently, the
rate of change of water volume V in the plain in a time
unit was:

$$\Delta Q = \frac{\Delta V}{\Delta t} = \frac{V_1 - V_2}{t_1 - t_2} . \qquad (5)$$

Since $V_1 = f(H_1)$ and $V_2 = f(H_2)$, it follows

$$\Delta Q = \frac{f(H_1) - f(H_2)}{t_1 - t_2} . \qquad (6)$$

Since the outflow Q_o could be obtained from ΔQ determined
in this manner, the average water level was taken as the value
H, or

$$H = \frac{H_1 + H_2}{2} . \qquad (7)$$

This water level H, together with the antecedent precipitation index, defined indirectly the change in every gradient
which influenced the capacity of all sinkholes.

Determination of M. As previously explained the parameter I_{pp} defines in some way the groundwater levels, because
larger antecedent precipitation would result in higher groundwater levels. However, the same previous precipitation will
differently affect the groundwater regime, depending on the
season. During dry summers the same antecedent precipitation
would affect the groundwater levels, and thus the capacity of
sinkholes, differently than during wet winters. In addition,
the biological cover, evapotranspiration, temperature, humidity of the air, and similar factors differ from season to
season. For all these reasons, the seasonal parameter M
had to be introduced. This parameter was introduced by a
sequence of months, with August being one and so on to July
being twelve. The underground was usually filled with water
from autumn to spring. The above sequence is a function of
the climate, and is valid only for the regime of rivers flowing
into the Adriatic Sea in Yugoslavia.

4. Mathematical Model.

The outlined variables define the hydraulic effects on
outflows of enclosed karst plains in an indirect way, yet
they have different dimensions. For that reason a regression
type mathematical model rather than a functional type is
selected. Both linear and nonlinear regression equations are
analyzed, the linear equation in the form

$$Q_o = A_o + A_1 H + A_2 M + A_3 I_{pp} \, , \qquad (8)$$

and the nonlinear equation in the form

$$Q_o = A_{11} + A_{12} H + A_{13} M + A_{14} I_{pp} + A_{22} H^2 +$$

$$+ A_{23} H M + A_{24} H I_{pp} + A_{33} M^2 + A_{34} M \cdot I_{pp} +$$

$$+ A_{44} I_{pp}^2 \, . \qquad (9)$$

The multiple linear regression, Eq. (8), was shown to be
satisfactory, and was used by selecting values of independent
variables in Eq. (8), which correspond to special times of
emptying plains. As described above, it was possible to form
a series of equations in which the unknowns were the regression

coefficients A_o, A_1, A_2, and A_3. These regression coefficients were then estimated from these equations by the least-squares method. To measure how good was a regression equation with these coefficients, multiple correlation coefficient and partial correlation coefficients were used. The multiple correlation coefficient was obtained by

$$R_{1.23...n} = \sqrt{1 - \frac{\sigma^2_{1.23...n}}{\sigma^2_1}} , \qquad (10)$$

where

$$\sigma^2_{1.23...n} = \frac{\Sigma X^2_1 - A_1 \Sigma X_1 - A_2 \Sigma X_1 X_2 - ... - A_n \Sigma X_1 X_n}{N} , \qquad (11)$$

with

$$\sigma^2_1 = \frac{\Sigma (X_1 - \overline{X}_1)^2}{N} , \qquad (12)$$

and A_1, A_2,...,A_n the regression coefficients and N the sample size. The partial correlation coefficients were obtained by

$$R_{12.34...n} = \frac{R_{12.34...n-1} - R_{1n.23...n-1} \cdot R_{2n.34...n-1}}{\sqrt{(1-R^2_{1n.23...n-1})(1-R^2_{2n.34...n-1})}} , \qquad (13)$$

with

$$X_1 = Q_o; \ X_2 = H; \ X_3 = M; \ X_4 = I_{pp}, \quad \text{in this case.}$$

5. Testing the Method on Case Studies.

The applicability of the method was checked on several karst plains (poljes) of Eastern Herzegovina: Nevesinjsko, Fatničko, Dabarsko, Mokro and Popovo Polje.

Nevesinjsko Polje. The catchment of the Nevesinjsko Polje is $A = 485$ km^2. Figure 3 gives the graphical presentation of how the multiple correlation coefficient changed in function of α or K of Eq. (4). By changing K the explained variance of Q_o changed. In case of the Nevesinjsko

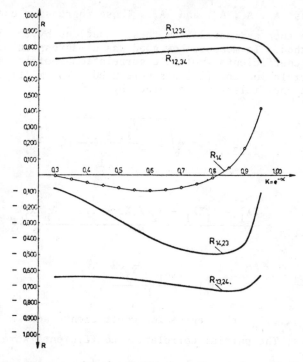

Fig. 3. The Changes in the Multiple $(R_{1.234})$ and the Partial
Correlation Coefficients $(R_{12.34}, R_{13.24}, R_{14.23})$
for the Multiple Linear Regression of the Sinkholes
Outflow, for the Nevesinjsko Polje (Enclosed Karst
Plain) as Functions of the Parameter K.

Polje, the optimal value was K = 0.80, at which the multiple
correlation coefficient was at a maximum, or $R_{1.234}$ = 0.869,
and $R_{1.234}^2$ = 0.755. The regression equation for the sinkholes
outflow is

$$Q_o = 58.55 + 0.0279 \ H - 5.8868 \ M - 0.2585 \ I_{pp} . \quad (14)$$

The partial correlation coefficients are: $R_{12.34}$ = 0.798,
$R_{13.24}$ = -0.714 and $R_{14.23}$ = -0.495. In this case the
multiple correlation coefficient was relatively small (0.87).
The reason were the errors in determining Q_o and I_{pp}. In
determining Q_o, the estimation of Q_d was essential, which
was determined at a cross section rather distant from the
flooded plain. Between the measurement cross section for the
inflow into the plain and the flooded plain itself there were
other inflows but also there were some water losses along the

riverbed. They essentially affected the precision in determining Q_o. Besides, the high altitude of the catchment had often the precipitation in the form of snow, which melted later, so that I_{pp} did not measure exactly only the effect of precipitation on the groundwater regime. This was evident by somewhat small absolute value of the partial correlation coefficient of Q_o on I_{pp}, given H and M. However, the seasonal measure, M, corrected this deficiency of I_{pp}, showing a relatively high effect on Q_o, because the partial correlation of Q_o on M, given H and I_{pp}, was -0.714. Figure 4 gives flood level, inflow, outflow and average daily precipitation hydrographs of the Nevesinjsko Polje. Table 1 presents the data for the regression analysis and predicted outflows.

Fatničko Polje. For the Fatničko Polje only the surface (orographic) catchment was known (A_{or} = 40 km^2), but not the underground catchment area. For the optimal K = 0.85 (see Fig. 5), the multiple correlation coefficient was $R_{1.234}$ = 0.922, with $R^2_{1.234}$ = 0.850. The multiple linear regression equation of the outflow capacity is:

$$Q_o = 38.31 + 0.0198\ H - 1.8948\ M - 0.4953\ I_{pp} \quad . \quad . \quad . \quad . \quad (15)$$

The partial correlation coefficients are $R_{12.34}$ = 0.835, $R_{13.24}$ = - 0.464, and $R_{14.23}$ = - 0.892. For the Fatňicko Polje all inflow into the plain comes at the karst springs at the rims of this plain, so that no difficulty was encountered as in the case of inputs into the Nevesinjsko Polje. The snow accumulation and melt had only a slight influence, since it was of short duration. Figure 6 gives the graphical presentation of flooding in the Fatničko Polje. Table 2 gives the data, particularly the observed and estimated values of outflow capacity of the Fatničko Polje.

Dabarsko Polje. The catchment of the Dabarsko Polje is A = 178 km^2. For the optimal K = 0.95 (see Fig. 7) the multiple correlation coefficient was $R_{1.234}$ = 0.869, with $R^2_{1.234}$ = 0.755. The multiple linear regression equation of the sinkholes outflow capacity is:

$$Q_o = 38.74 + 0.0064\ H - 0.9870\ M - 0.0891\ I_{pp}. \quad\quad (16)$$

328

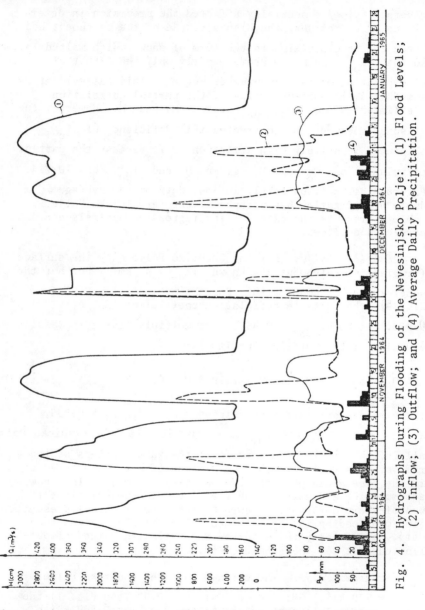

Fig. 4. Hydrographs During Flooding of the Nevesinjsko Polje: (1) Flood Levels; (2) Inflow; (3) Outflow; and (4) Average Daily Precipitation.

The partial correlation coefficients are $R_{12.34} = 0.747$, $R_{13.24} = -0.702$, and $R_{14.23} = -0.863$.

Similarly as for the Nevesinjsko Polje and for the same reasons, the effect of errors in basic data was reflected in somewhat smaller multiple correlation coefficient. Namely a small river enters the Dabarsko Polje and its inflow water

Table 1. Observed (Q_o) and Estimated (Q_o^*) Outflow Capacity
of Sinkholes of the Nevesinjsko Polje.

	Q_o	H	M	I_{pp}	Q_o^*	$Q_o - Q_o^*$
1.	75.74	2526	3	108.79	83.19	- 7.45
2.	72.07	2288	3	87.04	82.18	-10.11
3.	68.54	1195	3	11.68	71.19	- 2.65
4.	39.72	2059	8	68.39	51.18	-11.46
5.	65.53	2485	9	33.40	66.22	- 0.69
6.	74.43	2293	9	7.05	67.68	6.75
7.	57.81	2387	7	57.19	69.11	-11.30
8.	51.77	1060	7	54.93	32.70	19.07
9.	106.93	2763	5	53.44	92.33	14.60
10.	81.46	2228	5	4.33	90.11	- 8.65
11.	107.64	2265	3	29.69	96.36	11.28
12.	116.45	2671	4	36.19	100.12	16.33
13.	64.05	1167	4	17.06	63.13	0.92
14.	95.87	2500	6	64.98	76.13	19.74
15.	70.72	2219	6	40.86	74.53	- 3.81
16.	60.53	1760	8	7.63	58.55	1.98
17.	20.82	779	8	5.27	31.81	-10.99
18.	77.11	1135	5	7.35	58.86	18.25
19.	78.09	2325	4	12.35	96.63	-18.54
20.	82.84	2375	5	15.57	91.31	- 8.47
21.	67.74	1505	5	23.52	65.00	2.74
22.	71.00	2405	6	21.43	84.74	-13.74
23.	93.38	2352	5	14.50	90.97	2.41
24.	95.22	2573	5	30.05	93.08	2.14
25.	33.50	1620	9	34.60	41.79	- 8.29
26.	89.34	2615	6	15.95	92.01	- 2.67
27.	70.72	2040	6	15.40	76.13	- 5.41
28.	32.65	1515	8	44.89	42.09	- 9.44
29.	80.38	2325	9	28.90	62.92	17.46

Q_o = the observed, Q_o^* = the estimated outflow.

at the control cross section does not necessarily equal the
total inflow which floods the plain. In addition, less data
were available for the regression analysis, thus, decreased
accuracy of the prediction equation. The partial correlation
coefficient of outflow to the season showed also the influence
of snow. Figure 7 gives the same graphs for this plain as
Figs. 3 and 5 for the previously described cases. To observe
the water flow through the main sinkholes, a special measuring
equipment was installed in the Dabarsko Polje. Figure 8 gives
the graphical presentation of flooding in the Dabarsko Polje,
with the observed and estimated outflows from the plain. It
can be noticed that there were significant differences in
observed and estimated outflows from the plain in winter
months (December, January and February). The explanation was
the snowfall which remained on the ground and did not influence
the outflow capacity to the extent as predicted by I_{pp},
namely the obtained outflow was lower than the actual outflow.
Table 3 gives the data and these outflows.

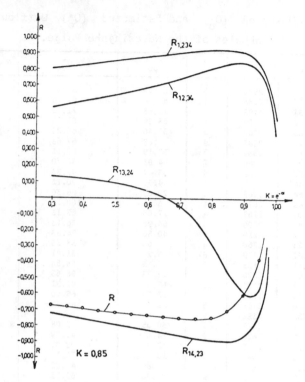

Fig. 5. The Changes in the Multiple $(R_{1.234})$ and the Partial
Correlation Coefficients for the Multiple Linear
Regression Equation of the Sinkholes Outflow Capacity
For the Fatničko Polje, as Functions of the Parameter
K.

Mokro Polje. The Mokro Polje has the catchment of A =
105 km^2. Figure 9 shows for the optimal value K = 0.75
the corresponding multiple correlation coefficient $R_{1.234}$ =
0.786, with $R^2_{1.234}$ = 0.622. The multiple linear regression
equation of the outflow capacity is

$$Q_o = 5.309 + 0.0069 \ H - 0.1522 \ M - 0.0094 \ I_{pp}. \qquad (17)$$

The partial correlation coefficients are $R_{12.34}$ = 0.780;
$R_{13.24}$ = - 0.271; and $R_{14.23}$ = - 0.147. From the partial correlation coefficient of Q_o on I_{pp}, it can be seen that the
influence of antecedent precipitation in case of the Mokro
Polje was small. Therefore, this method had a limited application. The multiple correlation coefficient was relatively

331

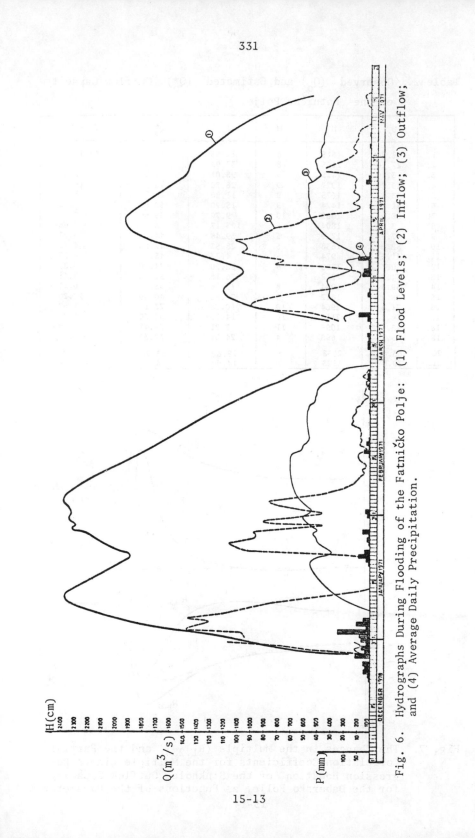

Fig. 6. Hydrographs During Flooding of the Fatničko Polje: (1) Flood Levels; (2) Inflow; (3) Outflow; and (4) Average Daily Precipitation.

15-13

Table 2. Observed (Q_o) and Estimated (Q_o^*) Outflow Capacity
of the Fatničko Polje.

	Q_o	H	M	I_{pp}	Q_o^*	$Q_o - Q_o^*$
1.	43.90	818	8	12.55	33.19	10.71
2.	27.10	1195	8	37.93	28.11	- 1.01
3.	3.10	1415	9	93.01	3.31	- 0.21
4.	29.20	1927	9	28.72	45.32	-16.12
5.	43.6	1675	9	11.80	48.70	- 5.10
6.	41.7	1424	9	15.20	42.02	- 0.32
7.	35.0	1062	10	9.70	35.66	- 0.66
8.	3.0	1804	5	123.17	3.68	- 0.68
9.	47.5	1759	5	39.48	44.23	3.27
10.	52.0	1658	5	28.53	47.65	4.35
11.	41.6	974	5	4.77	45.83	- 4.23
12.	30.7	1389	8	52.20	24.90	5.80
13.	54.7	2218	7	36.16	51.22	3.48
14.	59.4	1994	8	19.16	53.29	6.11
15.	28.2	1612	8	29.85	40.40	-12.20
16.	71.5	2964	10	10.28	73.17	- 1.67
17.	56.2	2116	10	14.35	54.30	1.90
18.	43.0	1095	11	7.71	35.41	7.59
19.	25.5	693	4	24.51	32.36	- 6.86
20.	63.4	2038	6	28.60	53.28	10.12
21.	39.8	1323	7	14.69	44.06	- 4.26

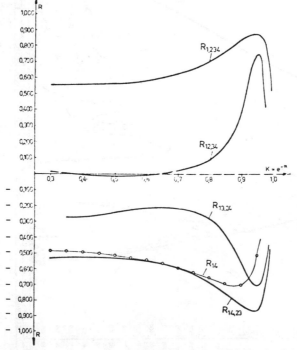

Fig. 7. The Changes in the Multiple ($R_{1.234}$) and the Partial
Correlation Coefficients for the Multiple Linear Regression Equation of the Sinkholes Outflow Capacity
for the Dabarsko Polje, as Functions of the Parameter K.

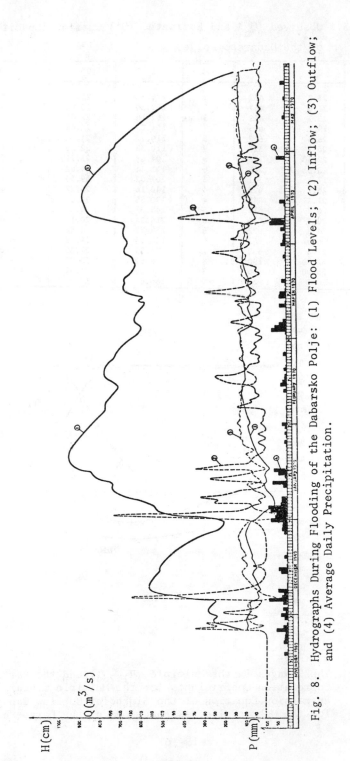

Fig. 8. Hydrographs During Flooding of the Dabarsko Polje: (1) Flood Levels; (2) Inflow; (3) Outflow; and (4) Average Daily Precipitation.

Table 3. Observed (Q_o) and Estimated (Q_o^*) Outflow Capacity
of the Dabarsko Polje.

	Q_o	H	M	I_{pp}	Q_o^*	$Q_o - Q_o^*$
1.	23.2	432	9	126.73	21.32	1.88
2.	21.6	467	5	179.36	20.80	0.80
3.	22.3	422	5	162.18	22.04	0.26
4.	19.2	625	7	154.05	22.08	- 2.88
5.	25.3	602	8	116.27	24.32	0.98
6.	20.2	327	9	110.38	22.10	- 1.90
7.	22.50	185	9	104.68	21.71	0.79
8.	23.0	205	6	113.44	24.02	- 1.02
9.	17.8	361	3	207.02	19.63	- 1.83
10.	26.7	623	4	140.16	26.27	0.43
11.	27.2	545	4	120.55	27.52	- 0.32
12.	26.7	617	5	148.31	24.52	2.18
13.	20.2	1053	6	216.94	20.19	0.01
14.	24.8	972	6	158.72	24.86	- 0.06
15.	24.6	802	6	148.64	24.68	- 0.08
16.	27.8	630	7	94.85	27.39	0.41
17.	22.80	190	8	78.62	25.05	- 2.25
18.	25.00	36	8	80.38	23.91	1.09
19.	20.7	37	5	166.6	19.2	1.50

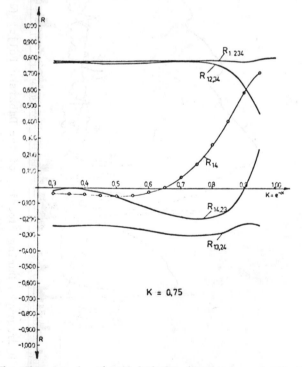

Fig. 9. The Changes in the Multiple ($R_{1.234}$) and the Partial
Correlation Coefficients for the Multiple Linear
Regression Equation of the Sinkholes Outflow Capacity
for the Mokro Polje, as Functions of the Parameter K.

small, since the regression equation of outflow capacity did
not reflect all the basic variables that affect this sinkhole's
capacity. Figure 9 gives the effect of the parameter K on
correlation coefficient, while Fig. 10 presents the flood
hydrographs of the Mokro Polje, with basic data given in
Table 4.

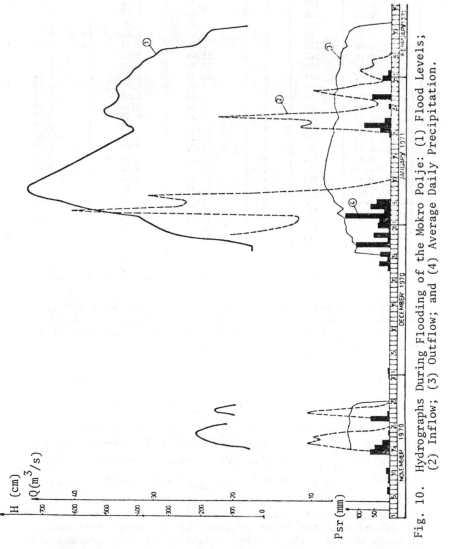

Fig. 10. Hydrographs During Flooding of the Mokro Polje: (1) Flood Levels;
(2) Inflow; (3) Outflow; and (4) Average Daily Precipitation.

Popovo Polje. The catchment area of the Popovo Polje is
$A = 2,712$ km^2. Precipitation was not essentially important
in the Popovo Polje for the outflow capacity, since the system
of underground channels was well developed, so that the

Table 4. Observed $(\bar{Q}_o)$ and Estimated (Q_o^*) Outflow Capacity
of the Mokro Polje.

	Q_o	H	M	I_{pp}	Q_o^*	$Q_o - Q_o^*$
1.	6.41	155	5	6.36	5.57	0.84
2.	6.72	322	6	9.34	6.55	0.17
3.	6.60	255	6	5.25	6.12	0.48
4.	4.44	285	7	21.45	6.03	- 1.59
5.	5.67	165	8	9.05	5.16	0.51
6.	5.68	178	6	2.06	5.62	0.06
7.	5.16	158	7	23.53	5.12	0.04
8.	5.94	218	5	29.76	5.79	0.15
9.	5.40	246	6	10.07	6.01	- 0.61
10.	4.98	145	8	9.25	5.01	- 0.03
11.	6.71	175	3	50.49	5.60	1.11
12.	6.50	160	4	26.39	5.57	0.93
13.	5.45	170	6	6.34	5.52	- 0.07
14.	6.74	272	6	15.00	6.15	0.59
15.	5.52	259	4	35.23	6.17	- 0.65
16.	5.98	366	4	23.86	7.03	- 1.05
17.	6.87	462	5	23.55	7.54	- 0.67
18.	4.98	228	6	23.95	5.76	- 0.78
19.	5.54	354	8	18.43	6.36	- 0.82
20.	5.99	420	5	40.44	7.09	- 1.10
21.	4.88	172	5	8.47	5.67	- 0.79
22.	7.61	422	7	15.52	7.04	0.57
23.	7.48	344	7	13.86	6.51	0.97
24.	5.24	228	8	28.62	5.41	- 0.17
25.	9.72	654	6	36.79	8.61	1.11
26.	8.71	570	6	15.52	8.22	0.49
27.	7.59	486	6	6.55	7.72	- 0.13
28.	5.98	281	9	36.06	5.56	0.42

piezometric levels around the plain were low, as shown by
various investigations. For the optimal value K = 0.60
(see Fig. 11) the multiple linear regression equation of the
outflow is

$$Q_o = 22.80 + 0.0772 \, H - 0.3908 \, M + 3.972 \, I_{pp} \, , \qquad (18)$$

which may not be valid because I_{pp} enters into it with a
positive sign, contrary to Eqs. (1)-(4) through the multiple
correlation coefficient was relatively high, namely $R_{1.234}$ =
0.933 with $R_{1.234}^2$ = 0.871. The partial correlation coefficients are $R_{12.34}$ = 0.929; $R_{13.24}$ = -0.300; and $R_{14.23}$ =
0.121. These partial correlation coefficients show clearly
that for the Popovo Polje the outflow capacity was predominantly
influenced by water levels and not by the antecedent precipitation. However, the outflow capacity may be decreased when
the sinkholes were obstructed by debris occasionally carried
by high water flows, which factor was difficult to predict.
Table 5 gives the basic data, similar to those of Tables 1
through 4.

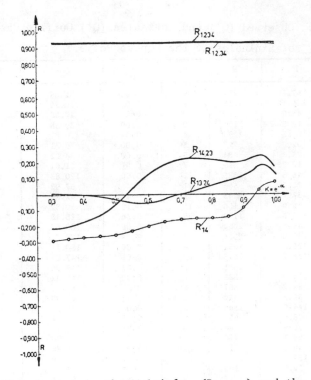

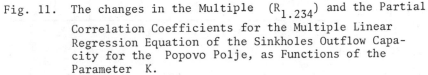

Fig. 11.   The changes in the Multiple $(R_{1.234})$ and the Partial
Correlation Coefficients for the Multiple Linear
Regression Equation of the Sinkholes Outflow Capa-
city for the Popovo Polje, as Functions of the
Parameter K.

6.   Conclusions.

The proposed method gives results of practical use
though some difficulties in its application remain. The more
accurate basic data, the better results would be obtained.
Number of factors should be taken into account in the proposed
method, in addition to using the index of antecedent precipitation. Further studies on these factors should include the
investigation of underground network of channels by using
piezometer boreholes, detailed hydrogeologic exploration of
the area involved, possibilities of obstruction of sinkholes
during floods, and similar aspects. The method was shown to
be reliable in determining the water budget that flows through
an enclosed karst plain, with the estimates being on the
conservative side.

Table 5.   Observed (Q_o) and Estimated (Q_o^*) Outflow Capacity
of Sinkholes of the Popovo Polje.

	Q_o	H	M	I_{pp}	Q_o^*	$Q_o - Q_o^*$
1.	157.3	1451	9	0.08	131.65	25.65
2.	126.1	1258	9	0.02	116.50	9.60
3.	48.0	365	10	0.00	47.08	0.92
4.	12.5	151	10	0.00	30.55	-18.05
5.	104.3	1277	4	0.04	120.01	-15.71
6.	102.0	757	5	0.00	79.31	22.69
7.	78.3	484	5	0.00	58.22	20.08
8.	12.5	149	7	0.01	31.61	-19.11
9.	140.6	1325	11	0.00	120.83	19.77
10.	81.7	566	11	1.44	67.92	13.78
11.	37.7	285	11	0.42	42.20	- 4.50
12.	12.9	150	11	0.19	30.82	-17.92
13.	125.8	1142	5	0.36	110.48	15.02
14.	149.4	2080	7	0.00	180.69	-31.29
15.	147.0	2014	7	0.04	175.74	-28.74
16.	125.3	1689	8	0.00	150.11	-24.81
17.	133.7	1618	10	0.81	147.07	-13.37
18.	163.4	1681	7	0.01	149.90	13.50
19.	134.0	1583	7	0.00	142.32	- 8.32
20.	84.2	607	8	0.59	68.87	15.33
21.	39.8	330	8	0.21	45.99	- 6.19
22.	144.5	1502	5	0.03	136.97	7.53
23.	78.8	657	6	0.13	71.71	7.09
24.	70.8	544	6	0.08	62.78	8.02
25.	88.1	778	7	0.22	81.00	7.10
26.	149.1	1512	10	0.05	135.86	13.24
27.	124.4	1017	11	0.26	98.06	26.34
28.	12.9	160	11	1.92	38.5	-25.60
29.	99.5	747	3	2.32	88.16	11.34
30.	16.7	230	3	0.17	40.08	-23.38

Q_o = the observed, Q_o^*= the estimated outflow.

7.   References.

[1]   Ristić, D., Brief method for the determination of outflow
capacity in the final stage of the emptying of flooded
karst plains [In Serbo-Croatian]: Gradjevinar, No. 1,
Zagreb, 1963.

[2]   Interregionaljniy seminar po gidrologicheskomu i
vodnomu balansu [In Russian]: Belgrade, 1960.

[3]   Obradović-Sentić, An outline of statistical analysis [In
Serbo-Croatian]: Naučna knjiga, Belgrade, 1967.

[4]   Jevdjević, Vujica, Hydrology I [In Serbo-Croatian]:
Belgrade, 1956.

DISCUSSION

Yevjevich.   The use of the variable M, the month or the
season of the year, must represent a cyclic phenomenon related
to the water budget of a karst polje (plain). The evaporation
should be that variable, as related to heat supply, wind
velocities (diffusion) and the area of the watershed and the

flooded plain. Using the month of the year, or any other
time interval, as a variable takes care only of the deterministic (periodic) component in the fluctuation of evaporation
and evapotranspiration of the watershed of a polje, including
the evaporation from the flooded polje. It neglects the
significant stochastic variation in evaporation. One could
then expect that the temperature and eventually the wind
velocity at one or two gauging stations, if measured, may
produce a better representation of evaporation than the
calendar unit along the year.

The index of antecedent precipitation is computed by
multiplying the daily precipitation by $K_t = \exp(-\alpha t)$, with
α a constant determined by using the multiple regression.
For the greater partial correlation coefficient of the total
outflow capacity Q_o of the polje in relation to the antecedent precipitation index (I_{pp}), keeping the other independent
variables inside the regression equation, and for varying
values of $K = \exp(-\alpha)$, the maximum absolute value of this
partial correlation coefficient gave the best value of
$K = \exp(-\alpha)$. First question is what determines the relationship of $R_{14.23}$ to K, and can it be explained by physical
factors? Second question is, why the curves of $R_{14.23}$ vary
so much from one polje to another in the examples given?

Žibret. The average monthly temperature was not used
as a variable in the regressive equation. It should be expected that temperature would give a higher correlation than
the calendar intervals (months). However, the month sequence
number, besides measuring the evapotranspiration, contains
indirectly the effects of temperature. Since the proposed
method uses a calculation over a long time, with the data
used in computations accumulated over a reasonably long
period, the temperature was not used because the long-range
observations were not available.

The varying parameter K, or the varying coefficient α,
was optimized by the method given in the paper (Figs. 3,5,7,9,
and 11). An analysis of the relationship of the parameter K
to some other indicators, such as geologic, climatic and
similar factors, was not undertaken. The sensitivity of the
function $R = f(K)$ to K was different for the Nevesinjsko
Polje in comparison with that of the Popovo Polje. It seems
that the karst poljes of the upper horizons of the Trebisnjica
River basin have exibited extremes in the function $R = f(K)$,
whereas the Mokro Polje and the Popovo Polje of the lower
horizon have the regression relationship nearly independent
of K. To restate it in another way, in the latter case, the
rainfall does not affect the capacity of sinkholes. A more
detailed geologic analysis should produce a better answer to
this problem.

DETERMINATION OF FLOW THROUGH FLOODED KARST POLJES BY USE OF POLJES AND PIEZOMETRIC BOREHOLES WATER LEVELS

by

Izet Avdagić, Civil Engineer, Institute of
Water Resources Engineering, University of Sarajevo

Synopsis. A flooded karst polje (the karst plain), is a subsystem of water retention in a river basin. It relieves parts of the underground hydraulic system from excessive pressures. In most cases of flooded poljes, water inflows and outflows occur through submerged inlets and outlets, respectively. Depending upon the mechanism of inlet and outlet activity and physical properties, water enters or leaves the plain by springs, estavelas and sinkholes. Under flooded conditions of these plains, the flow is determined for certain zones by the use of the level differences between the water level in the polje and a level or pressure measuring point in a conveyance channel, or by using the velocity head at the measuring point of the channel. The dynamic and continuity equations are used for determining the inflow and outflow of a polje. A constant outflow capacity occurs in some parts of the subsystem under flood conditions. Therefore, it is feasible to calculate the flow through channels or at the sinkhole zones. The calibration of a subsystem can be performed in different cases to different degrees of accuracy.

1. Introduction.

Water levels in flooded karst poljes have been measured for many years, mainly to record the total duration of floods. However, water resources development in karst areas requires the knowledge of both the inflow and the outflow, which could not be obtained from the available data on water levels of the polje only. Solutions are found for simple cases but with unsatisfactory accuracy. A method for flow determination through springs, estavelas and sinkholes under flood conditions and under pressure is presented in this paper. Their flows during the conditions of non-flooded karst poljes are determined by hydrometric methods.

The method presented in this paper is based on measurements of water level differences. A systems approach is used in defining the relationship between the flow and the measured level differences. The karst plain of the Fatničko Polje, which acts as a subsystem in a hydrologic system is used as an example of the method developed.

2. Hypotheses on the Hydraulic Mechanism of a Flooded Karst
   Polje.

   *Position and function of a karst polje in a karst hydro-
   logic-hydraulic system.* A karst hydrologic-hydraulic system
   consists of a catchment and underground channels. Developed
   channels make an underground flow system in which the function
   of each individual channel can be changed as to the flow
   direction, depending on piezometric relationships. A catchment with its water infiltration makes the first part of the
   system. The underground channels of the system can be either
   under pressure, or with free surface flow, or partly under
   pressure and partly with free surface flow.

   Depending upon the hydrogeological conditions of the
   system, a catchment may be schematized by a certain number of
   water retentions. Figure 1 presents a scheme of a simple
   system of a flooded karst polje with an inflow and an outflow
   only. It may be conceived as a three-reservoir system, one of
   which (II, karst polje) is only periodically flooded. Flooding
   occurs due to limited capacity of outflow channels during flood

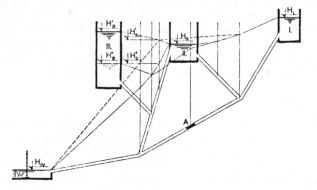

Fig. 1.   Schematic Representation of a Simple System of Flooded
          Karst Polje: Reservoir I, Simulating the Catchment
          Area of High Altitudes; Reservoir II, Simulating the
          Flooded Karst Polje with Direct Recharge Area;
          Reservoir III, Simulating the Intermediate Catchment
          and Indirect Area of High Altitudes; Reservoir IV,
          Simulating the Outflow; A, a Zone with Highly
          Restricted Water Transmission Capacity.

periods, so some channels discharge water into the reservoir
II. With a system of practically unlimited flow capacity, the
karst poljes are not ordinarily flooded. During floods,
parts of the system with restricted flow capacity are under
pressure, while the other parts of the system, or when the
system outflow capacity is relatively large, most of the
channels have free surface flow.

Characteristic water features of a karst polje. The
characteristic water features of a karst polje are springs,
estavelas and sinkholes. Under the flood conditions the flow
measurements can be made at flooded springs in the same way
as the flow measurements at sinkholes and estavelas. The
flow features at estavelas and sinkholes are less often investigated, so some general description is warranted here.
Estavelas and sinkholes are parts of underground channels
through which the water inflow and the outflow of karst
poljes occur. They often appear as both the sinkhole and
estavela zones. The term zone means a group of interconnected
sinkholes and/or estavelas. There can be several sinkhole and
estavela zones in a karst polje, which may or may not be
connected. These zones may have either different or the same
mechanism and different boundary conditions. Zones are defined
by piezometric levels and their relationships. Under flood
conditions the sinkholes are under pressure. Estavelas always
act under pressure. Flow discharge through sinkholes and flow
direction and flow discharge at the estavelas depend on their
geometric and hydraulic characteristics. Under flood conditions, the geometric features of sinkholes and estavelas may
be regarded constant, so that flows depend only on piezometric
relations in the system of underground channels.

Estavelas are karst water features through which both
the inflow and the outflow of a karst polje occur. By their
hydraulic mechanism they resemble sinkholes of the underground channels which are under pressure, but connected with
the channels in which the pressure varies considerably. They
differ from sinkholes only by their position in the system. As
per the scheme of Fig. 1, estavelas are connections between
the retentions I and II. Connections of channels in that part
of the system is such that they enable the water to flow into
retention II through the same channel under certain piezometric
conditions, while for the other piezometric conditions the flow
from retention II occurs through the same channel. Sinkholes
are water features with the only function of receiving outflow
from a karst polje, (See Fig. 2).

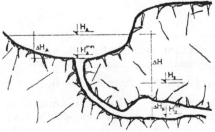

The outflow through flooded
sinkholes with constant geometric
characteristics is a function
only of the piezometric condition in the channel connecting
retentions II and III in Fig. 1,
with the piezometric levels at
the borehole A, defining these
conditions, namely

$$Q_o = f(H_A, H_{II}) \ , \qquad (1)$$

Fig. 2. Schematic Representation of a Sinkhole.

in which, H_A = the piezometric level at a point A, and H_{II} = the level in the retention II.

Significant variations in the level H_{II} and in the flow occur in sinkholes or zones of sinkholes with channels under pressure when they are connected with other channel subsystems of large pressure changes. When level variations are so large that $H_{II} < H_A$, sinkholes then act as springs, or they become estavelas. Then the inflow and outflow are functions of the water level in the polje above the sinkhole and water levels in channels. Figure 3 shows the example of the Fatničko Polje case as the dependence of flow discharge only upon the water level in the polje, which is a highly scattered graph of points. Depending on characteristics of the channel subsystem and the levels H_A and H_{II}, the flow discharge through sinkholes can be either approximately constant or only a function of the level H_{II} in the retention.

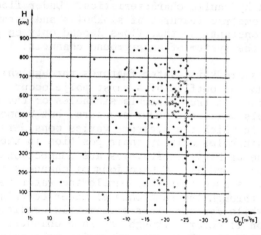

Fig. 3. Relationship of Outflow Through a Sinkhole and the Water Level of the Fatničko Polje for Sinkholes with Large Variations in H_{II}, with Possibilities of $H_{II} \gtreqless H_A$.

Very small fluctuations of outflow occur through sinkholes when the level variations of H_A and H_{II}, namely ΔH_A and ΔH_{II} very slightly affect the level difference $\Delta H = H_{II} - H_A$, which determine the outflow (See Fig. 4). Under the condition of $\Delta H_A << \Delta H >> \Delta H_{II}$, $Q_o \approx$ constant. For sinkholes which have pressure changes ΔH_A in the piezometer much smaller than the

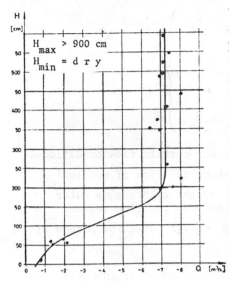

Fig. 4. Relationship of Out-
flow through a Sink-
hole and the Water
Level in the Fatničko
Polje for Sinkhole
Zone for which ΔH_A <<
ΔH >> ΔH_{II}.

total difference ΔH_{II} between
the level in the polje and the
piezometric level inside the
sinkhole, or where ΔH and
ΔH_{II} are of approximately the
same order (ΔH_{II} < ΔH >>ΔH_A),
the outflow is a function of
the water level above the sinkhole only, namely $Q_o = f(H_{II})$.

The description of the
work of sinkholes shows that a
large number of sinkholes are
in effect estavelas, which has
been confirmed by measurements
on some of the largest sinkholes. The only question that
remains is how often H_A can
be greater than H_{II}. Nearly
every year, in the course of
several days, these large sinkholes act as springs. Therefore, the period or the probability of the activity of a
channel at sinkhole as a spring
should be the criterion for the
classification or the naming it
either as a sinkhole or as an
estavela.

Measurements of inflows and outflows through underground
channels into or from a polje usually show a turbulent flow
regime. With estavelas and for very short periods, the flow
regime is intermediate turbulent to laminar and even laminar.
This occurs in periods of changes in flow direction. Because
these periods are usually very short, errors caused by these
changes in flow regime are small and have a limited effect on
the computations of the total water budget.

3. A Model for Defining the Relationship Between the Outflow
and the Measured Piezometric Levels in and Close to Karst
Poljes.

Based upon the above description of flow mechanism of
underground channel systems, the inflows and outflows of the
karst polje system can be determined by using the dynamic and
continuity equations. Dynamic equations for n flow zones
during the time interval j can be written in the following
form

$$Q_{j,1} = k_1 \Delta H_{j,1}^{a_1}$$

$$Q_{j,2} = k_2 \Delta H_{j,2}^{a_2}$$

$$\cdots \cdots \cdots$$

$$Q_{j,n} = k_n \Delta H_{j,n}^{a_n}$$

$$(2)$$

with k_i and a_i = the constants for certain flow conditions. Coefficients k_i depend on the shape and size of outflow openings, or in a strict analysis on the velocity of water flow, while the exponents a_i depend on the flow regime. In this paper k_i is referred to an average value for a zone of various openings.

For a flooded karst polje with n zones or channels, the water continuity equation of the polje for the time interval j is

$$\sum_{i=1}^{n} Q_{j,i} = \frac{\Delta W_j}{\Delta t_j} \qquad (3)$$

with

$$\Delta W_j = W_{j-1} - W_j \qquad (4)$$

and

$$\Delta t_j = t_{j-1} - t_j \qquad (5)$$

with W_j = the total water volume of the flooded karst polje, and ΔW determined from the changes in water levels in the polje and from the relationship of the water storage to the level.

From Eqs. (2) and (3), then

$$\sum_{i=1}^{n} k_i \Delta H_{j,i}^{a_i} = \left(\frac{\Delta W}{\Delta t}\right)_j . \qquad (6)$$

To determine $2n$ unknown coefficients k_i and a_i in Eqs. (2) and (6), measurements of ΔH and ΔW for a number of time intervals are needed.

The unknown coefficients are determined by minimizing the difference of the terms

$$\sum_{1=1}^{n} Q_{j,i} \quad \text{and} \quad (\frac{\Delta W}{\Delta t})_{j} \quad , \quad \text{namely}$$

$$\min \left\{ \sum_{j=1}^{m} \left[\sum_{i=1}^{n} Q_{j,i} - (\frac{\Delta W}{\Delta t})_{j} \right]^{2} \right\} \tag{7}$$

with m the number of time intervals of observations. By substituting $Q_{j,i}$ as in Eq. (6) then

$$\min \left\{ \sum_{j=1}^{m} \left[\sum_{i=1}^{n} k_{i} \Delta H_{j,i}^{a_{i}} - (\frac{\Delta W}{\Delta t})_{j} \right]^{2} \right\} \tag{8}$$

with the required number of observations $m = 2n + r$. The greater r the more accurate are the results. In this manner coefficients k_1, k_2,...,k_n and the exponents a_1, a_2,...,a_n are determined with a minimum error. Errors in the above coefficients may occur because of the errors in level measurements, nonsimultaneity in level observations, inaccuracy of the relationship $W = f(H)$, etc.

Piezometric differences ΔH can be determined as differences of water levels in the polje and in the piezometer borehole, or simply as the velocity head at the representative inflows and outflows. According to the assumed flow mechanism at a given spring, sinkhole or estavela zone, the flow velocities through various openings of the same zone are proportional. In order to obtain the piezometer level, it is sufficient to determine it only at a point of the zone, or for an individual spring, sinkhole or estavela directly at these water features. The exponents a_i as functions of the flow regime can be determined either from measurements or by calculations. As already stated, a constant flow rate depends on the position of the channel in relation to the water level of the karst polje. In specific cases of very flat poljes the flood level fluctuations may be small, and all channel entrances or outlets are at the same level -- say they are at the bottom or on the rim of a polje -- the determination of a_i is relatively simple, since for small level fluctuations under the flood conditions they are constant. In practice, however, water level fluctuates in a large range in most karst plains. In such cases it is necessary to divide this total range into zones, so that for each zone the conditions of inflows and outflows produce an average, constant a_i. This requires a number of equations of the type of Eq. (8), together with the

precise specifications of conditions under which the individual
set of equations should be used for computing the inflows and
outflows under the conditioons of flooded karst poljes.

4. Application of the Method.

     The method outlined is tested on the Fatničko Polje in the
Eastern Herzegovina. It is an enclosed karst plain at the
elevation of 470 m.a.s.l. Numerous water features of this
polje can be sorted in the three most important groups, with
different elevations, as shown in Fig. 5, namely:

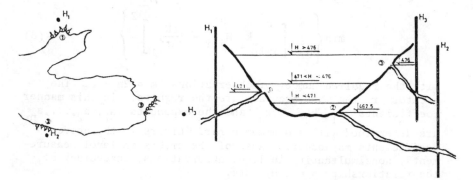

Fig. 5. Positions of Zones of Water Features and Recording
         Gauges in the Fatničko Polje.

     (1) The zone of very large ephemeral springs, such as
Obod, Baba Jama and Pribabići, which at their maximum flow
give more than 40 m³/s. This zone is at the northeastern rim
of the polje, below the village of Kalac. Springs are ascend-
ing, with the overflow for Obod and Baba Jama at the elevation
of 476 m.a.s.l.

     (2) The zone of the Pasmica Sinkhole, situated at the
southern rim of the polje, below the village of Padjeni. It is
in the lowest part of the polje. The elevation of this zone
is 462.5 m.a.s.l.

     (3) Estavelas near the Lepernica Cave. This zone is
situated on the southwest rim of the polje, at the elevation
471 m.a.s.l.

     Among other water features, the ephemeral springs Veliki
i Mali Nežir are also of some importance.

     Floods in the polje last on the average about 140 days
per year. According to the records of the Hydro-Meteorological
Service, the maximum registered flood level is 500.80 m.a.s.l.

on 30 December 1950, with a corresponding water storage in the plain of 228×10^6 m^3.

The inflow and outflow occurs through the three zones (see Fig. 5): the spring zone near Obod (1), the zone of estavelas near Lepernica (3), and the sinkhole zone near Pasmica (2). Sinkholes in the Pasmica area periodically act also as springs. According to data during the 100 days of flood in the polje, of the year 1971, the sinkholes acted as springs for 16 days while for about four days there was no inflow or outflow. Flow measurements were made at the Obod Spring during two years, and it was found that the spring has not acted as a sinkhole during that period.

It was assumed in the flow computations that each zone acts as an estavela zone, for a general case. In selecting the computational scheme the correct physical approach must be taken into account, since only such an approach can ensure constant coefficients of the system of Eq. (6). Coefficients of the system of equations for the three zones depend on the mean elevation of each zone, on the water level in the karst polje, and on the pressure or the water level in piezometer boreholes, respectively for every zone, by which the drop of pressure at each zone is determined due to flow into or out of the plain.

It is possible to decrease the required number of systems of equations if some well defined characteristics of each subsystem are taken into account. For the Fatničko Polje these special characteristics have resulted in the formulation of only four systems of equations, as given in Table 1, and schematically represented in Fig. 5. The symbol H refers to levels in the polje, while H_1, H_2, and H_3 refer to levels in the piezometer boreholes in the immediate vicinity of the polje, one for each of the three zones.

Because of a slight influence of H_2 for H < 471 and a great influence on flow capacity, the difference $\Delta H = H - 462.50$ was used for the water level in the polje instead of ΔH_2, in the system of equations III and IV. Coefficients k_i are approximately constant in each system of equations. Measurings in the main channels have shown that the flow is turbulent and under pressure, with the coefficient $a_i = 0.5$.

During the period of investigations in 1971-72, the Fatničko Polje was flooded for 100 days. All piezometric levels were observed every day. There were 66 observations related to system I, 14 to system II, 9 to system III, and 7 to system IV.

Table 1. Formulation of Four Systems of Equations for the
Fatničko Polje.

Systems of equations (each for the same characteristics of the subsystem)	Limit Conditions	
	Water elevation in the polje	Levels in the piezometer
I	H > 476	-
	471 < H < 476	H_1 > 476
	H < 471	H_3 < H
II	471 < H < 476	H_1 < 476
III	H < 471	H_1 < 476
		H_3 < H
IV	H < 471	H_1 > 476
		H_3 < H

The unknown coefficients of flow capacities were determined for each of the four cases by solving the corresponding
system of equations. The final equations with these coefficients, to be used for computations of inflows and outflows are:

$$Q_I = - 0.074 + 13.445 \, \Delta H_1^{0,5} - 3.433 \, \Delta H_2^{0,5} + 16.172 \, \Delta H_3^{0,5} \quad (9)$$

$$Q_{II} = - 0.007 - 0.898 \, \Delta H_1^{0,5} - 7.242 \, \Delta H_2^{0,5} + 10.810 \, \Delta H_3^{0,5} \quad (10)$$

$$Q_{III} = 0.230 - 16.440 \, \Delta H^{0,5} \quad (11)$$

$$Q_{IV} = - 0.040 + 8.800 \, \Delta H_1^{0,5} - 8.110 \, \Delta H^{0,5} + 12.160 \, \Delta H_3^{0,5} \quad (12)$$

Equations (9) through (12) are used according to conditions of subsystems, namely first by a classification of layer
zones based upon the water levels, and then by computing the
net flows by summing up the obtained positive and negative
flows. Positive flows are inflows into and the negative flows
are outflows from the polje.

The correlation coefficients between measured net flows
and the computed net flows, these latter obtained by using the
registered water levels for systems of equations I, II, III and

IV, are: $r_1 = 0.978$, $r_2 = 0.942$, $r_3 = 0.972$ and $r_4 = 0.924$, respectively.

The flow through small openings was analyzed from the point of view of their importance and the flow regime in the system II of equations. This is the case when water levels in the polje are between 471 and 476 m.a.s.l. and $H_1 < 476$.

Under these conditions, and assuming both a laminar and a turbulent regime, the flow of approximately 0.5 percent of the corresponding total flow is obtained for the zone (1). Because of a small contribution of this flow it is difficult to finally evaluate the results of the type of flow regime only by the correlation coefficients, namely of 0.942 for the laminar and of 0.947 for the turbulent regime.

For Eqs. (9) through (12) the intercepts (-0.040 to 0.230) are close to zero. This means that the system has been hydraulically well defined, namely that the regime of the flow, measuring points and elevation limits for layer zones, are well selected.

The comparison of the computed total outflow with the total inflow shows the outflows to be somewhat larger than the inflows for each flood wave. The reason for this is always the initial flows of water waves during the flow through polje and channels with a free surface, but computed as flows under pressure. These results are shown in Fig. 6 to illustrate the error when the difference in flow regimes is neglected. Figure 7 shows the net flows of direct measurements obtained as $\Delta W/\Delta t$ from the original data, and the corresponding computed net flows, determined by using the differences of water levels between the piezometers and the polje.

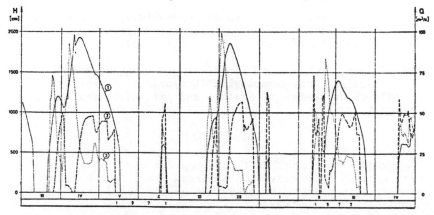

Fig. 6. Hydrographs of Inflow and Outflow of the Fatničko Polje for the Year 1971-72.

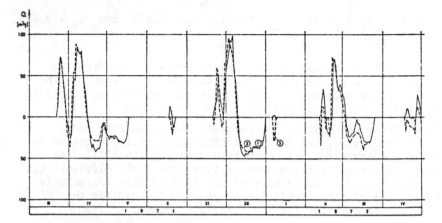

Fig. 7. Hydrographs of Net Flows (Either Inflow or Outflow)
for the Fatničko Polje: (1) Observed Flows, (2)
Computed Flows, and (3) The Free Surface Flows
Through the Polje and the Channels.

5. References

Ristić Danilo, Problems in determining capacity of sinkholes:
    Report, Third Conference of Yugoslav specialists in
    hydraulic research, Opatija, pp. 65-73, 1962.

Ristić Danilo, Summary method in determining the capacity of
    sinkholes in the final stage of water outflow from
    periodically flooded poljes: Report, Third Conference of
    Yugoslav specialists in hydraulic research, Opatija,
    pp. 74-78, 1962.

Djurović Miroslav, Ein Beitrag zur Hydrogeologie der Karsttäler
    (Contribution to hydrology of karst valleys): Die
    Wasserwirtschaft (Germany), Heft 4, 1964.

Avdagić Izet, Mechanism of functioning of sinkholes and
    estavelas: Acta carsologica (Krasoslovni zbornik) VI/14,
    Slovenian Academy of Science and Art, Ljubljana, pp. 209-
    218, 1974.

DISCUSSION

Yevjevich. Figure 1 of this paper shows a point or a
short section A, conceived as a narrow place in the karst
channel   system, with the idea that during floods this point or
short section forces water to flow into the karst polje (plain).
This concept of concentrated narrow points or short constricted
sections in the underground system of karst channels looks like
an analogy with the control cross sections in a free-surface

channel. Narrow points or constricted sections in a karst
system of channels under pressure are only concentrations of
head losses. Basically, the system of channels as a whole
always has a well-defined capacity of water flow for given
boundary conditions. Therefore, this loss concentrations at
narrow control points or sections are an unrealistic assumption
as a predominate control of underground karst water regimes.

Boreli. The presented example by Avdagić of utilization
of a schematic model of privileged flow routes seems to be vali-
dated as a good approach for simulation of underground karst
flow environments. The model is simple; it is of conduit-type
approach. It is supported by the fact that closing the outlet
of a spring in the Fatničko Polje resulted in an exceptionally
large pressure increase in the upstream underground channels.
Another successful example of this conduit-type model is related
to a coastal spring of brackish water at Ain Zaiana in Libya.
A system of flow equations for this case contained: continuity
equations of water and salt; dynamic equations for the system
of conduits analogous to that used by Avdagić; equality of
pressure at branching and joining points of channels under
pressure, taking into account differences in densities of
saline, fresh, and brackish waters.

When piezometric levels and salt concentrations were known,
a valuable information concerning the system could be obtained,
which was effectively implemented at the Ain Zaiana Spring.
However, the system seemed significantly more complex than that
presented in Avdagić'es paper. An investigation of flow directions in coastal zones was made easier by the fact that salt
serves as a natural traser, which provides also for a series of
supplementary equations in the model.

Avdagić. Water retentions and higher piezometric levels of
underground courses are not caused in karst plains only by
bottlenecks, but also by a limited flow capacity of the entire
system of channels. This limited capacity may be a result of a
short or long but narrow section of channels, or it may be
caused by a simple constricted cross section at a point.
Examples may be found at Postojna at the karst Pivka River.
Knowledge of such channel point or section locations and of the
obstacles for water movement during high flows is always necessary in order to establish a model which determines the flow
capacity, by using the measurements at various features such as
springs, sinkholes, and estavelas of karst plains.

In his discussion, Boreli termed the model a pipe-like
model. I disagree with this definition. Even though it was
schematized as a pipe-like model, expressions used to describe
the phenomenon can equally be applied to the flow through both
the priveleged routes and the porous media. In the example
presented, when the conditions required that the priveleged

routes be excluded, the linearity law was used. These situations occurred in the second set of equations for the conditions when the water was at $H_1 >$ 476 m.a.s.l, that is when the main priveleged route of the Zone 1 was excluded.

EXAMPLES OF DETERMINATION OF VOID VOLUME
IN KARST FORMATIONS

by

Antun Stepinac, Professor of Civil Engineering,
University of Zagreb, Yugoslavia

Synopsis. The problem of void volume determination in
karst formation is dealt with by considering examples. Such
cases have been selected for study where the outflow can be
determined without large errors.

Selected areas were classified into three categories: (A)
those with a high surface retention; (B) those with a small
surface retention; and (C) those without a surface retention.
Three calendar years, one hydrologic year, always taking the
same years, and a 10-year period, have been used as investigation material.

The objective was to find for each case and analyzing
both the particular years and the 10-year period such maximum
retention quantity that regulates the natural outflow. It
was found, however, that the analysis of particular years
did not give satisfactory solutions.

Results of particular years may be affected by previous
water recharge, depletion of the underground, different annual
precipitation and a distorted surface runoff during the
recession period studied.

It was finally inferred that the selected 10-year period
should be used in the form of modular coefficients. Such an
approach made it possible to define the maximum natural
retention which regulates the outflow from karst formations.
The resulting underground storage volumes, both absolute and
specific, expressed in unit area in m^3/km^2 or in unit of rock
mass volume in lit/m^3, are comparable for all cases studied.

The selected representative study period did not contain
either an extremely dry or an extremely wet year. A longer
study period (say 40 years) should give an improvement in
the estimate of karst underground water storage capacities.

1. Introduction.

To obtain some, even rough, information on void volume
available within a karst formation by the analysis of actual
outflow from underground is only one possible approach to use
by either a theoretical or a practical method.

Difficulties arise in determining the relevant catchment
areas, degree of karstification, geologic and hydrologic
aspects, and basic parameters. It is virtually impossible--
without extensive investigations and observations of groundwater piezometric levels--to determine the water table cases,
and thereby also--on the basis of total water outflow--the
absolute and specific volumes of voids within the rock.

It is often impossible to determine the flow of karst
waters to individual springs by the primary and secondary
tectonic fissurations. Rock fissures affect the continuity
as well as the connection between the underground channels.
It is often better to consider catchments of a wide spring
zone, for which it is often easier to define the area, than
those of individual springs. The total water storage volume
in karst underground differs from time to time depending on
distribution of water inflows in relation to the available
underground storage capacity.

After a prolonged drought period, the long duration of
intensive rainfall will recharge the underground very fast
initially, the actual inflow rates depending on the capacity
of sinkholes, capacity and distribution of underground
channels and outflow capacities at lower levels.

Considering this evaluation an important, practical
problem, examples of underground recharge and depletion over
a period of 10 years were investigated, by selecting a period
which comprises years of characteristic flows and their
distribution over the seasons.

2.   Selection of the Period and Area of the Study.

Based on the analysis of recorded outflows, the period
between 1949 and 1958 was selected as the most representative
regarding the sequences of dry and wet years. The selection
of representative study areas was made in such a way that
the available observations permitted the determination of
underground recharge and depletion. These areas were classified according to their specific characteristics. The first
area selected was the catchment of the Grab and Ruda Springs.
This catchment contains the large polje (plain) of Buško
Blato, characterized by surface water accumulation when the
underground is saturated or when the inflow exceeds the
capacity of drainage system. However, since the drainage
capacity is large at the south and southwest rims of this
plain, flooding of Buško Blato is an indicator that the
underground is filled with water. The second area was
the catchment of karst springs in the Zrmanja River valley,
from Žegar to Jankovića Buk. That catchment includes the
plateau of Gračac, subject to flooding, in a lesser degree than
the Buško Blato. Floods of that plateau were brief, the

maximum drainage capacity being approximately the average
maximum surface inflow. The third area was the catchment of
the Getina River headwaters, with no significant surface
storage but with similar characteristics as the catchment of
the Grab' and Ruda Springs.

3. Study Approach.

The above three cases are first considered from the
hydrogeologic aspects in order to define the respective catchment areas as realistically as feasible. Water budgets of
outflows from the underground are determined for a 10-year
observation period. Recession curves have been determined
from the observed outflow hydrographs. Of particular importance
were those hydrograph parts which are between the time of
complete cessation of infiltration and the time of the new
infiltration. These hydrograph parts were the basis for
determination of recession rate.

It was difficult to find long periods completely free of
inflow to the underground, whether it is from surface streams
or from direct precipitation infiltration. The effect of
precipitation depends on intensity, duration and distribution
of rainfall, and the season of the year. In studying the
underground water depletion, it was necessary to take into
account both the inflow from the streams (if any) and the
direct contribution by rainfall. In this study, the inflow
was determined by using the representative rainfall gauging
station for each of the above three case areas. In analyzing
the recession curves, special attention was paid to those
parts of hydrographs which had the greatest accuracy, regardless of whether a high or a low flow was experienced at the
initial point of these parts.

If two recession parts were similar, then the transition
times from a discharge Q_1 to a discharge Q_2 should be the
same. However, these times for the same initial discharge
are different because of different conditions prevailing in the
underground, as shown in Fig. 1.

The final objective of this study is to determine the
maximum storage volume of active voids affecting underground
flow regulation within the karst formations. Either the
specific volume per km^2 of the catchment area or per m^3 or km^3
of the rock mass can be used.

4. Catchment of the Grab and Ruda Springs.

Catchment area. By its geological structure, the immediate
catchment area of the Grab and Ruda Springs is 385 km^2.

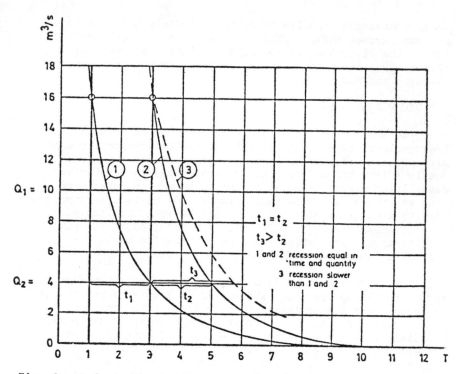

Fig. 1. Hydrographs Outflow Recession for Initially Equal
        Discharges.

Considering differences in main features, the area was
divided into three zones: A-from the sinkhole line at the
Buško Blato to the Grab and Ruda Springs, with 172 km^2; B-
containing the Buško Blato, with 157 km^2; and C-the hinterland
of the Buško Blato, with 56 km^2, as shown in Fig. 2. Separation in three zones was justified on the basis of different
intensities of underground recharge and depletion.

     The zone A was most active in recharge and depletion,
because it is in a direct contact with the well-developed
sinkhole zone at the southwest and west rims of the Buško
Blato as well as with faults oriented in the direction of
the Cetina Valley.

     The zone B, the plain of the Buško Blato, was in lime-
stones of indeterminate depth, covered with alluvial and
lacustrine sediments sporadically reaching up to 40 m in depth.
At the central part of the polje these deposits were highly
impermeable, but toward the edges where they thinned out they
were permeable [1]. Outflow from the Buško Blato by

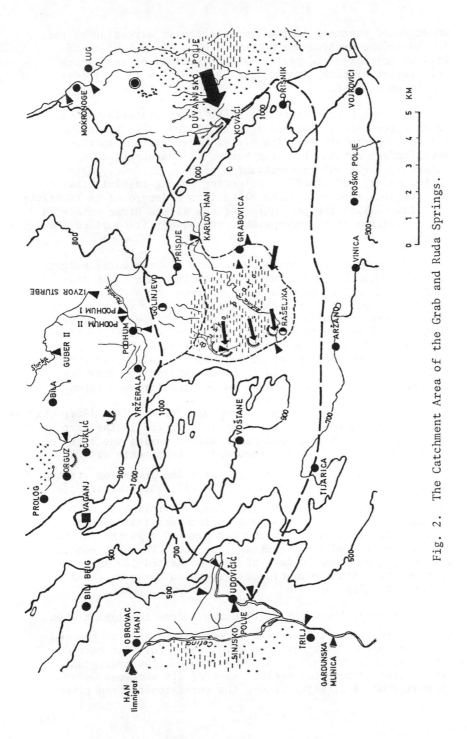

Fig. 2. The Catchment Area of the Grab and Ruda Springs.

underground channels in the south-southeast direction at the
Jabuka-Aržano section was prevented by a heavy barrier of
Liassic dolomites and partly by the vertical or very steep
orientation of rock strata [2]. The sinkhole line divides
the zones A and B.

The zone C represents the Buško Blato hinterland, which
feeds water both to the underground of the Buško Blato and to
the Buško Blato itself. The Ričina River is an important
water budget component. This zone C is characterized by
numerous, large but intermittent springs (Mukišnica, Agino
Vrelo, Kuželj and others), indicating during rainfall that the
infiltration from the Buško Blato into underground is restricted. The smaller the percentage of the Ričina River waters in
the replenishment of underground, the higher its surface flow
discharge.

Outflow from the Underground. The 10-year water budget
for the period 1949-1958 was used with the mean daily discharge at the Grab and Ruda Springs, from which the mean 10-
day discharges, as sufficiently representative for the overall
ten-year period are computed. The general recession curves
contain both the surface runoff and the direct infiltration
from rainfall during the period of recession. The years which
give the maximum net depletion volumes are 1952, 1954 and
1958. Of these, 1954 proved to be convenient for analysis,
and years 1952, 1958 and 1949/50 were used for comparison.

Characteristics of the Hydrograph for the Year 1954. In
1954 a large inflow to the underground started in the last
two decades of February, and particularly during the month of
March. The maximum outflow recorded in this month was 70
m^3/sec. In the second 10 days of March the recession started
and lasted to the second 10 days of April, when the average
daily discharge decreased to 15 m^3/sec. A reliable and continuous recession curve was well defined for that period,
referred to as Curve I. During the next 20 days the inflow
and outflow showed a substantial increase. The next recession
started at the third 10 days of May and lasted 120 days, or
four months, with the continuous recession curve referred to
as Curve II (Fig. 3).

By transposing Curve II to Curve I from the moment when
on the former the rate of 15.8 m^3/sec was reached to the end
of the recession, a single recession curve for that year was
obtained, as shown in Fig. 3. When the outflow hydrograph
was plotted in semi-log scales, some of its sections were
approximated by straight lines, the recession section given by

$$y = ae^{-bx} ,$$ (1)

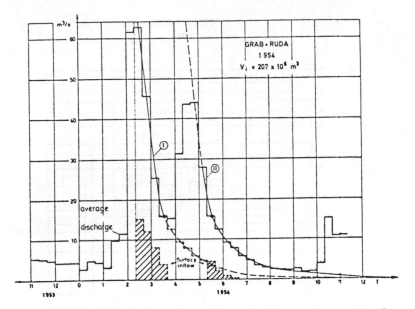

Fig. 3. The Hydrograph and the Recession Curves for 1954 for
the Grab and Ruda Springs.

with y in m^3/sec, and x = the time, or (after Maillot)

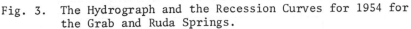

$$Q = Q_o \, e^{-b(t-t_o)} \tag{2}$$

with a composite recession, and parameters a and b differing from section to section (Fig. 4) to be estimated by the
method of least squares.

Active Void Volume in 1954. The outflow from the second
10 days of February to the second 10 days of April plus from
the second 10 days in June to a complete recession in the
second 10 days of October with a total duration of the recession
period of 250 days in 1954 was $V_o = 207 \cdot 10^6 \, m^3$, as the
integration of recession curve. The inflows during the recession period were: (a) the Ričina River, $V_r = 39.7 \cdot 10^6 \, m^3$,
and (b) direct infiltration precipitation, $V_p = 28 \cdot 10^6 \, m^3$,
computed for A = 385 km^2, P = 350 mm, C = 0.21, and P_e =
73 mm, where A = the catchment area, P = the precipitation,
C = the runoff coefficient, and P_e = the net infiltration precipitation. The rainfall had no effect on the increase of
surface streams flows. The maximum active storage capacity

GRAB • RUDA
1954

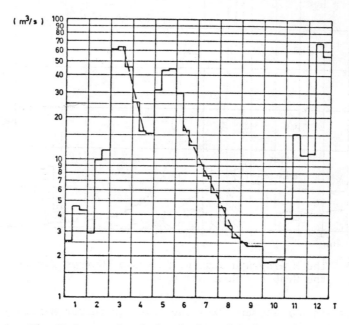

Fig. 4. The Hydrograph of the Grab and Ruda Springs in Semi-Log Scales for the Year 1954.

of the underground was then: $V_u = V_o - (V_r + V_p) = [207.0 - (39.7 + 28.0)] \cdot 10^6 = 139.3 \cdot 10^6 \; m^3$.

The comparison between the recession curves of 1954 and 1952 showed that the recession curves were of the same form (Fig. 5), although the recession started at a relatively low discharge in 1952.

The inflow-outflow budget for 1952, taking the interval from February 21 to March 20 and from April 11 to November 20 (Fig. 5) gave: $V_o = 150.2 \cdot 10^6 \; m^3$ as outflow, $V_r = 26.1 \cdot 10^6 \; m^3$ as inflow by surface streams, and $V_p = 7.7 \cdot 10^6 \; m^3$ as inflow from direct infiltration, with $V_u = V_o - (V_r + V_p) = [150.2 - (26.1 + 7.7)] \cdot 10^6 = 116.4 \cdot 10^6 \; m^3$. Similarly, water budget in 1958 from the beginning of the recession to its end gave: $V_o = 253.2 \cdot 10^6 \; m^3$; $V_r = 82.3 \cdot 10^6 \; m^3$ and $V_p = 62.0 \cdot 10^6 \; m^3$, with the active void volume

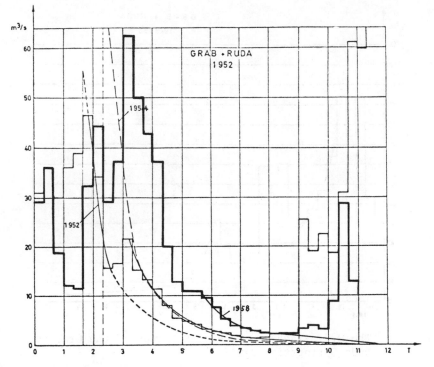

Fig. 5. The Hydrograph and Recession Curves of the Grab and Ruda Springs in 1952, 1958 with Recession of 1954.

$$V_u = V_o - (V_r + V_p) = [253.2 - (82.3 + 62.0)] \cdot 10^6 \text{ m}^3 = 109.2 \cdot 10^6 \text{ m}^3.$$

Analyzing the hydrologic instead of the calendar years, the year 1949/50 was found suited for considering a large storage capacity of the underground (Fig. 6). The outflow for both recession periods in 1949/50 was computed by the integration of recession curves (Fig. 6). The total outflow for periods was $V_1 = 442.8 \cdot 10^6 \text{ m}^3$. During the recession period the underground received $V_r = 88.0 \cdot 10^6 \text{ m}^3$ from the Ričina River and $V_p = 49.0 \cdot 10^6 \text{ m}^3$ from infiltration (P = 460.6 mm, C = 0.26 and P_e = 128 mm). The volume of actively filled voids was $V_u = V_o - (V_r + V_p) = [442.8 - (88.0 + 49.0)] \cdot 10^6 = 305.8 \cdot 10^6 \text{ m}^3$.

This is a rather large value. In relation to the estimated catchment area of 385 km^2, the specific void volume in the active rock mass was

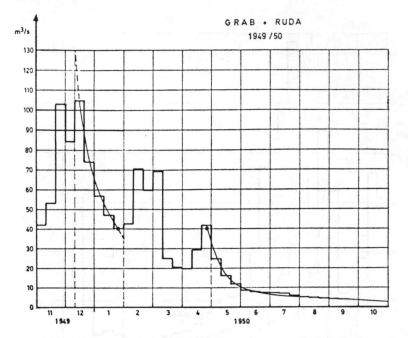

Fig. 6. The Hydrograph and Recession Curves of the Grab and
Ruda Springs in 1949/50.

$$sV_s = \frac{V_u}{A} = \frac{305.8 \cdot 10^6}{385} = 0.792 \cdot 10^6 \ m^3/km^2.$$

Taking the elevation of Buško Blato (700 m.a.s.l.) as the
upper level and the elevation of Sinjsko Polje (300 m.a.s.l.)
as the lower level, it follows that 1 km^2 with the depth of
400 m would give a rock mass of $4 \cdot 10^8 \ m^3$. Based on an
ideal prism, the specific pore volume per m^3 of the rock mass
would then amount to

$$sV_u = \frac{0.792 \cdot 10^6}{4 \cdot 10^8} = \frac{0.792}{400} = 0.00198 \ m^3/m^3 = 0.198\% = 1.98 \ lit/m^3.$$

Analysis by Using the Overall 10-Year Period. To get a
better picture of fluctuations which occur in outflows and
inflows in the karst underground considered, the overall 10-
year period is used by a comparative analysis of mass curves
of inflows and outflows, expressed in form of modular coefficients, for both the considered springs and for the reference
stream [3], as shown in Fig. 7.

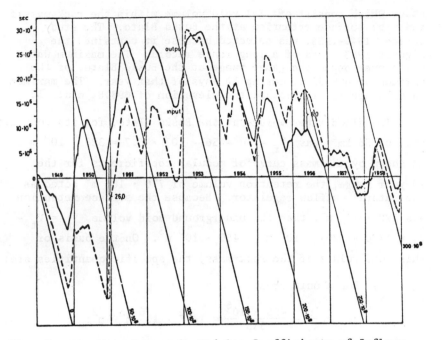

Fig. 7. The Mass Curves in Modular Coefficients of Inflows
and Outflows of the Grab and Ruda Springs for the
Period 1949-1958.

With the modular coefficients of discharges, $k = Q/Q_a$,
their mass curves, expressed in seconds are,

$$\Sigma k \Delta t = \sum \frac{Q}{Q_a} \Delta t \; , \qquad (3)$$

with the modular coefficients of the outflow of the Grab and
Ruda Springs and the inflow of the Ričina River near Karlov
Han, as the main or reference stream.

For the extreme ordinates of outflow and inflow mass
curves, the maximum surface and underground retention capacity
of the catchment area of 385 km^2 inside of which the flow at
the Sinjsko Polje level through the Grab and Ruda Springs
is naturally regulated, was

$$V_t = 34 \cdot 10^6 \; Q_a = 34 \cdot 10^6 \cdot 22.6 = 770 \cdot 10^6 \; m^3 \; .$$

The average Grab and Ruda outflow is $Q_a = 22.6 \; m^3/sec$.
The outflow from the underground is regulated by the retention

17-11

space which consist of: (a) void volume within the rock massif and, (b) surface retention at the Buško Blato. The study period, 1949-1958, was selected because it contained the highest 1953 flood of a long-range record. The maximum water stage overtopped the gauge range at the Buško Blato, of the maximum of 698.80 m, during 10 days of that year. The maximum water stage likely reached the elevation of 698.84 m.a.s.l.

The flood water volume at the Buško Blato, for its constant area of 56 km^2, was $V_f = Ad = 56 \cdot 10^6 \cdot 5.7 = 320 \cdot 10^6$ m^3. As shown by the mass curve of modular coefficients for the 10-year range, the retention volume of $770 \cdot 10^6$ m^3 acted as the natural outflow regulator. Because the surface retention was $320 \cdot 10^6$ m^3, then the underground void volume $V_u = V_t - V_f = (770 - 320) \cdot 10^6$ m$^3 = 450 \cdot 10^6$ m^3. On the basis of this void volume of the rock mass, the specific quantities are:

(a) For a unit area:

$$sV_s = \frac{V_u}{A} = \frac{450 \cdot 10^6}{385} = 1.17 \cdot 10^6 \text{ m}^3/\text{km}^2;$$

(b) For the gross volume of the rock mass, with its total height of $H = 400$ m between the lower (Sinjsko Polje) and the upper (Buško Blato) elevations

$$sV_u = \frac{sV_s}{V_m} = \frac{1.17 \cdot 10^9 \text{ lit}}{4 \cdot 10^8 \text{ m}^3} = 2.93 \text{ lit/m}^3 .$$

Based on the mass curves of the modular coefficients, the characteristic inflows and outflows are represented in cartesian coordinates (Fig. 8), from which it follows as in the previous cases that the natural retention volume is $V_t = 34 \cdot 10^6 \cdot 22.6 = 770 \cdot 10^6$ m^3.

The above results are only approximations, though good indicators as to the direction in which further investigations should be carried out. The relative meaning of obtained figures, of specific void volume (lit/m^3 of the rock mass) is shown on the following example. The karst massif falls steeply toward the Grab and Ruda Springs area. Assuming a lower horizon 300 m higher than it is, the catchment area would not change essentially, neither would the outflow or the specific retention volume by square kilometer. A substantial change would, however, occur in the specific void volume of the rock mass, because the new position would be at a

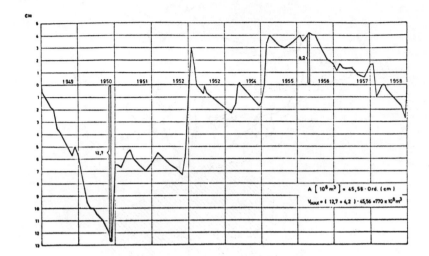

Fig. 8. The Characteristic Replenishment and Recession of
the Underground of the Grab and Ruda Springs Catchment in a 10-Year Period.

highly karstified zone, with a high percentage of voids. The
obtained specific void volume should be considered only as the
average value, the actual value being either higher or lower,
which depends on tectonics and the degree of karstification.

5. Catchment Area of the Springs in the Zrmanja Valley Between
Žegar and Jankovića Buk.

General Information. The karst zone between Žegar and
Jankovića Buk is composed of a whole range of small or large
karst springs, the most important being Krupa, Krnjera and
Dobarnica. That zone drains the whole catchment area of the
Gračac Plateau (Fig. 9). The catchment area gravitating
toward the Gračac Plateau is 563 km^2, as defined by both the
topographic and geologic factors. The main rivers in this
area are Ričica, Krivak and Otuča. Directly toward these
spring zones, water is contributed by a catchment area of
approximately 206 km^2, which contains also the Gračac Plateau.
The flooded area of this plateau under the maximum flood conditions is 12 km^2. The total catchment area contributing water
to the spring zone of the Zrmanja Valley (Žegar-Jankovića Buk)
is then 769 km^2, as shown in Fig. 9.

Average 10-Year (1949-1958) Runoff. The average flows
are as follows:

- the Gračac Plateau of 563 km^2 Q_a = 17.6   m^3/s

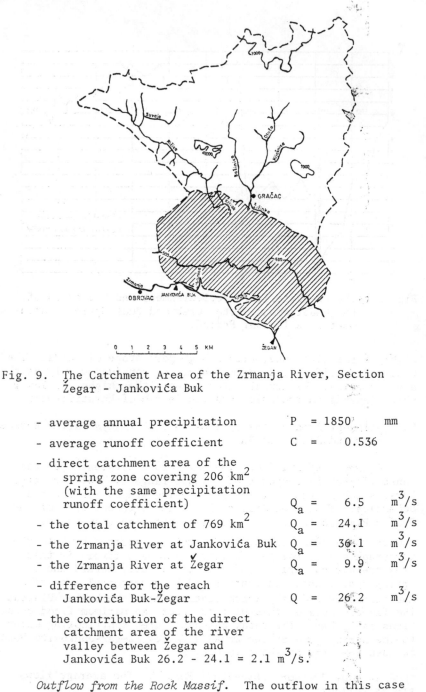

Fig. 9. The Catchment Area of the Zrmanja River, Section
Žegar - Jankovića Buk

- average annual precipitation P = 1850   mm

- average runoff coefficient C =   0.536

- direct catchment area of the
  spring zone covering 206 km^2
  (with the same precipitation
  runoff coefficient) Q_a =   6.5 m^3/s

- the total catchment of 769 km^2 Q_a =   24.1 m^3/s

- the Zrmanja River at Jankovića Buk Q_a =   36.1 m^3/s

- the Zrmanja River at Žegar Q_a =   9.9 m^3/s

- difference for the reach
  Jankovića Buk-Žegar Q =   26.2 m^3/s

- the contribution of the direct
  catchment area of the river
  valley between Žegar and
  Jankovića Buk 26.2 - 24.1 = 2.1 m^3/s.

Outflow from the Rock Massif. The outflow in this case
was analyzed in the same way and for the same characteristic
years as for the Grab and Ruda Springs. The basic year 1954

had two recession curves, more favorable for analysis than for the Grab and Ruda Springs. A particularly favorable situation was for the recession range between the maximum outflow and the low flow of 5 m^3/sec. (Fig. 10).

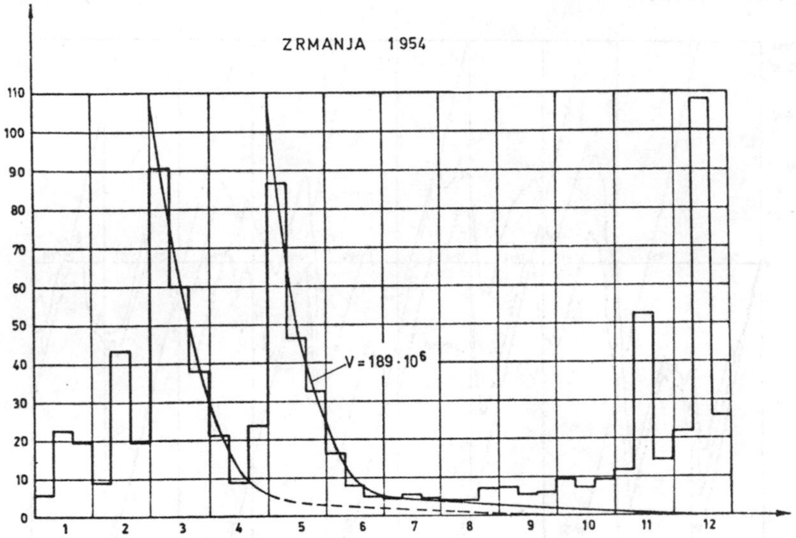

Fig. 10. The Hydrograph and the Recession Curves for the Year 1954 for the Zrmanja River at the Section Žegar - Jankovića Buk.

The active void volumes found for the above years were:

1954	$V_u = 69 \cdot 10^6\ m^3$
1952	$V_u = 62 \cdot 10^6\ m^3$
1958	$V_u = 90 \cdot 10^6\ m^3$
1949/1950	$V_u = 179 \cdot 10^6\ m^3$.

Analysis of the Overall 10-Year Period. According to the classification used, the Zrmanja River headwaters would fall into the B category. It is characterized by periodical surface water storage, but in a much lesser measure than at the Buško Blato. Retention basin of the Gračac Plateau is comparatively shallower, with numerous local hills. A record stage depth was 2.52 m. Covering an area of 12 km^2, the miximum surface retention volume is $12 \cdot 10^6 \cdot 2.52 = 30 \cdot 10^6\ m^3$.

Using the same method as in the case of the Grab and Ruda Springs and the modular coefficients [3] and Eq. (3), the maximum budget of inflows and outflows is $\Sigma k = 191.5$ -

176.6) $10^6 = 15 \cdot 10^6$ sec, or $V_t = \Sigma k\, Q_a = 15 \cdot 10^6 \cdot 26.2 =$
$393 \cdot 10^6\ m^3$, as shown in Fig. 11. The reference inflow is
represented by the sum of flows of the Ričica, Krivak and
Otuča Rivers.

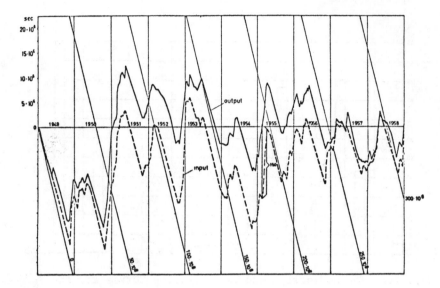

Fig. 11. The Mass Curves in Modular Coefficients for the
Period 1949-1958 for the Section Žegar - Jankovića
Buk of the Zrmanja River.

The average runoff of the section Jankovića Buk-Žegar,
$Q_a = 26.2\ m^3/sec$, contains also $1.1\ m^3/sec$ as the inflow
between Žegar and Jankovića Buk. Assuming a linear change
of flow, the discharge at Jankovića Buk is by $2.1\ m^3/sec$ lower,
with the average discharge of $24.1\ m^3/sec$. The total retention
is $V_t = 15 \cdot 10^6 \cdot 24.1 = 363 \cdot 10^6\ m^3$, the surface retention
$V_f = 30 \cdot 10^6\ m^3$, so that the void volume of the underground
is $V_u = 333 \cdot 10^6\ m^3$.

The specific void volumes computed both by unit area is

$$sV_s = \frac{V_u}{A} = \frac{333 \cdot 10^6}{206} = 1.616 \cdot 10^6\ m^3/km^2 .$$

The mean elevation difference between the Gračac Plateau
and the spring area in the Zrmanja Valley is about 500 m. The
specific void volume by unit of rock mass is consequently

$$sV_u = \frac{aV_s}{5.25 \cdot 10^8} = \frac{1.616 \cdot 10^6}{5.25 \cdot 10^8} = 0.00306 \ m^3/m^3 = 0.306\% = 3.06 \ lit/m^3$$

6. The Cetina Headwaters Catchment Area.

General description. The Cetina catchment area (Fig. 12) was classified into the C category [4]. However, the most difficult task was the determination of the contributing direct catchment area of the headwaters zone.

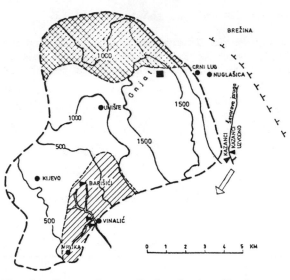

Fig. 12. The Catchment Area of the Cetina Headwaters up to Vinalić.

From the Kazanci Sinkhole along the southwestern part of the Livanjsko Polje a fault line was taken as the north-eastern watershed of the Cetina River headwaters. Such conclusion was supported by the fact that at the north-eastern part of the Livanjsko Polje there is an opposite fault zone extending up to the Vrbica Estavel, meaning that the underground of the Livanjsko Polje did not significantly contribute water to the Cetina headwaters. The waters coming from the Šator Mountain run through the Livanjsko Polje by the Ševarova Jaruga toward the Kazanci Sinkhole.

In the quoted study [4] the water of the Kazanci Sinkhole were not attributed to the Cetina headwaters. This led to the conclusion that the water of the whole Šator Mountain area and of a part of the Livanjsko Polje, including the Ševarova Jaruga, had no connection with the Cetina headwaters. Thus, the watershed line of the direct catchment area ran practically

north-south up to the fault near Vrlika, cutting also a part
of the Pašić Polje.

Consequently, it was estimated that the total catchment
of the Cetina headwaters upstream of the Vinalić is 336 km^2,
including 42 km^2 of the area from which the water comes to
the Cetina River by surface runoff only, and a part of 70 km^2
contributing water to the Cetina indirectly. Consequently,
the net water contributing area for the study of underground
void volume was 224 km^2, as shown in Fig. 12.

Outflow from the Underground. Analyzing again the same
characteristic years as for the two previous areas, the maximum
underground storage volumes were obtained for the Cetina
River headwaters:

1954	$V_u = 96.3 \cdot 10^6$ m^3
1952	$V_u = 74.0 \cdot 10^6$ m^3
1958	$V_u = 134.0 \cdot 10^6$ m^3
1949/1950	$V_u = 111.0 \cdot 10^6$ m^3 .

The basical year also was 1954, as shown in Fig. 13.

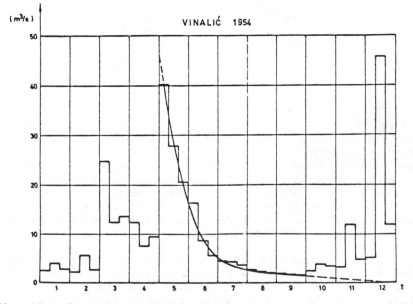

Fig. 13. The Hydrograph and Recession Curve for the Year 1954
of the Cetina River Headwaters.

Similarly as for the preceding two cases, an overall analysis was made for the Cetina headwaters for the 10-year period. The mass curves of inflows and outflows, in modular coefficients, are presented in Fig. 14.

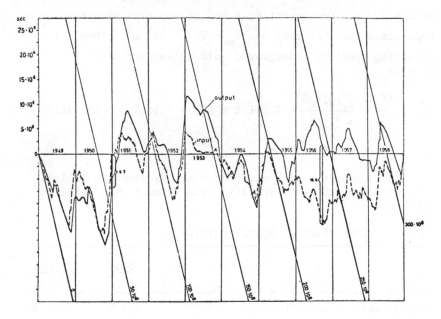

Fig. 14. The Mass Curves of Inputs and Outputs in Modular Coefficients of the Cetina Headwaters for the Period 1949-1958.

The retention volume, or the void volume of the underground regulation of natural outflow, was determined as $V_u = T Q_a = (23.3 \cdot 10^6) \, 11.6 = 268 \cdot 10^6 \, m^3$.

Specific Retention Volumes. Assuming the catchment of the Cetina Headwaters of 224 km^2, and that the Vinalić gauge station included also the surface runoff from an area of 42 km^2, the average discharge from the underground storage, is approximately 11.0 m^3/sec. The underground void volume is $V_u = T Q_a = 23.3 \cdot 10^6 \cdot 11.0 = 256 \cdot 10^6 \, m^3$. The specific volume by unit area becomes

$$sV_s = \frac{256 \cdot 10^6}{224} = 1.15 \cdot 10^6 \, m^3/km^2.$$

The specific void volume by unit rock mass was computed on the basis of the head between the average elevation of the catchment area above the sea level and that of the headwaters area, using the hypsometric curve. Namely, the average elevation of the catchment is 1090 m.a.s.l., and level of outflows at the Cetina River is 370 m.a.s.l., giving the head of $H = 720$ m. Consequently, 1 km^2 of the area with $H = 720$ m represents the rock mass of $V_m = 7.2 \cdot 10^8$ m^3. Then the resulting specific underground void volume per unit of rock mass is

$$sV_u = \frac{sV_s}{V_m} = \frac{1.15 \cdot 10^6}{7.2 \cdot 10^8} = 0.00160 \ m^3/m^3 = 0.160\% = 1.60 \ lit/m^3 \ .$$

7. Comparison of Results.

The comparison of specific volumes is given in Table 1, while the comparison of specific void volumes is given in Table 2.

Table 1. Comparison of Specific Volumes.

Area	A km^2	P mm	Q_a m^3/s	Head H_m	V_u 10^6 m^4	Specific Volumes	
						10^6 m^3/km^2	lit/m^3
1. Grab and Ruda	385	1404	22.2	400	450	1.170	2.93
2. Zrmanja	206	1850	24.1	525	333	1.616	3.06
3. Cetina Headwaters	224	1580	11.5	720	256	1.150	1.60

Table 2. Comparison of Specific Void Volumes for Three Areas.

	Grab and Ruda A = 385 km^2, H = 400 m		Žegar-Jankovića Buk A = 206 km^2, H = 525 m		Cetina Headwaters A = 224 km^2, H = 720 m	
	10^6 m^3	10^6 m^3/km^2	10^6 m^3	10^6 m^3/km^2	10^6 m^3	10^6 m^3/km^2
1954	139	0.352	69	0.333	96	0.430
1952	116	0.302	62	0.300	74	0.308
1958	109	0.283	90	0.435	134	0.598
1949/50	306	0.802	179	0.865	111	0.495
Average	167.5	0.433	100	0.485	104	0.456

Differences in specific volumes of Table 1, expresses in m^3/km^2 are comparatively high. Several factors may have produced them: capacities of sinkhole drainage, precipitation differences, variations in the erosion and corrosion history of the three areas, errors in determining watershed areas, the rock mass volume, errors in data.

It can be inferred from Table 2 that the area of the Cetina headwaters in 1949/50 had a strikingly low specific void volume by unit area in relation to that of the Grab and Ruda and the Zrmanja areas. However, for the four-year average, the specific volume of the area of the Cetina head-waters was comparable with the specific void volumes of the other two areas. The Cetina headwaters area had practically no surface retention which could, in conjunction with precipi-tation, affect favorably the underground replenishment as was the case with the Grab and Ruda and the Zrmanja areas. The differences of the individual years were an indicator that the study of the void volume in karst and comparison of results based on short time intervals (say one year) may lead to erroneous conclusions.

Other Comparisons. Heights of ideal prisms representing the rock masses were different in the three cases. The com-parison on the same basis was therefore impossible, and should be done only on the basis of specific conditions. For instance, if the specific void volume obtained for the Grab and Ruda Springs was taken as a reference value, the question remains what were the heights of the ideal prisms representing the rock masses of the Cetina headwaters and the Zrmanja River, for which the specific void volumes would be the same as for the Grab and Ruda catchment. The comparison is made by the following parameters:

(a) For the Grab and Ruda Springs,

Void volume   : $V_u = 450 \cdot 10^6 \ m^3$

Ideal prism height : $H = 400 \ m$

Specific void volume: $sV_u = 0.00293 \ m^3/m^3$

(a) The corresponding values for the Cetina headwaters:

Void volume   : $V_u = 256 \cdot 10^6 \ m^3$

Direct catchment: $A = 224 \qquad km^2$

Assumed   : $sV_u = 0.00293 \ m^3/m^3$ (same as for the Grab and Ruda Springs),

$$H = \frac{V_u}{A \cdot sV_u} = \frac{256 \cdot 10^6}{224 \cdot 0.00293 \cdot 10^6} = 392 \ m$$

The height difference between the prisms was only 8 m, from which it may be concluded that the considered areas (Grab and Ruda and the Cetina headwaters) belong to similar

categories regarding the limestone rock structure, degree of
karstification and meteorologic conditions.

(b) The corresponding values for the Zrmanja area,

Void volume   : $V_u = 333 \cdot 10^6$ m^3

Direct catchment: $A = 206$ km^2

Assumed   : $sV_u = 0.00293$ m^3/m^3

with

$$H = \frac{V_u}{A \cdot sV_u} = \frac{333 \cdot 10^6}{206 \cdot 0.00293 \cdot 10^6} = 550 \text{ m.}$$

The height difference between the prisms is 150 m. In
order to have the same prism height as in the case of the
Grab and Ruda area (400 m), the catchment area with the same
specific volume should be by 79 km^2 bigger for the Zrmanja Area.

8. Conclusions.

The obtained total and specific void volumes of karst
rock mass, as shown in Table 1, could not be taken as very
accurate, primarily for the season that the obtained results
were based on a relatively short observational period. The
selected 10-year period was representative, especially from
the aspect of the maximum surface flood retentions. A longer
period of 30-40 years would improve values on the underground
void volumes.

Results obtained and methods used to reach them are good
indicators for future studies, as a guidance for investigations to be undertaken for certain objectives.

9. List of Major Symbols.

A = area in km^2

Q_a = average discharge in m^3/s

P = total precipitation in mm

P_e = effective precipitation in mm

k = modular coefficient Q/Q_a

V = total retention volume in 10^6 m^3

V_f = surface retention in 10^6 m^3

V_u = underground retention in 10^6 m^3

V_o = total outflow volume in 10^6 m^3

V_p = volume of inflow due to precipitation in 10^6 m^3

sV_s = specific void volume per unit area in m^3/km^2

sV_m = specific volume per unit of rock mass in lit/m^3.

10. References.

[1] Boreli, M., Pavlin, B., An approach to the problem of underground water leakage from storage in karst regions: UNESCO; IHD, Vol. 1, 32-62, Dubrovnik, 1965.

[2] Herak, M., Possibilities of further development of the Cetina River waters: Feasibility Report, Split, 1963.

[3] Žugaj, M., Determination of underground retention in karst by analysis of runoff characteristics: Documentation, Civil Engineering Department, Zagreb.

[4] Magdalenić, A., Hydrology of the Cetina Drainage Basin: Yugoslav Karst, Zagreb 1971.

DISCUSSION

Yevjevich. The question whether a maximum void space in a volume of karst rock could be conceived, must be answered in the light that the water space volume is a function of the dynamic flow conditions. If one talks of probabilities of the total volume of low flows of a karst spring, then one must introduce also the concept of probabilities of the total void space emptied during a recession curve. This becomes particularly important when water flows through a karst underground system (water enters at one end of the karst system and leaves it at a spring). Exceptions of various types exist. However, the total water in void spaces of a system with a large karst spring is rarely expected to completely flow out.

The void space must be divided into the part which can be emptied by gravity force and that which either cannot empty or require exceptionally long time to empty. The effective porosity, or that porous volume that participates in current filling and emptying of seasonal and wet-to-dry year fluctuations, is of the most practical interest. The total rock mass is then between the upper and lower states of water levels as the gross rock volume, and the effective porosity is the net volume. Their ratio gives the percent of rock being used as water storage. Because the sets of upper and lower water levels are random variables, so must also be the net and gross volumes of the rock mass. Therefore, the concept of maximum void space of the karst underground water systems does not look as a feasible and practical hydrologic concept.

Duckstein. This paper puts forth a detailed analysis of the uncertainty in determining the volume of underground karst voids. An alternative approach to this problem may be the use of a conceptual physical karst model coupled with the simulated precipitation and runoff input. Such an approach would take into account the dependence between years and would extend the historical series in the sense of including wet or dry periods that have not been yet observed at that given location but that may occur in the future.

Boreli. The use of a simplified model, that is the difference between the average elevation of the river basin and the elevation of the spring, to define the specific void volume, sV_u, could completely distort the actual storage characteristics of the rock mass. The specific void volume which would be equivalent to the effective porosity, E, is defined by the amplitude of oscillation of underground water. If the estimation were based on these results, the values of sV_u, which were given in the paper as 2 to 3 $1/m^3$, or E = 0.2 to 0.3%, would be 1-2% instead, which is estimated, may be much closer to reality.

Ramljak. Researchers of the Trebišnjica Hydropower System carried out an experimental sealing of the empemeral Obod Spring at the Fatničko Polje, with the intention of decreasing the flow into the Polje and, thus alleviating the flooding of the Polje. The final purpose of this experiment was to assess the possibility of eliminating the construction of a tunnel between the Fatničko Polje and Bileća.

A manometer which was able to register a maximum pressure of 12 atmospheres was built in the sealed-off structure. After closing the spring with rains occurring immediately afterwards, the pressure rose to 12 atmospheres in 10 hours and the water appeared at about 120 m above the Obod Spring. Other springs appeared also, first at about the same elevation as the Obod Spring, and then, gradually, rose to the elevation of 120 m above the Obod Spring. Within one hour after the seal-off structure was destroyed, all the springs above the Obod Spring ceased to function, indicating they functioned only because of closing of the Obod Spring. Then, the water continued to flow out only at the Obod Spring, as before it was sealed off. Therefore, it was concluded that in this case the underground water retention was not very significant.

In this experiment the inflow into the Polje was decreased by about 50 m^3/sec. The rate of discharge from the newly created springs was only about 12 m^3/sec, estimating that the Obod Spring would have been discharging approximately 60 m^3/sec. if it had not been sealed off. However, despite these results the project was abandoned because of considerable damage resulting from the fact that the Obod Spring is located between two villages where new springs appeared, the traffic on the road above Obod was interrupted, power lines damaged, etc. It appeared necessary to consider a construction of the seal-off structure which could regulate the flow, to reduce the discharge into the polje without creating new springs in villages above the Obod Spring.

It is perfectly logical that the zone of extreme variations should, indeed, be of interest. This is emphasized in the introductory section of the paper, but perhaps it was not adequately described.

Stepinac. In the discussion of the maximum void volume in the paper, the question arises whether there is, in fact, a maximum volume. Examples indicate as much as a ten times greater volume than those described in the paper. It is essential to find the void volume of the environment in a zone of extreme underground water level variations, which can be achieved through extensive investigations, as emphasized in my introductory remarks.

Maximum void volumes are not given in the paper. Instead, only active void volumes in the zone of water table fluctuations between the water inlet and outlet are discussed. We. could have cited examples of significantly greater level changes, with the specific void volumes still smaller than given.

Parizek. The question is whether the data on the mean groundwater decline or recession of groundwater levels were used for the watersheds of springs investigated, along with spring flow recession curves, to determine effective porosity of the karst study areas or whether the analysis of the spring flow recession curve was made alone? This point was not clear from the text nor during the paper presentation. I am particularly interested in comparisons of results of such studies done separately using each method for the same watershed.

Two problems must be dealt with when attempting to predict the sustained yield of wells in carbonate rocks where fracture and secondary permeability and porosity dominate. One concerns the yield characteristics and unique behavior of individual wells completed within the aquifer and the other the regional behavior of the aquifer system taken as a whole when subjected to pumping stresses.

The problem of determining the sustained yield of individual and groups of wells in fractured, highly anisotropic carbonate aquifers was reviewed by Parizek and Siddiqui (1970)[1]. Yields of wells are particularly responsive to the position of the water table and its relationship to one or more producing zones which may be separated by non-productive rock. Yield may be dependent more upon the position of the water table with respect to these openings than to the proportion of saturated rock penetrated by the well bore.

They state[1]: "A permeability profile must be defined for these wells along with their available drawdowns, and the inclination of water-yielding openings. Permeability profiles may be roughly estimated from detailed driller's logs and caliper logs, and more precisely determined from flow meter surveys, packer tests and by pumping wells after successive increments of drilling or by a combination of increasing casing-lengths and extended drilling."

Pumping tests may be conducted after different casing settings and *well depths* to compare changes in specific capacity values. Tests also can be repeated after significant changes in water levels have occurred to determine the gain or loss in well yield. Available drawdown determinations are more difficult because available drawdown is dependent upon the inclination and position of significant water-yielding openings exposed within the borehole, seasonal variations in water-table position and draw-down-turbulence relationships.

Parizek and Siddiqui (1970)[1] found that for some gently dipping carbonate rocks openings frequently follow bedding planes or selected beds favoring conduit development. When this is known to be the case, pumping levels may be allowed to approach the top of one or another of the most productive zones encountered before significant reductions is well-yield are noted.

They state[1]: "Where openings are inclined, pumping levels should be kept well above the depth at which the opening was penetrated to minimize the rate of dewatering of conduits where openings occur higher in elevation adjacent to the well bore compared to where they were penetrated by the well bore. Test holes may be drilled immediately adjacent to the potential production well to define the inclination of individual conduits or wells test pumped where possible at rates sufficient to draw the pumping levels to the top of the opening in question. The latter is preferable because reductions in yield can be observed directly as a function of drawdown. To determine available drawdowns in fractured rocks, a permeability or yield profile, the inclination of openings adjacent to the well and seasonal variations in water levels must be known." The latter point cannot be overstressed because free-water surfaces in fractured rocks are subject to abrupt changes reflecting even small amounts of recharge and discharge. This is due to the low specific yields for these rocks. Seasonal water-level changes of 20 or more meters are common

---

1) Parizek, R.R., and S.H. Siddiqui, Determining the sustained yields of wells in carbonate and fractured aquifers: Groundwater, Vol. 8, No. 5, p. 12-20, 1970.

in many hydrogeologic settings in the Appalachian Mountain valleys and more than 30 m of water level decline has been observed during a six year sequence of dry years due to natural groundwater depletion.

Aside from a knowledge of the yield profile of each borehole in a well field and their available drawdowns it is still necessary to determine or estimate the coefficients of storage or specific yield and aquifer transmissivity to estimate sustained yields. This is often a difficult task using conventional pumping test methods and observation well data where aquifers are highly anisotropic because cones of depression frequently are highly distorted reflecting concentrated flow along fractures and enlarged channel ways. Elongated cones of depression are common along zones of fracture concentrations, some are star shaped on fracture trace intersections, or show other irregular configurations.

The problem of determining regional transmission and storage properties of fractured carbonate rocks can be resolved for practical purposes except where conduit flow predominates by viewing fractured aquifers on a larger scale. Although locally highly anisotropic, fractured aquifers may be viewed as being more nearly isotropic on a regional scale or display two principal directions of permeability distribution. Several approaches for estimating storage and transmissivity values thereby are possible. Large cones of depression developed around major pumping centers, well fields, limestone quarries, etc. can be examined using flow nets or by assuming reasonable values for coefficients of storage and transmissivity and recapitulating the known pumping history and water level behavior. (See for example Faulkner's paper in this proceedings). This can be done by digital simulation after estimating recharge, coefficients of storage and transmissivity, and comparing computed water levels with observed water-level data in areas undergoing little or heavy groundwater development.

Reliable gravity-yield and specific-yield data also can be obtained using the groundwater depletion method. Mean groundwater stage changes, for known groundwater basin areas must be determined along with base flow during a period of groundwater depletion. Gravity yield values are calculated for several prolonged inventory periods where recharge is negligible using the relationship: $S_g = H (Y_g)$, where $S_g =$ the change in groundwater storage during the inventory period; $H =$ the change in mean groundwater stages for a watershed of known area; and $Y_g =$ the gravity yield defined as the ratio of the volume of water soil or rock will yield by gravity to its own volume, during a period of groundwater recession.

Gravity yield values are time dependent as gravity drainage relates to the effective porosity, nature of permeability, grain size, etc. This point has been made abundantly clear by Stepinac and others speakers who have illustrated the time dependence of groundwater recession curves obtained on springs and streams. Frequently it has been possible to find rainless periods of a week or longer in the humid eastern U.S. or when minor summer showers are insufficient to meet field capacity requirements or cause changes in runoff. Prolonged cold spells in winter may be used when precipitation is stored in the watershed as snow or when ground-frost development is extensive. Normally gravity yield values thus obtained are lower than the ultimate specific yield values for these deposits but provide reliable estimates of specific yield when depletion periods last several or more weeks. If a series of time-gravity yield values are plotted particularly for prolonged depletion periods, it is possible to extrapolate the best fit line until it approaches the horizontal. The intercept of the horizontal line with the ordinate provides a good estimate of the specific yield for the deposit being drained. Fortunately, fractured rocks drain more rapidly than do soil and rock when intergranular permeability dominates. Hence the depletion period need not be as long as for the latter materials. The better intergranular and vugular porosity are developed, the longer the depletion period.

A common problem arises when using the depletion method. Groundwater basins and subbasin areas must be precisely defined and a representative network of observation wells must be available for each study area. Ideally, subbasins should be selected so that they are confined to a particular sequence of strata that are likely to have different storage properties. For example, we have found that some carbonate rocks have an estimated specific yield value of from 3 to 5 percent whereas other rocks in the same basin taken together have a value of 1.5 to 2 percent. Strata that are more highly fractured, have more closely spaced systematic joints, are located in the valley environment, or have shallow water levels all should have higher gravity and specific yield values when compared with the same rock in immediately adjacent settings.

Gravity- and specific-yield values should decrease with depth below land-surface because rocks are normally less decomposed and less well jointed with depth. Natural water-level fluctuations are usually restricted to the upper more permeable and porous strata. In some area, gravity yield values will be too low when computed for short drainage periods and too high when computed for shallow strata. These two factors probably tend to be self compensating.

Depth-specific yield data are essentially nonexistent in North America but are required in groundwater storage and

sustained-yield studies. I was pleased to see this point
discussed in detail by various Yugoslavian investigators.

Representative gravity yield values obtained by depletion
methods in the eastern United States are presented in Table 1.
These were obtained on a variety of fractured carbonate and
non-carbonate rocks in the Appalachian Mountain region
(Parizek, 1971)[2].

Elsewhere, permeability may be so well developed in carbonate aquifers that most nearby observation wells will respond
to pumping in a more ideal manner. Analysis of time-drawdown
data using conventional analytical techniques will suffice
to provide rather reliable values for the coefficients of
storage and transmissivity. Other well fields in our study
area did not respond in this manner. Coefficients of storage
and transmissivity obtained from various observation wells in
the same field or for the same unit of rock provide rather
conflicting results as one might expect for fractured carbonate rocks (Table 2). Often a range in values for coefficients
are obtained for the same time-drawdown data depending upon
the analysis technique adopted.

The biggest source of errors when estimating specific
yield or effective void volume of fractured rocks that may
be obtained by the groundwater depletion method results from
poor definition of the groundwater basin area tied to a particular point of groundwater discharge, inaccurate groundwater
flow measurements during the recession period, poor definition
of the mean groundwater stage change for the watershed under
study, poor definition of other sources of recharge and discharge to the aquifer during the inventory period, and un-
detected underflow contributions or losses of groundwater to
the watershed under study.

In the United States, the well control frequently is
abundant enough and geological controls governing a groundwater
basin areas well enough known that the problem of defining
basin area does not pose serious limitations. High gravity
yield values have been obtained in my studies for subbasin
groundwater depletion investigations conducted on watersheds
located in high relief areas. Here, groundwater underflow
into the basin was apparent where gravity yield values of 20

---

2) Parizek, R.R., Sustained yield of wells in fractured carbonate rocks: in Hydrogeology and Geochemistry of Folded
   and Faulted Carbonate Rocks of the Central Appalachian Type
   and Related Land Use Problems: Mineral Conservation Series,
   Circular 82, Earth and Mineral Sciences Experiment Station,
   The Pennsylvania State University, Univ. Park, Pa., 181 p.
   Edited by R.R. Parizek, W.B. White and D. Langmuir, 1971.

to 30 percent were obtained for rocks where values should not exceed 2 to 3 percent. This underflow problem should be particularly serious in high mountain areas as along the Dalmation Coast of Yugoslavia.

Table 1. (from R.R. Parizek, 1971)[2], Gravity Yield Values for Fractured Carbonate and Noncarbonate Rocks in the Central Appalachian Region Obtained by the Depletion Method.

Rock Type	Gravity Yield	Duration in Days	Source of Data
Oswego Sandstone, Tuscarora Quartzite	1%	5	Konikow (1969)
Junita Formation, residual soils, colluvium and stream alluvium in the Nittany Valley area.	2 1/2%	40	
80% of Basin area underlain by Cambro-Ordovician Carbonates and 20% by the above formations and deposits in Spring Creek	1.5%	--	Giddings (1974)
Cambro-Ordovician Carbonates in the Lebanon Valley area of Pennsylvania	5%	--	H. Meisler (1963)
Siltstone, Shale, Sandstone, stream alluvium and colluvium	12.4% 8.4%	8 8	G.C. Cline (1968)
Conestoga Formation finely to coarsely crystalline limestone; schistose and conglomerate in part, residual soil and stream alluvium in little Conestoga Creek Basin, Penna.	2.7% 6.2%	7 8	H. Meisler and A. E. Becher (1971)
Brandywine Creek Basin, Penna.	7.0%		Olmsted and Hely (1962)

Table 2. Summary of Pumping Test Data Showing Specific Capacity
and Coefficient of Transmissivity Values for Selected
Wells Located Within Fractured Carbonate Aquifers.
(From Siddiqui[3], 1969; and Parizek and Siddiqui[1],
1970).

Well No.	Formation	Specific capacity gallons per minute per foot of drawdown per foot of saturated rock penetrated x 10^{-3}	Coefficient of Transmissivity
G-10	Gatesburg Fm.	471.47	18300-42400
UN-2	Gatesburg Fm.	123.9	10500-57500
UN-3	Gatesburg Fm.	120.81	17200-63500
Un-14	Gatesburg Fm.	172.34	16800-30500
UN-16	Gatesburg Fm.	53.64	5650-11700
UN-17	Gatesburg Fm.	187.97	16220-53000
UN-20	Gatesburg Fm.	1.45	313-740
UN-22	Gatesburg Fm.	31.34	705-2500
UN-23	Gatesburg Fm.	111.89	2310-7800
UN-24	Gatesburg Fm.	132.60	43000-75000
UN-25	Gatesburg Fm.	30.0	1670-3450
UN-26	Gatesburg Fm.	119.99	46350-81000
SC-5	Gatesburg Fm.	2202.56	109000-186000
SC-15	Gatesburg Fm.	27.66	2500-5000
SC-16	Gatesburg Fm.	1656.82	422000-225000
SC-17	Gatesburg Fm.	3.33	85-370
SC-18	Gatesburg Fm.	1590.01	345000-560000
SC-19	Gatesburg Fm.	371.50	33400-60000
116	Nittany Dol.	224.09	1385-9070
401	Nittany Dol.	6.68	-----
412	Gatesburg Fm.	0.70	128-330
415	Gatesburg Fm.	930.0	15000-68400

Stepinac. In the Parizek's discussion the stress is on
the use of pumping wells for determing the volume of underground
voids under the conditions of varying groundwater levels in
different rock poreous media. My paper would definitely treat
this problem if data for such an approach were available.

In the paper the karst cases were selected with springs
of low level positions, for which the most likely underground

3) Siddiqui, S. H., Hydrogeologic Factors Influencing Well
Yields and Aquifer Hydraulic Properties of Folded and
Faulted Carbonate Rocks in Central Pennsylvania: Ph.D.
dissertation, Department of Geosciences, The Pennsylvania
State University, 502 p, 1969.

watersheds could be geologically defined and outflows may be
determined at any time. If a system of wells and pumps were
economical to use, then the karst spring function would cease.
One can visualize the outflow of the natural Karst springs
as the total outflow of pumps of a set of wells.

Table 2 given by Parizek, with the specific capacities
of wells, is a good way to present the results. In a hypothetical case of wells and pumps in the areas studied in the
paper, similar variations in specific capacities would be
normal to expect, depending whether a well would be located
in solid Karst rocks or in primary or secondary fault or
fissure zones.

The approach of determining the void volumes in a Karst
rock mass, as shown in the paper, had as an objective to find
out the order of magnitude of the total void volume in a
relatively well defined region geologically, on the basis of
input-output water budget. Evidently, such an approach has
its shortcomings, especially as it concerns the lack of
measurements on inputs, as the case was with the Vinalić
region, with the insufficiently well defined maximal groundwater levels and the time of the total depletion of the underground. To come close to the maximum groundwater levels, two
cases are selected with floods on the upper water levels (at
Buško Blato, and at Gračac Plateau).

The selected period of ten years definitely did not
include the extreme wet and dry years. Neither the obtained
maximum underground retention was an ideal quantity. Regardless of it, the cumulative input and output water quantities
in that period showed a method which should be continued in
investigations to come up with still more realistic values.
The well located piezometer boreholes in a sufficient number
would likely give the ideal, average underground levels. The
comparison of changes of levels in the underground with the
outflowing water during the time Δt, would throw more light
on this problem, particularly with the partial changes of
groundwater tables. The large number of piezometers would
permit the drawing of isolines of the water table, as a further
contribution to determination of rock void volumes.

The investigation by wells and pumping has its importance
in cases when the outflows can not be measured, such outflows
as Karst springs under the sea, lakes, in large rivers, etc.

INFLUENCE OF RESERVOIRS ON CHANGES IN NATURAL FLOODING OF UPSTREAM KARST PLAINS

by

Milorad Milićević, Civil Engineer, Chief of Construction,
Electric Power Authority BH, Trebinje, Yugoslavia

Synopsis. The backwater curves of levels of surface karst reservoirs may produce an increase in the recession curves of inflows from karst aquifers into them, which curves can serve as indicators of changes in the water regime upstream of reservoirs. These changes occur as rises in groundwater levels with an increase of groundwater storage, or as an increase in flooding of upstream, natural, periodically-flooded karst plains (poljes). The users of reservoirs may face several legal and administrative problems due to these increases. Besides, the longer water at these higher levels stays in flooded plains, the larger may be the volume of water lost to adjacent karst catchments.

This paper is an attempt to find methods for identifying the eventual changes in upstream water regimes by reservoirs in karst. Taking into account that effects of reservoirs on the water regime of flooded plains may be rather brief, the solution of the problem should be looked for by using the statistical relationship of parameters of the water regime and the catchment hydrometeorologic data not influenced by a reservoir.

The statistical relationship is determined for the period prior to reservoir construction, for which observations are usually available, and then applied to the period of the eventually changed regime. These changes can then be identified by comparing the estimated and the observed flood characteristics of karst plains during the period of reservoir existence. Provided sufficiently long observations are available, the statistical relationship between the parameters of water regime and the catchment hydrometeorologic data, can be obtained also during the period of changed regimes. By comparing these statistical relationships of natural and changed regimes, it is possible to discriminate the eventual changes. The advantage of the method presented is the use of hydrologic variables of the catchment, that are regularly observed.

1. Introduction.

By constructing surface reservoirs in karst regions the recession curves of water inflows from interconnected karst aquifers may change, which indicate changes in the groundwater regime. These changes may be in the form of a general increase of underground water levels and an increased and prolonged

18-1

flooding of upstream karst plains. These plains (poljes) are periodically flooded under the natural regime. A cascade of closed karst plains, with water communicating among them through underground channels only, is a common phenomenon in Yugoslavian karst regions.

While some factors of the changed water regime may be positive (as an example, the increase of groundwater levels), the prolonged and increased flooding of karst plains decreases the agricultural production and can cause water losses to adjacent karst catchments.

This paper presents the investigations leading to discrimination of possible changes in water regime by considering the period before the construction of a large reservoir as the natural or pre-reservoir water regime of interconnected underground aquifers and karst plains, and the period after the reservoir is created, as the changed or post-construction water regime. This may help the users of a storage reservoir to forecast the inflow of water from the underground into the reservoir, and planners to better design such reservoirs during the feasibility studies.

2. Methods of Investigation.

To find the consequences of surface reservoirs in karst in the form of changed hydrogeologic conditions and flood regime of upstream karst plains is not a simple task. It is more difficult to do it if the period available for the identification of changes is too short to discriminate them as significant, say if the period of the new regime is only a couple of years. The problem in this paper is approached by establishing the statistical relationship between the water regime parameters and the catchment hydrologic variables under the natural regime. Usually sufficient observations of all variables are available for this relationship. Then it is investigated whether this relationship is changed during the operation of the surface reservoir.

The influence of surface karst reservoirs on the water regime in the interconnected underground karst aquifers or systems of karst channels, as well as on the flood regime of adjacent karst plains can be identified:

(1) By testing the homogeneity in the series of annual (or monthly) highest water levels, flood volumes and flood durations in karst plains, and comparing the natural and the new water regimes; and
(2) By finding the correlative relationships between the variables related to water inflow into the karst plains and the hydrologic variables of the catchment.

Testing homogeneity of series. The method of testing the homogeneity of series uses the series of highest water levels, flood volumes and flood durations in karst plains for the pre-reservoir and post-construction periods. The pre-reservoir natural water regime is compared with the post-construction water regime by analyzing the frequency distributions of flood-related random variables of individual months in which floods occur. Then the projected probabilities of occurrence of these flood-related variables during the post-construction period from the frequency curves of pre-reservoir period make feasible to discriminate whether the changes in the water regime have occurred or not.

To discriminate the changes, rather long series of ob-servations are needed, of at least ten years for both the natural and the changed regime. The data available on the natural regime is usually longer than for the post-construction regime, because the problem of increased flooding may be posed soon after the beginning of reservoir operation. There-fore, the test of homogeneity of series cannot be carried out in the classical way. However, by investigating how certain variables of post-construction period relate to statistical properties and frequency distributions of these variables in the pre-reservoir period, some inference can be made on changes.

Correlation analysis. By establishing the relationship of variables of water regime, which serve for the discrimina-tion of changes, to catchment hydrologic variables, which are not affected by the reservoir construction, changes in water regime can be investigated, and not only by mere indications but by numerical identification. For such discrimination of changes, reliable historic hydrologic data are needed, at least for ten years, provided these ten years have experienced high floods.

The simple water-budget equation, for any time interval Δt, connecting runoff to precipitation is

$$Q = P - E \pm R , \qquad (1)$$

where Q = the runoff, P = the precipitation, E = the evapora-tion, evapotranspiration and other losses (percolation out of the catchment), and R = the retardation of water in karst aquifers, in systems of underground karst channels and flooded karst plains. Classical hydrologic services usually supply the information on Q and P, while E must be estimated and R determined in order to predict the runoff by using the precipitation.

The difference between precipitation and evaporation and other losses out of catchment, conceived as the runoff deficit, is often called the effective precipitation, $P - E = P_e$. It is reasonable to postulate that the retardation R is dependent on effective precipitation, or

$$R = f(P_e) \ . \tag{2}$$

The capacity for water retention of the karst underground depends upon its hydraulic and geometric characteristics. The geometry of underground channels may be considered as fixed for the periods considered, while the hydraulic parameters vary with and are dependent upon the effective precipitation, because the part of infiltrated precipitation forms both the underground and surface water pressure gradients controlling the flow capacities.

The difficulty arises when the effective precipitations P_e is to be expressed as a function of time. The use of the antecedent precipitation index, I, is attractive, and herein assumed to be of the form

$$I = \sum_{i=0}^{n} h_i k^i \ , \tag{3}$$

where h_i = the daily precipitation (averaged over the catchment area), i = the number of previous days with $i = 0, 1, 2, \ldots, n$, and k = a variable parameter. The I-index for any day is the sum of previous daily precipitation values multiplied by k^i. The index gives a measure of effects of the preceding precipitation, by using for n up to a month or less than it. The parameter k of the antecedent precipitation index varies, in principle, following the evaporation and evapotranspiration sequences of warm or cold weather.

Extremes of runoff deficit do not follow exactly the temperature extremes. For the Trebišnjica River basin in Yugoslavia, used here as an example, the shift is of about two months. The minimum runoff deficit is in March and the maximum is in September. Therefore, the sequential calendar number of weeks could be used to take care of this cyclicity in the correlation analysis, representing the average characteristics of evaporation and evapotranspiration, as shown in Table 1.

The special problem is the runoff from snow melt, and more so since in the catchment investigated, no snow survey is made, except for short periods in recent times. A relationship between the terrane elevation above the sea level and the runoff from snowmelt can be established, provided the ground is saturated with water at that time. However, if there is a retention capacity for water infiltration, no runoff may result

Table 1. Cyclicity of Evaporation and Evapotranspiration in Form of Indexing the Weeks of the Year for the Trabišnjica River Basin.

Week	θ	Week	θ	Week	θ
1.I-7.I	10	7.V-13.V	8	3.IX-9.IX	25
8.I-14.I	9	14.V-20.V	9	10.IX-16.IX	26
15.I-21.I	8	21.V-27.V	10	17.IX-23.IX	25
22.I-28.I	7	28.V-3.VI	11	24.IX-30.IX	24
24.I-4.II	6	4.VI-10.VI	12	1.X-7.X	23
5.II-11.II	5	11.VI-17.VI	13	8.X-14.X	22
12.II-18.II	4	18.VI-24.VI	14	15.X-21.X	21
19.II-25.II	3	25.VI-1.VII	15	22.X-28.X	20
26.II-4.III	2	2.VII-8.VII	16	29.X-4.XI	19
5.III-11.III	1	9.VII-15.VII	17	5.XI-11.XI	18
12.III-18.III	0	16.VII-22.VII	18	12.XI-18.XI	17
14.III-25.III	1	23.VII-29.VII	19	19.XI-25.XI	16
26.III-1.IV	2	30.VII-5.VIII	20	26.XI-2.XII	15
2.IV-8.IV	3	6.VIII-12.VIII	21	3.XII-9.XII	14
9.IV-15.IV	4	13.VIII-14.VIII	22	10.XII-16.XII	13
16.IV-22.IV	5	20.VIII-26.VIII	23	17.XII-23.XII	12
23.IV-29.IV	6	27.VIII-2.IX	24	24.XII-31.XII	11
30.IV-6V	7				

from snowmelt. To take care of the snowmelt runoff in the correlation analysis, the sum of the average daily air temperatures over the river basin for the time interval of analysis is used. To further improve the correlation, the water levels or discharges of the river entering a flooded, closed karst plain can be also used as independent variables.

The general correlation function is then:

$$W_m = f(I, \theta, T, H, \Sigma h), \tag{4}$$

with W_m = the maximum flood volume in the closed karst plain, I = the antecedent precipitation index, θ = the week number index (measuring the runoff deficit), T = the average air temperature, H = the water level in the river immediately upstream of flooded, closed karst polje, and Σh = the sum of

daily precipitation in the period of increased flooding of the
karst polje.

The correlative association with the least variance of
residuals can be obtained by varying the parameter k. Taking
into consideration the large amount of input data, the problem
must be treated on a digital computer. As the first approach,
the linear multiple correlative association is investigated in
the form:

$$X_1 = A_o + A_1 X_2 + A_2 X_3 + A_3 X_4 + A_4 X_5 + \ldots \qquad (5)$$

with X_1 = the maximum flood volume in the karst plain as the
dependent variable, and X_2, X_3, X_4, X_5, . . ., the so-called
independent variables, as described previously.

All the data needed for the correlation analysis is processed for a certain number of floods in karst plains of the
historic period of the pre-reservoir regime. It was desirable
to include as many floods as possible, but at least twenty.
The following correlation parameters are to be estimated:
multiple correlation coefficients, partial correlation coefficients, regression coefficients, standard deviation of residuals, and multiple correlation coefficients obtained by
deleting from the analysis one by one the independent variables.

The antecedent precipitation index in the computer program designed could cover the antecedent period up to n = 60
days. The variable parameter k in this index could be
varied from 0.40 to 0.95, at increments of 0.05. The maximum
multiple correlation coefficient of the multiple linear regression analysis determines the selection of the k and n
values.

The correlation association as well as the effects of
each independent variable on the multiple correlation coefficient are then assessed. If this coefficient is found to be
greater than 0.90, the correlative association is considered
satisfactory. When this coefficient is found smaller, the
analysis of runoff deficit is repeated, searching for new
approaches to assess the proper effective precipitation, provided the accuracy of input data was sufficient.

By properly describing the correlative relationship for
the natural regime, it is then feasible to numerically determine the eventual significant departures in the water regime
after the reservoir was built. When sufficiently long series
of observations were available for the changed-regime period,
a similar correlative relationship between the highest floods

in closed karst plains and catchment hydrometeorologic variables can be established. By comparing these relationships,
obtained for periods before and after the reservoir was built,
the discrimination of changes in flood regime of karst plains
could be made.

If the post-construction observational period is too
short, the correlative relationship obtained for the pre-
reservoir regime can be used to predict what would be the
natural regime in post-construction period, provided the
antecedent precipitation index and other hydrometeorologic
variables of the catchment were also observed in the post-
construction period. The comparison of these predicted values
of maximum floods with the observed floods can then be used to
show the changes if any in flooding of closed karst plains.

3.   Application of the Method Outlined to the Case Study of
     the Trebišnjica River.

Introduction. In order to apply the method outlined, the
backwater effects of the Bileća Reservoir at the Trebišnjica
River in Yugoslavia on floods in the Fatničko Polje (a closed
karst plain) was used as a case study, showing the correlation
relations before and after the construction of the reservoir.
The basic parameters of the system of the Trebišnjica River,
with the surface storage of the Bileća Reservoir, with its
underground karst aquifer, systems of underground channels, and
the upstream closed karst Fatničko Polje, are: (a) catchment
area at the Grančarevo Dam creating the reservoir, $A = 1,331$ km^2;
(b) average annual precipitation at the catchment area, $P_a =$
1,800 mm, and (c) average discharge of the river, $Q = 79.8$ m^3/s.

The Trebišnjica River begins at the karst Bileća Spring,
and sinks into the underground at the Popovo Polje. The
catchment area, situated between the elevations of 335 m
(Bileća Spring) and about 2000 m of highest mountains, is
made of karst plateaus and cascade of closed karst plains. The
Gatačko Polje is the karst plain at the highest elevation of
960 m, then Cerničko (900 m), Fatničko (470 m) and Bilećko
Polje (430 m), as shown in Fig. 1.

Precipitation is unevenly distributed over the basin and
over the year, with the winter-spring flood period of karst
plains and the dry summer period. Only the perennial rivers,
the Gračanica and the Mušnica Rivers, flow through the Gatačko
Polje. Hydrogeologic conditions are similar for all closed
karst plains: the springs occur at the northeast rims of
plains and sinkholes at the southwest rims.

The geology of the Fatničko Polje, the case study of
eventual increase of floods, and its surroundings includes

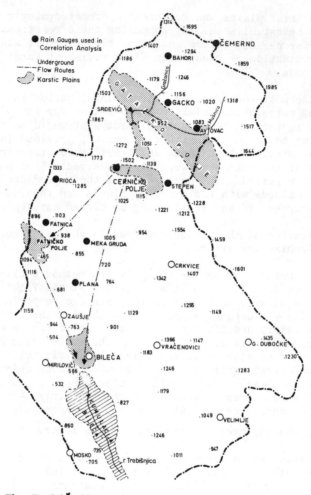

Fig. 1. The Trebišnjica River Catchment Area at the Grančarevo Dam Profile.

mainly sedimentary rocks of the Mesozoic, Tertiary and Quaternary. Extensive geological and geophysical surveys have shown
the existence of Eocene flysh, mainly in form of clay marls at
a depth of more than 100 m. Although this structure does not
stretch further than the outskirts of the plain, the flysh serves as water barrier. As the consequence, several small, but
permanent springs as well as a number of large but temporary
springs (Obod, Baba Jama, etc) occur at the contact of the
limestone and the flysh. During the high-precipitation season
the flysh zone backs the groundwaters, so they partially
appear at the large springs, flooding the plain. However,
water bypasses the barrier and flows towards the Trebišnjica
River springs. During the low-precipitations season, the

flysh barrier makes all water to flow to springs of the
Trebišnjica River. It has been verified by dye tracers, that
a direct underground connection during the low-precipitation
season exists between the water at the Gatačko Polje and the
Trebišnjica River. During the high-precipitation season an
overflow of underground water occurs from the line Gatačko
Polje-Trebišnjica Springs into the Fatničko Polje. The
flooding of the Fatničko Polje thus occurs, in an average
year, of about 120-140 days. The maximum flood observed in
the Fatničko Polje in the period 1949-1974 had a volume of
225.8 millions m^3 (see Fig. 2).

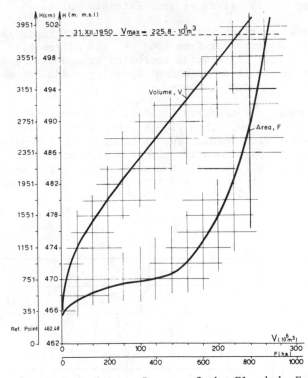

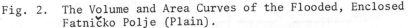

Fig. 2. The Volume and Area Curves of the Flooded, Enclosed
Fatničko Polje (Plain).

Groundwater piezometric levels in boreholes around the
Fatničko Polje, under the natural regime, are as follows:
(a) during the flooded plain, the groundwater levels follow
the fluctuation of water levels in the plain, while (b) during
the dry season the piezometric levels are 94.5 m below the
bottom of the plain (elevation 368.00 m above the sea level).

Major effects of reservoir construction. The large
Grančarevo concrete-arch dam was built on the Trebišnjica River

18 km downstream from the Bileća Springs in 1967. The Bileća
Reservoir thus created has a surface storage capacity of 1,270
millions m^3 (about one million acre-feet). The maximum
water level in the reservoir is 75 m above the springs of the
Trebišnjica River. The level difference between the bottom of
the Fatničko Polje and the Trebišnjica River springs is
130 m, so that the level difference between this plain and the
maximum reservoir level is reduced to 55 m. This means that
the maximum reservoir level is about 32 m above the natural
underground piezometric levels below the Fatničko Polje during
the dry season. For a full surface reservoir there is a
large underground storage coupled with the surface storage,
stretching nearly all under the Fatničko Polje.

In the continuous survey for control of imperviousness
of the Bileća Reservoir from 1967 on, the piezometric levels of
many geophysical exploration boreholes around the reservoir,
as well as a wealth of catchment hydrologic and hydrometeorologic data, have been gathered.

The reservoir capacity is about 50 percent of the average
annual water inflow. This gives a good within-the-year and
over-the-year flow regulation. Because of this regulation
potential, but particularly because a sequence of dry years
occurred from 1967 to 1974, the reservoir was filled to the
maximum level only once, in Spring 1970. Figure 3 shows the
reservoir level hydrograph for this period.

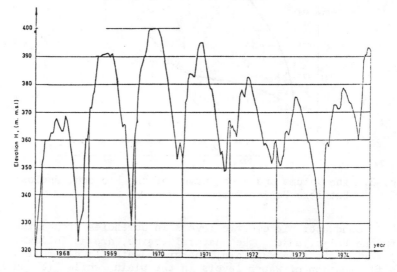

Fig. 3. The Level Hydrograph of the Storage Reservoir Bileća
for the Period 1967-1974.

By analyzing the piezometric groundwater levels of a
large number of exploration boreholes in the area around the

reservoir and around the Fatničko Polje, and by comparing the hydrographs of outflow (emptying of the flooded plain) of the Fatničko Polje in pre-reservoir and post-construction periods, it can be ascertained that the levels of the reservoir up to the elevation 360 m above the sea level, with the maximum reservoir level of 400 m, do not change the natural flood water regime of the Fatničko Polje. Therefore, only the floods of the Fatničko Polje, that occur when the reservoir levels were above 360 m elevation, have been used in comparing the pre-reservoir and post-construction regimes. Figure 4 gives the synoptic charts of floods in the Fatničko Polje, with the maximum flood levels and the number of flood days, for both the pre-reservoir and post-construction period.

— Pre—Construction Period

Year	I	II	III	IV	V	VI	VII	VIII	IX	X	XI	XII	Σ days	Max. Flood cm
1949													93	1949
1950													104	3828
51													177	3801
52													145	3105
53													72	3715
54													127	2485
55													164	2119
56													89	1110
57													87	1729
58													152	2348
59													130	2380
1960													195	2360
61													99	1930
62													152	2360
63													151	2705
64													136	2722
65													179	2976
66													134	2139
67													80	1380
	20.4	14.4	18.1	16.5	9.4	1.4	—	—	0.5	5.6	20.4	22.0	128.7	

— Post—Construction Period

Year	I	II	III	IV	V	VI	VII	VIII	IX	X	XI	XII	Σ days	Max. Flood cm
1968													145	2166
69													190	1896
1970													192	3382
71													172	2382
72													93	1400
73													67	1602
74													163	2725
	22.6	22.1	18.0	19.3	12.8	6.4	—	0.4	2.7	5.1	13.3	20.7	143.4	

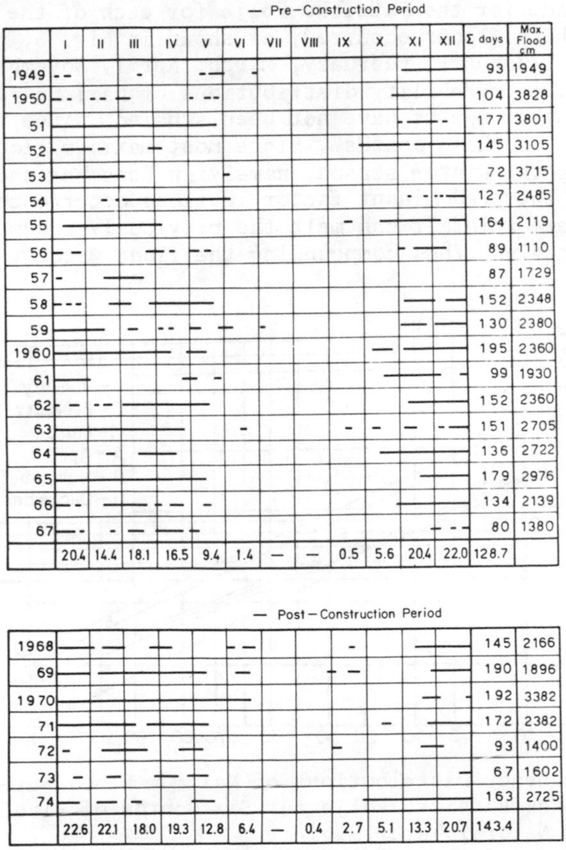

Fig. 4. The Synoptic Charts of Periodic Flooding of the Closed Fatničko Polje (Plain) for the Pre-Reservoir Period (Upper Chart), and the Post-Construction Period (Lower Chart).

Testing the homogeneity of series for the case study. Reliable data are available on floods in the Fatnicko Polje since 1949 for the natural regime, or during 19 years. For the post-construction period, the number of occurrences of flood elevations in the Fatnicko Polje, with the Grancarevo Reservoir levels higher than 360 m above sea level, was only twelve. Therefore, the classical approach of testing the homogeneity of series hardly applies. Because of it, the analysis of frequency distribution of floods was carried out only.

For the natural regime, an estimation of lognormal probability distributions of maximum flood volume in millions m³ (hm³) was made for the Fatnicko Polje for each of the six months in which floods occurred, as shown in Fig. 5, namely for months of January, February, March, April, November and December. The probability distributions of maximum flood volumes in other months have not been studied, since floods seldom occur in those months. Since most maximum floods occur during the winter season, namely in December and January, rainfall is the predominant factor in flood occurrence. However, the warm rainfall can melt the previously accumulated snow in mountains, thus compounding the flood water volumes.

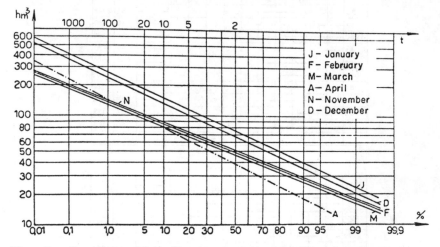

Fig. 5. Frequency Distributions of Maximum Flood Water Volumes in the Fatnicko Polje for Six Months of Floods for the Natural Water Regime.

Table 2 gives the return period of all flood events observed in the Fatnicko Polje during the post-reservoir regime, obtained by using the flood frequency distribution curves for the natural regime.

Table 2. Return Periods in Years of Post-Construction Regime
of Floods of the Fatničko Polje, Determined by Flood
Frequency Curves of the Pre-Reservoir Regime.

Date of Max. Flood	Water Level at the Bileća Reservoir	Max. flood volume in millions m^3	Flood volume Return Period in years
18.2. 69	368.0	25.40	1.1
2.3. 69	390.04	68.60	5.0
11.6. 69	391.03	9.84	-
25.1. 70	385.08	168.80	15.0
23.4. 70	399.81	188.00	980.0
11.1. 70	373.66	107.10	3.5
28.3. 71	386.66	26.10	1.1
14.4. 71	393.24	74.10	9.5
2.3. 72	375.26	37.00	1.4
25.4. 72	379.98	6.95	1.0
8.5. 74	376.68	10.62	-
3.11. 74	389.27	134.18	95.0

It can be seen from Table 2 that all the post-construction
floods have the usual return period except the flood of April,
1970. Any final conclusion about the change in flood regime of
the Fatničko Polje after the construction of the Bileća Reservoir based on the above analysis would be premature and unsubstantiated. This is more so true, since the post-construction
period is only seven years long, most of them on the dry side.
For a more reliable comparison the necessary period of observations should be at least 10 years.

Correlation analysis for the case study. For the correlation analysis, the data are necessary for: floods in the plain,
precipitation on the catchment, air temperatures in the catchment area, and water stages of rivers upstream of the karst
plain. The shortest observation period available is for precipitation, namely only since 1954. Therefore, the data are
used only for the period from 1954 onwards, in spite that the
observation periods for other variables were longer.

For the selected period of the natural regime, namely
1954 to 1967, 50 flood events of the Fatničko Polje were analyzed. For each maximum flood the following variables are treated:
maximum flood volume, average daily precipitation on the

catchment for the period of previous 30 days, ΣT the sum of
air temperatures in the catchment area for the period of rising
floods in the Fatnicko Polje and five days before that, and ΣH
or sum of daily water stages in the Musnica River for the
period of rising floods and five days before it.

The catchment area, including the Fatnicko Polje, has 10
precipitation gauges. The analysis of their representativeness
has shown that no one of these 10 gauges separately could be
considered as a representative of the average precipitation
on the catchment. Therefore, the data from all precipitation
stations have been used in the analysis, with the average
catchment precipitation for subsequent days determined.

4. Analysis of Results.

The prepared input data were processed in the form of
three series:

(i)   the maximum flood volumes in the karst polje for the
reservoir pre-construction period;
(ii) the maximum flood volumes in the karst polje for the
reservoir post-construction period; and
(iii) the maximum flood volumes for the whole period of
observations.

The results of correlation analysis are given in Table 3.
For each of the three periods processed, the multiple correlation coefficients, R, are given, first computed with all the
four independent variables, then deleting one by one of the independent variables. The multiple correlation calculated with
all the independent variables in all cases is shown to be
greater than 0.970. In all the cases processed, the largest
correlation was obtained for the same precipitation index
k = 0.95. On the basis of the multiple regression equation
obtained, the maximum flood volumes in the karst polje for the
post-construction period are predicted, as shown in Fig. 6.

For the twelve flood cases that occurred in the post-
construction period, the flood variables have been predicted
by the correlation relationship and the regression coefficients
obtained for the natural regime. The estimated maximum floods
in the Fatnicko Polje, that should have been expected, without
any change in the post-construction period, are given in Table
4, compared with those observed in the Fatnicko Polje in this
post-construction period.

For the highest flood volumes in the polje in the post-
construction period, the flood volumes estimated by Eq. (6), as
established for the pre-construction period, were lower than
those observed in nature. Other estimated floods mainly comply
with the ones actually recorded, as Table 4 shows.

Table 3

Multiple Regression Analysis of Floods
in the Fatnicko Polje

	Sample size	Independent Variables	k	R
Pre-Construction Period	30	$X_2\ X_3\ X_4\ X_5$	0.95	0.970
	30	$X_3\ X_4\ X_5$	0.95	0.969
	30	X_2 . $X_4\ X_5$	0.95	0.922
	30	$X_2\ X_3$. X_5	0.95	0.956
	30	$X_2\ X_3\ X_4$.	0.95	0.946
Post-Construction Period	24	$X_2\ X_3\ X_4\ X_5$	0.95	0.982
	24	. $X_3\ X_4\ X_5$	0.95	0.979
	24	X_2 . $X_4\ X_5$	0.95	0.868
	24	$X_2\ X_3$. X_5	0.95	0.980
	24	$X_2\ X_3\ X_4$.	0.95	0.933
Total	54	$X_2\ X_3\ X_4\ X_5$	0.95	0.974
	54	. $X_3\ X_4\ X_5$	0.95	0.972
	54	X_2 . $X_4\ X_5$	0.95	0.806
	54	$X_2\ X_3$. X	0.95	0.968
	54	$X_2\ X_3\ X_4$.	0.95	0.929

Testing the susceptibility of the multiple correlation coefficient to the sample size and the period of observations, it was found out that the series used in the analysis has been properly chosen. The homogeneity of the series of maximum flood volumes of both prior and after the construction of the reservoir was tested by using the U-test and the series was found to be homogeneous.

The analysis of obtained results show no significant changes in the flooding regime of the Fatnicko Polje, because the differences between the estimated and observed floods are within the accuracy of correlation analysis.

Maximum Flood Volume
in the Polje

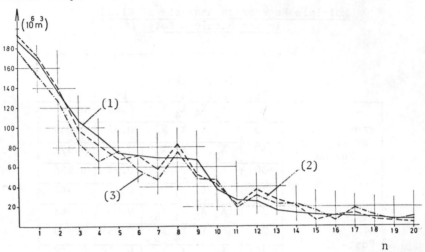

Fig. 6. Maximum Flood Volumes in the Fatničko Polje, in the
Descending Order of Recorded Volumes: (1) Recorded
Annual Maximum Flood Volumes; (2) Flood Volumes Pre-
dicted by Eq. (6) for Reservoir Post-construction
Period; and (3) Flood Volumes Predicted by Eq. (6) for
Reservoir Pre-construction Period, with n = the Number
of Highest Flood Volumes Included.

Table 4. Comparison of Estimated and Observed Flood Volumes in
the Fatničko Polje for the Post-Construction Period.

	Date	Reservoir Elevation	Maximum flood volume (hm^3)	
			Predicted	Observed
1	18. 2. 69	386.00	23.20	25.40
2	2. 3. 69	390.04	89.00	68.60
3	11. 6. 69	391.03	9.08	9.84
4	25. 1. 70	385.08	163.20	168.80
5	23. 4. 70	399.81	197.41	188.00
6	11. 1. 71	373.66	75.10	107.00
7	28. 3. 71	386.66	19.40	26.10
8	14. 4. 71	393.24	76.50	74.10
9	2. 3. 72	375.26	53.80	37.00
10	25. 4. 72	379.98	9.50	6.95
11	8. 5. 74	376.68	13.85	10.62
12	3.11. 74	389.27	127.40	134.18

DISCUSSION

Yevjevich. Figure 5 shows that the lognormal probability
distribution functions are used to fit the frequency distributions of maximum flood water volumes in the Fatničko Polje
for each of flood season months. Assuming that these fits do
not overestimate the return periods of extreme volumes, Table
4 shows that in the seven years of operation of the Bileća
Reservoir, four out of seven years have return periods greater
than seven (9.5, 15.0, 95.0 and 980.0). The two extreme values
of 95 and 980 years are most striking. The probability that
such four flood events occur in seven years under natural
conditions and the two extremes of 95 and 980 years, are so
small, that one has to question the conclusion of the paper
that there is no effect of the reservoir on flood volumes in
the Fatničko Polje. Either one must reject the selected
lognormal probability function as best to fit the maximum
flood volume frequency distributions, and look for another
function as a more appropriate distribution function, or the
conclusion must be drawn that the reservoir influences the
flooding of the Fatničko Polje.

Hajdin. A question is warranted in connection with this
paper, which also could be applied to a number of other papers.
Why not attempt, in modelling water flows, volumes, levels
or precipitation, a physical explanation of these relationships, making use of hydraulic information? More of it will
be presented in the general discussion concerning the planning
of future research in karst hydrology and water resources.

Duckstein. On strictly statistical grounds, Eq. 6 represents a linear regression for which five coefficients must be
estimated from a sample of 30. Only in the case the relation
between dependent and independent variables was based on a
physical information could such a regression equation provide
a reliable prediction for floods. The worth of a linear regression should be measured not only by the coefficient of determination, $R^2 = 0.86$, but also by the standard error of
estimates, as well as by other criteria. It would help if the
confidence band was plotted on a graph. Furthermore, the correlation matrix, given under the analysis of results shows a
correlation coefficient of 0.74 between variables 2 and 5, 0.70
between 3 and 5 and 0.63 between 4 and 5. The presence of
variable 5 introduces a considerable multicollinearity into the
model. Because of a small sample size a model with, at most,
two independent variables is warranted, so that it is appropriate to use a stepwise regression analysis, preferable without the variable 5. The first two variables, which result from
this analysis, should likely be kept only.

Ristić. One of the reasons for initiating many hydrologic
investigations is the need to study and discriminate the

possible influences of engineering undertakings in karst upon
the water regime in karst poljes, that is for the karst hydrologic systems as a whole. Such an objective may be the result
of various trends: (i) The undesirable effects of a structure
of a water resources system upon several terms of the hydrologic
system, which can provoke a conflict with some other water related interests in the catchment area; and (ii) An objective
to eventually start with the development of those water resources which before the engineering undertaking have been either
inaccessible or have become feasible to develop as a result
of construction of engineering structures of a water resources
system. These two problems are not standard, current problems
to be solved by simple approaches. They require a deep in-
volvement of a team of experts. Because the results of such
analyses in most cases have several legal, economic and politi-
cal repercussions, this task often is of a very delicate
undertaking. Having in mind difficulties to solve this type
of problem, the lack of a generally accepted methodology for
a solution of such problems, the paper should be considered as
a contribution which transcends the boundaries of discrimina-
ting effects of a particular reservoir on a particular karst
polje.

By properly selecting the independent variables in the
multiple regression equation, it is feasible, especially for
the data of the period prior to construction of the Bileća
Reservoir, to estimate the values of maximum flood volumes in
different years for a karst polje under consideration. Several
questions and problems deserve attention:

(i) It is stated in the paper that "it can be asserted
for sure that filling the Bileća Reservoir up to the elevation
of 360 m a.s.l. does not cause any change in water regime of
the Fatničko Polje": However, a number of flood waves was
not studied, so that the above conclusion seems unsubstantiated.

(ii) The frequency analysis of floods in the paper related only to the period November - April. The other floods
should have been also included in the analysis, because they
are a part of the problem, and, maybe, even more important
to study from the economic point of view.

(iii) It is difficult to explain the fact that in the
period of five years the flood volumes with the return
periods of 3, 5, 10, 15, 100 and 1000 years have occurred,
without an effect of the Reservoir on the Polje.

(iv) The time series of independent variables should
have been also analysed by the same method as used for the
analysis of floods.

(v) No explanation is given in the paper for choosing
the maximum flood water volume (V_{max}) as a representative

variable to study the effect of the Reservoir on the hydrologic
regime of the Polje.

The author of the paper has chosen to analyze a series
of maximum annual flood volumes, V_{max}, in the Polje as shown
in Table 2 of the paper. By a preliminary investigation by
this writer, this variable V_{max}, Fig. (a), did not show to be
sufficiently sensitive for discrimination, as shown by the
double-mass curve analysis of the precipitation and the maximum
flood volumes, Fig. (b). In an analysis of the problem, though
with two years of data only, the variable better suited for
statistical discrimination was the rate-of-change, ΔV_i, Fig.
(a), of the flood volume in the Polje. Though this variable
proved to be more sensitive than V_{max}, the discrimination with
the ΔV_i series was not conclusive either, because of a small
sample of the reservoir post-construction period. Finally, the
concept of the *coefficient* of monthly fillings was introduced,
and defined by

$$K_m = \frac{(\Sigma \Delta V_i)_m}{(\Sigma P)_m}$$

with the numerator being the total filling volume during a
month, and the denominator the corresponding precipitation
during the same month. This filling *coefficient* would be
better if, instead of the precipitation total, the rainfall
index is used as in the paper. From the double-mass curve
of this index versus the precipitation, Fig. (c), it is obvious
that the trend for a change under the reservoir conditions has
occurred in the polje in comparison with the pre-reservoir
condition.

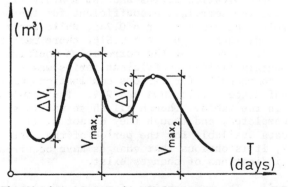

Fig. (a). The Maximum Retention Volume, V_{max}, and the
Incremental Volume, as Change Discrimination Variables.

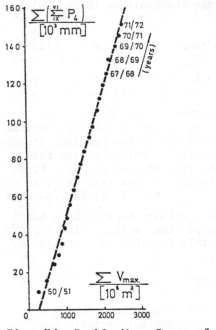

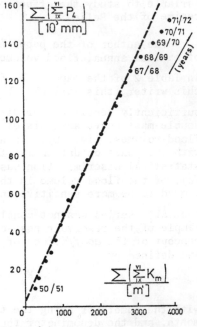

Fig. (b). Double-Mass Curve of
Precipitation Versus
Maximum Flood Volume.

Fig. (c). Double-Mass Curve
of Precipitation
Versus the Index K_m.

The indications that changes have been produced have been
subjected to preliminary statistical tests. Out of them,
the following aspects are stressed: (i) For the correlation
of monthly precipitation series and the monthly filling coefficient series, the correlation coefficient for the period of
pre-reservoir conditions is $r = 0.745$, while for the post-
reservoir conditions we get $r = 0.516$; there must be some
reason for the decrease of the correlation coefficient; and
(ii) The monthly filling coefficient series was statistically
tested for homogeneity for various combinations of series years
and two confidence levels, 90% and 95%. The results obtained
are given in the table. Though all these analyses have not
been yet completed, and though they do not utilize all the
observed data available for the period of the post-reservoir
conditions, it is obvious that changes have occurred and not
that some indications of changes exist.

Milčević. The homogeneity of series of highest water
level in the Fatničko Polje was tested by using the U-test.
It was established that the series is homogeneous. At the
very beginning of the work on this problem, a hydraulic model
was considered, but not found acceptable, because of the fact
that the underground channels were found not to be under
pressure along their entire lengths. For a hydraulic approach

Periods unmodified and modified conditions		Sample Size in Months		Homogeneous	
Unmodified (n_1)	Modified (n_2)	n_1	n_2	Level 95%	Level 90%
50/51-66/67	67/68-70/71	100	26	Yes	No
50/51-67/68	68/69-70/71	105	21	No	No
50/51-66/67	67/68-71/72	100	33	Yes	Yes
50/51-67/68	68/69-71/72	105	28	Yes	Yes

it would be necessary to use the underground water level observations, which cannot be proved not to be affected by the construction of the reservoir.

In the study tests on the sensitivity of change of the coefficient of multiple regression were carried out for a number of samples of various sizes. It was established that the selected number of samples and the selected period for the study, determined by the length of observations to the input, were quite adequate for the correlation analysis. The maximum monthly flood volumes in the polje were assumed to follow also some other distribution laws, except that presented in the paper, with similar results as those given in the paper obtained.

With regard to the discussion by Ristić, it is necessary to underline that investigations described in this paper did not have intention to offer a solution to a particular problem related to floods of the Fatničko Polje. Results of the analysis concerning the effects of the Bileća Reservoir upon the floods in the Fatničko Polje will be presented in the final report on the Trebišnjica system. Answers to specific comments on the papers are as follows:

The conclusion that the Bileća Reservoir with the water levels below 360 m.a.s.l. does not affect the hydrologic regime of the Fatničko Polje was arrived at after a detailed analysis of the groundwater hydrologic characteristics in the area between the polje and reservoir. This was feasible because the natural hydrologic characteristics were reconstructed for the lower water elevations of the reservoir. Nevertheless, the multiple regression analysis was applied to all flood volumes recorded in the period after the reservoir has entered into operation, also including those that occurred when the reservoir water levels were not above 360 m.a.s.l.

The statistical analysis of monthly flood volumes included only the events for the period November-April. Floods of other

months were not investigated for a simple reason that they were
infrequent, with no data for such an analysis. Probabilities
of floods in the Fatničko Polje during the operation of the
reservoir were not presented; however, it was pointed out that
some of those floods were unusually high. The probability
analysis of independent variables in multiple regression equation was not made, considering it unnecessary.

The maximum flood volume in this karst plain was selected
as the dependant variable, because this hydrologic variable
has a practical significance. However, the following variables
could have been well chosen: the maximum flood volume, the inflow into the polje, and the flood duration, because these
variables can be affected by the reservoir. The maximum flood
volume was regarded as the most convenient variable for the
analysis.

Ristić advanced the idea of using the variable of the
monthly inflow coefficient, as sufficient and representative
for the analysis. This coefficient is defined as the ratio of
the cummulative inflow into the polje and the corresponding
total precipitation. A careful examination of the flow conditions in karst polje systems reveals that there is not a very
direct relationship between the precipitation and the factors
of the hydrologic regime in a karst polje. More precisely,
these relationships are not clearly defined. The selection
of a fictitious coefficient for the investigation of a complex
phenomenon could additionally complicate the regression
analysis used. On the other hand, the maximum flood volume
allows that every flood event be considered, even if even no
more than one flood occurred annually. Ristić and the writer
disagree in the selection of a best methodology to be used in
this case. The multiple regression analysis for identification
of changes in karst hydrologic regimes of karst poljes, as
proposed in this paper, is basically a statistical technique.

USE OF PIEZOMETERS BOREHOLES FOR KARST INVESTIGATIONS
(A Preliminary Communication)

by

Petar Stojić, Civil Engineer,
Milorad Miličević, Civil Engineer, and
Petar Milanović, Geologist
Elektroprivreda BiH at Trebinje, Trebinje, Yugoslavia

Synopsis. Boreholes may be used as valuable tools for general hydrogeologic investigations leading to better understanding and description of the behavior of karst underground waters. It is, however, necessary to screen a large number of boreholes according to the response of their levels to various variables (to water levels in water courses, reservoirs, and karst plains retentions, and to precipitation). By using the correlation analysis, representative boreholes may be selected for continuation of observations. Examples of the types of results obtained by correlation and regression analysis are presented.

1. Introductory Remarks.

In order to obtain as much data as possible and to use it in the best feasible manner, investigations of the karst water resources require imagination and resourcefulness of researchers often working under the conditions of technological and financial constraints and using expensive exploration because of the complexity of karst conditions. Gathering of basic data on hydrology, geology, hydrogeology and engineering geology of a region is often based on the use of geological exploratory boreholes. At the same time, these boreholes are often used for continuous observations and investigations. The continuous observations of the piezometric levels belong to this additional potential of investigations by boreholes.

Since karst investigations require a large number of boreholes, many of which are located over a large, difficult to reach area, it is therefore difficult to obtain competent and reliable observers without exorbitant cost, and to process data rapidly. Competent observers guarantee the reliability of data, while a rapid processing of observations enable the investigators to respond to observed events of particular interest in a sufficiently brief time. Because the gathering and the processing of data is usually so slow, this process is not often feasible.

The catchment of the water resources system of the Trebišnjica River is among the most thoroughly investigated karst areas in Yugoslavia, and likely in the world. This region has an area of 7,525 km^2. Within the exploration works conducted in the region so far, more than 350 piezometric boreholes have been drilled and prepared for groundwater level observations. Boreholes are not evenly distributed over the region, since the largest number of holes have been drilled at the dam site and within the storage reservoir of Grančarevo. For instance, at the site of the Grančarevo Dam and in the larger area of the Bileća Reservoir (formed by the Grančarevo Dam), 90 boreholes were drilled for the purpose of investigating the rock perviousness and the grouting work, and for the reservoir leakage control.

Observations of groundwater level fluctuations in these boreholes were carried out mainly by the local inhabitants hired as observers. This is reflected in the reliability of gathered data. Thus, though the borehole had a cost of several hundred thousand new dinars, ($20,000 - $40,000 US), this investment was not fully utilized because it was difficult to assure reliable, quality observations. Therefore, it is necessary to study in further detail whether automatic recording and transmission of groundwater piezometric levels would be economically justified. As this approach requires much larger investments, it is expected that its application would be economical only if extended to boreholes which would represent the groundwater levels of a sufficiently large area. By using the information thus obtained from the representative piezometric boreholes, many difficulties, gross errors and pitfalls could be avoided. For that reason, a comprehensive analysis of data gathered from observations at piezometric boreholes for several years has been initiated.

2. Analysis of Piezometric Level Observations.

At the initial phase of this analysis, serious difficulties arose, among which the most important were:

(a) Lack of general geologic data presented on the same topographic maps;
(b) Lack of general topographic maps (of the same scale) containing hydrogeologic, hydrologic and meteorologic gauging stations;
(c) Characteristics of investigation boreholes, surface water gauges and meteorologic stations not being either determined or classified uniformly;
(d) No level hydrographs available for a large number of boreholes, and when available some of them not plotted properly for study; a diversity of scales was one of the greatest difficulties;
(e) The time intervals of gathering data, especially from the piezometric boreholes, varied so much (3, 5, 7 etc. days), that it was not feasible to use the originally tabulated data for the correlation analysis.

The available data had to be plotted and analyzed case by case, with an example shown in Fig. 1, and then classified, which made the following phase of the study feasible.

The main purpose of data processing was to perform the correlations between the piezometric levels in boreholes with the precipitation and the water levels in flooded karst plains and storage reservoirs. The final objective was to select the representative piezometric boreholes, if any, which could produce the general information of groundwater conditions in the observed area.

The first results of correlation analyses showed that it was feasible to define the stochastic relationships with various degrees of correlative links, with an example shown in Fig. 2. For sufficiently high correlation coefficients, it was then feasible to predict the events at the other boreholes by starting from observations in representative boreholes. This then reduced the necessary number of observational boreholes.

Correlations were performed between:

(1) groundwater levels of two boreholes (example, Fig. 2):

(2) groundwater level in a borehole and the level of a water course (examples, Figs. 3 and 4).

(3) groundwater level and precipitation (example, Fig. 5).

The results of correlation analysis between the levels of piezometers show considerable differences, which are the consequence of unequal hydrologic parameters of the underground porous media. First results showed that the correlation coefficients vary in a wide range. In some cases, even the linear correlation coefficient was relatively high with the nonlinear correlation having a much greater correlation coefficient. Figure 2 shows the linear regression between the levels of piezometers K-1 and F-1 for the monthly and 12-day interval values, both with a very high correlation coefficient. However, when the correlation analysis was made between the water level at the river gauging station at Bileća and the groundwater level in the piezometer PB-1 (Fig. 3), with data for the period of seven years, the plotted points indicate a nonlinear relationship. Another example (Fig. 4) shows that the regression between the level of the same watercourse and the level of the piezometer L-1 was linear. However, it was difficult to draw a conclusion with respect to the degrees of correlations, because the corresponding correlation coefficients were not determined.

412

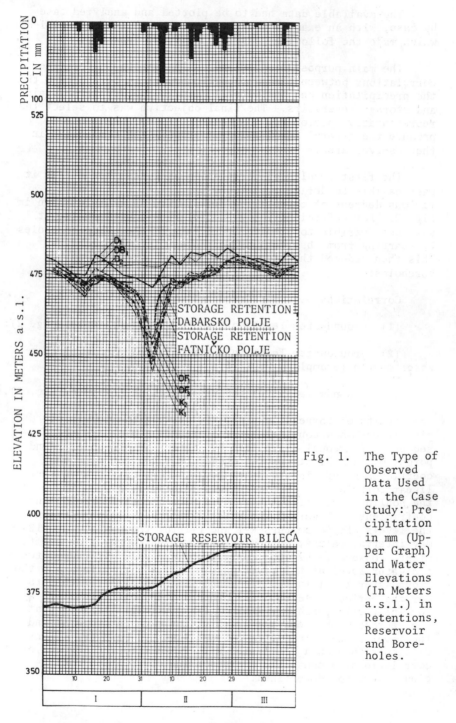

Fig. 1. The Type of Observed Data Used in the Case Study: Precipitation in mm (Upper Graph) and Water Elevations (In Meters a.s.l.) in Retentions, Reservoir and Boreholes.

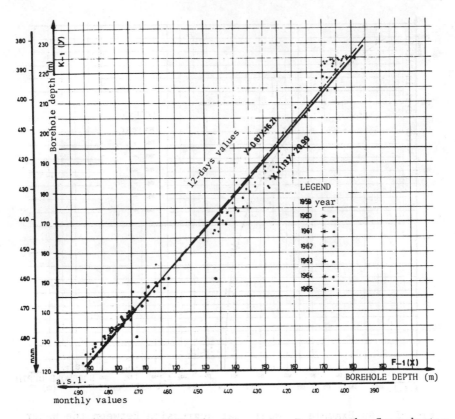

Fig. 2. An Example of Linear Regression Between the Groundwater
Levels in Two Boreholes (Piezometer Boreholes K-1 and
F-1).

The analysis of the relationship between the precipitation
and the water level in the piezometer B-9 showed a large dispersion of points, so that the correlation was expected to be
very low (Fig. 5). Similar analyses for many other boreholes
in different areas showed a similar scatter of points. The
writers of this paper want to underline that somewhat better
relationships were obtained when the analysis included the
index of precipitation rather than the simultaneous precipitation data.

While processing the piezometric data it was noticed that
certain boreholes appeared to be the isolated cases, so that
the data obtained from them were not representative of the
data in surrounding large areas. Some boreholes responded to
precipitation quickly, while some others did not respond at
all.

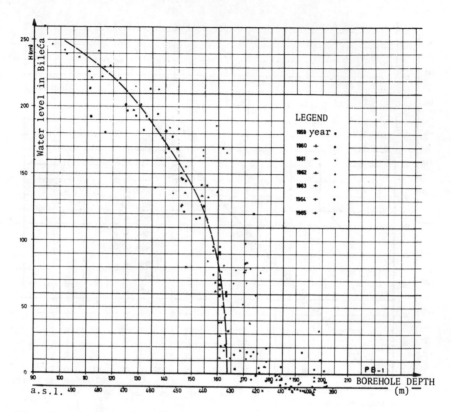

Fig. 3.   An Example of Nonlinear Regression Between the Water
Level in Bileća (Surfaced Water Level) and the Level
in the Borehole PB-1).

3.   Conclusion.

The results presented do not yet lead to definite conclusions, therefore, investigations of karst water resources
by use of piezometers should definitely be continued.

DISCUSSION

Yevjevich.   Since the piezometric levels in boreholes
record the energy head minus the velocity head $(\alpha V^2/2g)$, there
may be a significant difference between the energy and piezometric lines. This difference depends on the borehole position in relation to and the connections with the water flowing
karst channels. Therefore, the interpretation and use of
levels must be careful in drawing final conclusions. The basic
problem in using the boreholes to extract information on the
underground flow regime and water properties of karst porous
media is how to reduce the number of boreholes to an optimum

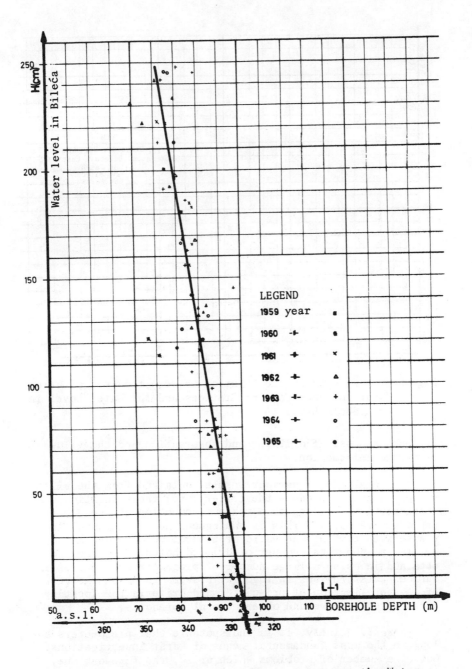

Fig. 4. An Example of Linear Regression Between the Water
Level in Bileća (Surface Water Level) and the Level
In Borehole L-1.

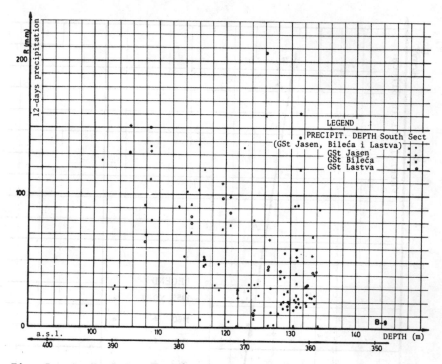

Fig. 5. An Example of the Relation Between the Precipitation
Data of Four Gauging Stations and the Water Level in
Borehole B-9.

between the cost of drilling and observation and the value of
extracted information.

The analysis of various results obtained from the existing
boreholes should produce the criteria for their location and
justification, leading to a maximum reduction of the number of
unproductive holes. This is analoguous to a continuous increase with time of the ratio of productive oil boreholes
drilled to the total number of drilled holes. The knowledge
obtained in using a large number of piezometric boreholes in
various karst regions in Yugoslavia seems to be on the verge
of a generalization of principles and criteria for locating
karst investigative and observational boreholes.

Boreli. Likely, it is indisputable that piezometers belong to the most fundamental means of karst investigations.
Out of a number of problems which arise, the foremost one,
stressed in this paper, is the representativeness of piezometers for the surrounding region. The final criterion in
the piezometric data considerations is their utilization to
solve the inverse problem in order to find the parameters of

the environment and the components of the water budget, besides
the objectives of other investigations. The reliability of
data warrants some observations.

Under certain conditions and by the very nature of their
construction, the piezometers cannot be representative. This
is primarily relevant for the case where the vertical gradients
are large, such as for the infiltration under a dam, when the
length of the perforated part of a piezometer casing is relatively large. Under such conditions the levels indicated by
piezometers are weakly defined. It follows, therefore, that
in order to obtain truly representative measurements from
piezometer boreholes, it is necessary to precisely specify the
vertical zone along which the piezometer casings are perforated.
This problem can arise with small vertical gradients as well,
if the rock mass is highly heteregenous, i.e., with distinct
permeable and impermeable zones.

It is perfectly normal that the representativeness of
piezometers be tested by correlation and by using the approach
described by the authors. Water levels in piezometers located
near the reservoirs should be highly correlated with the
reservoir levels and precipitation.

It should be emphasized that such correlations always
assume some apriori model of the system. Unusual behavior
of some piezometers frequently is an interesting indicator
of the corresponding, specific, often very significant, hydrogeologic relationship, which cannot be discovered unless the
piezometers, which do not satisfy a certain simple model, were
rejected as unrepresentative. The first and most fundamental
condition for the representativeness of a piezometer is that
its perforated part is located in a zone with a relatively
high permeability, but isolated from the surface layers which
include shallow subsurface priviledged routes. During intensive rainfall, piezometers might be filled with water from these
layers (See the figure). The correlation with rainfall may
then be quite high, yet these piezometers should not be considered representative.

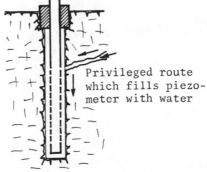

Privileged route
which fills piezo-
meter with water

Milićević. The existing piezometers in the Trebišnjica River basin are not used generally to measure the water flow. There were several attempts to measure $V^2/2g$ in a closed karst channel, but with a varying degree of success. These measurements were made by means of Pitot tubes or a special hydrometric wing. The greatest problem in such measurements was the fixing of the equipment in a stable position in an area of rapid flow, sometimes exceeding 16 m/s.

A CAPACITANCE METHOD FOR LEVEL MEASUREMENT OF LIQUIDS

by

Dragoljub Milatović, Professor of Electrical Engineering
Ljiljana Milošević, Electrical Engineer, and
Emin Skopljak, Electrical Engineer,
University of Sarajevo, Yugoslavia

Synopsis. An electronic instrument for recording water
levels in karst areas is described for the cases in which the
access is difficult during most of the year. The instrument
is autonomous in operation, of relatively small size, its
cost being about US $2,000, and very reliable in operation.
It consists of two transmission stations, a capacitance probe
and a power supply module. The instrument is all solid-state
and no special maintenance is required. The connection between the measuring point and the point of recording is insured
by an R.F. link in the V.H.F. band. Because of its advantages
of low weight and autonomous power supply, the measuring point
can be changed as desired. By operating a push button switch
at the point of recording, an exact reading of water level at
the measuring point is received in half a minute. The instrument is composed of standard electronic components and can be
made in any electronic shop.

1. Introduction.

Recording hydrologic data in the field is a necessary and
costly process, and often unreliable. The procurement of data
from the not readily accessible points and during the unfavorable climatic conditions, imposes the search for a
reliable method that would depend neither upon the weather
conditions nor upon the accessibility to a measuring point.
Such adverse conditions are specific to measurements in karst
areas of Yugoslavia. Therefore, efforts have been undertaken
to find a suitable method and instrument for recording water
levels at inaccessible points, with levels subject to large
and rapid changes. The data transmission is by radio communi-
cation equipment, considering that such a solution incorporates
high reliability and low cost under the field conditions. For
level measurements the capacitance method developed is rapid,
reliable and technically feasible.

2. Capacitance Transducers.

When two metal plates of an area S are arranged at a
distance d, and the material in between has a relative
dielectric constant ε, a capacitor of the following capacitance will result

$$C = \varepsilon_o \, \varepsilon \, \frac{S}{d} \tag{1}$$

where ε_o = the dielectric constant in vacuum, given by

$$\varepsilon_o = \frac{1}{36\pi} \, 10^{-9} \left[\frac{\text{Farad}}{\text{m}} \right].$$

If magnitudes S, d or ε are influenced by some non-electrical factor, the capacitance C will then depend on that factor, and thus the capacitance transducer of a non-electrical into an electrical factor can be realized. Various types of capacitance transducers differ in that the affected magnitudes can be S, d or ε, but their common feature is that they are all passive-type transducers. However, the capacitance transducers are not purely capacitance devices, because they are always associated with certain inductance and resistance. The inductance can be generally neglected, but the resistance is fairly high. These properties of the capacitance transducers can be illustrated by the equivalent circuit, as shown in Fig. 1.

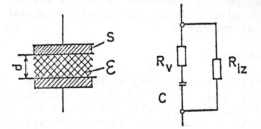

Fig. 1. Equivalent Circuit of the Capacitor in a Capacitance Transducer: R_v = The Loss Resistance in Dielectric, and R_{iz} = The Insulation Resistance Depending on Conductivity of Dielectric and the Plate Holder.

The resistance R_v depends on frequency, and R_{iz} is not affected. When the transducer supply is d.c., R_{iz} is very essential, but with an a.c. supply it has no influence if the frequency of a.c. supply is selected fairly high as to insure the relationship $\frac{1}{\omega C} \ll R_{iz}$.

A capacitance transducer must be electrically connected to the instrument, and this connection via a connecting conductor can be presented in the form of an equivalent circuit, as shown in Fig. 2. The magnitudes: R, L, R'_{iz} and C_p

as defined in Fig. 2 affect the sensitivity of the capacitance
transducer as well as are sensitive to moisture and temperature.

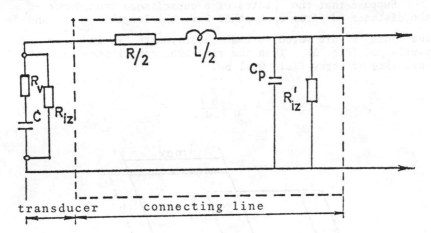

Fig. 2. Equivalent Circuit of the Capacitance Transducer and
         the Connecting Line: R = The Ohmic Resistance of
         Connecting Line, L = The Inductance of Connecting
         Line, R'_{iz} = The Insulation Resistance Between Lines,
         and C_p = The Capacitance Between Lines.

Care must be taken for the following condition to be met:

$$R, \omega L \ll \frac{1}{\omega C} \ll R'_{iz}, \frac{1}{\omega C_p} .$$

In considering the influence of connecting lines (especially
at higher frequencies), it is necessary to use short, low
capacitance lines, or special connecting methods in order to
reduce the possible errors. Disadvantages of capacitance
transducers are: high internal resistance that requires very
high internal resistance of connecting lines and unfavorable
sensitivity to fluids with $\varepsilon > 1$, such as oils, and specially
to water with $\varepsilon \simeq 80$. Therefore, when such a fluid is
placed between the plates of a capacitance transducer, its
resulting capacitance will be influenced by the change of
relative dielectric constant of the dielectric. Convenient
properties of capacitance transducers are: clear arrangement,
universal applicability, extremely high sensitivity and cap-
ability to record rapid changes of non-electrical magnitudes.
It can be applied at high temperatures.

3. Influence of Plate Area Variation Upon the Variation of Capacitance of the Capacitance Transducer.

Suppose that the plates of a capacitance transducer at the distance d from each other have the length ℓ_{max}, and the width b are moved so that their length ℓ is always overlapped (Fig. 3). Then the resulting capacitance without influence of stray field will be,

$$ C = \varepsilon_o \varepsilon \frac{b\,\ell}{d} \qquad (2) $$

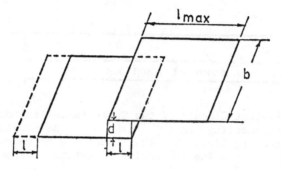

Fig. 3. Dependence of Capacitance on the Degree of Overlapping of Plates of a Capacitance Transducer.

Considering that all of the above magnitudes are constant (b, ε, ε_o, d), the ratio between C and C_{max} at $\ell = \ell_{max}$ is contained in the following equation which is applicable for the plate-type capacitance transducers

$$ \frac{C}{C_{max}} = \frac{\ell}{\ell_{max}} \; . \qquad (3) $$

The corresponding relations are linear under the condition that the associated magnitudes are constant. However, in shifting the plates it is difficult to maintain an accurate direction and a deviation of plate distance d, namely Δd is introduced. For that case, Eq. (3) is no more correct, and is modified into the form

$$ \frac{C}{C_{max}} = \frac{\ell}{\ell_{max}} \left(\frac{1}{1 - \frac{\Delta d}{d}} \right) , \qquad (3a) $$

and for $(\Delta d/d) \ll 1$, Eq. (3a) becomes

$$\frac{C}{C_{max}} \approx \frac{\ell}{\ell_{max}} \left(1 + \frac{\Delta d}{d} \right) \cdot \tag{4}$$

The graphical representation of Eq. (4) is given in Fig. 4.

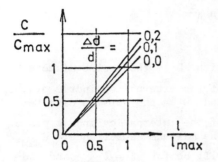
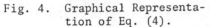

In practice, however, it is impossible to avoid the small deviations Δd, so that the capacitance transducers with plates are not used in the engineering investigations. An alternative construction of the capacitance transducer with plates in which the influence of the deviation Δd is reduced is shown in Fig. 5.

Fig. 4. Graphical Representation of Eq. (4).

The equation applicable to this case is:

$$\frac{C}{C_{max}} = \frac{\ell}{\ell_{max}} \frac{1}{1 - \left(\frac{\Delta d}{d} \right)^2} \, , \tag{5}$$

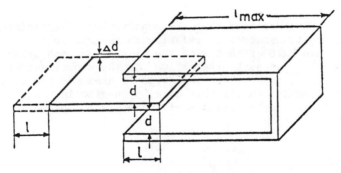

Fig. 5. Improved Construction of the Capacitance Transducer.

and for $(\Delta d/d)^2 \ll 1$, Eq. (5) becomes,

$$\frac{C}{C_{max}} = \frac{\ell}{\ell_{max}} \left[1 + \left(\frac{\Delta d}{d} \right)^2 \right] \cdot \tag{6}$$

The application of the capacitance transducer of Fig. 5 is reasonably feasible.

For practical applications, however, the construction of the cylinder type capacitance transducer (Fig. 6) is more feasible. The capacitance of the cylindric capacitor is

$$C = \varepsilon_o \, \varepsilon \, \frac{2 \, \pi \, \ell}{\ln \frac{D_s}{D_u}} \, , \qquad (7)$$

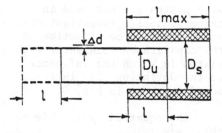

with D_s = the inside diameter of the external cylindric plate, and D_u = the outside diameter of the internal cylindric plate. The maximum capacitance, C_{max}, will be for $\ell = \ell_{max}$ and $\Delta d = 0$, respectively for $(\Delta d/d)^2 \ll 1$,

Fig. 6.   Cross Section of Cylinder Type Capacitance Transducer.

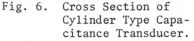

$$\frac{C}{C_{max}} \approx \frac{\ell}{\ell_{max}} \left\{ 1 + \frac{1}{2} \left(\frac{\Delta d}{d} \right)^2 \right\} . \qquad (8)$$

From Eq. (8) it follows that the sensitivity of cylindric capacitance transducers in relation to the change Δd is reduced to one half of that with the plate type capacitance transducers. The next alternative for the capacitance transducer is shown in Fig. 7. This type is used for level measurements of liquids, so for this case, by neglecting Δd, one can write the same equation as for the plate type capacitance transducer, namely

$$\frac{C}{C_{max}} = \frac{\ell}{\ell_{max}} \qquad (9)$$

4. Measurement of Levels of Liquid with Cylinder Type Capacitance Transducer.

The objective is to record level variations of a liquid by using a specially constructed cylinder type capacitance transducer, as shown in Fig. 8. Suppose the vessel A contains the liquid with a varying level. The change of the level of the liquid is water). The tube B is equipped with a cylinder made of a conducting material G. Via conductors, mercury is connected to the equipment for transmission of information at

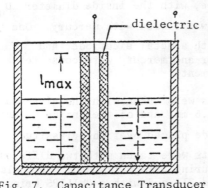

a distance, either by radio transmission or by line transmission. The same applies to the metal cylinder, so in this way the two cylindric electrodes with a glass tube in between are formed, and thus the cylinder type capacitance transducer is formed with the variation of capacity depending upon ε, h, D_u, and D_s, with D_u = the internal diameter of glass tube, and D_s = the external diameter, namely, D_u = the outside diameter of

Fig. 7. Capacitance Transducer for Level Measurements of Liquids.

mercury column, and D_s = the inside diameter of external metal electrode. Between the cylindric electrodes of diameters D_u and D_s is the glass as dielectric.

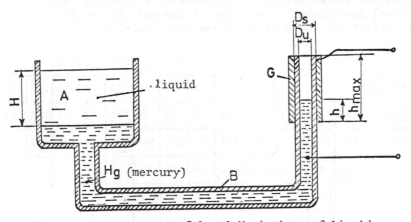

Fig. 8. Measurements of Level Variations of Liquids.

Suppose that the relative dielectric constant ε is a true constant, and that the glass tube has an equal cross section and wall thickness, so the following relation can be written

$$C = k\,h, \tag{10}$$

in which the constant k includes all the constants from Eq. (7). This type of transducer has been developed in the laboratory of the Institute for Hydraulic Engineering in Sarajevo. Variations of transducer capacitance C were measured in dependence of mercury column height in the conductance metal cylinder. A U-shaped glass tube, with the inside diameter D_u and the outside diameter D_s, was filled with mercury. One arm of the tube was equipped with a metal electrode, and finally, both the metal cylinder and mercury were connected by lines to the measuring equipment.

First group of measurements were taken with the glass tube of the outside diameter D_s = 4.6 mm, and of the inside diameter D_u = 2.2 mm. The metal electrode placed over the glass tube was made of copper. Measurements were taken with two different instruments, namely with a measuring bridge TESLA of Czechoslovakian manufacture (Tables 1 and 2), and with a PHILIPS bridge (Table 3). These measurement results are given in Fig. 9 as graphs D_1, D_2 and D_3, respectively. From the data in Tables 1-3, and Fig. 9, the conclusion can be drawn that the change of capacitance of this cylinder type capacitance transducer is linear in relation to the height change of the mercury column, namely upon the liquid level in the vessel A of Fig. 8. Some deviations from the straight line are the result of subjective error due to reading accuracy, and of unequal geometry of capacitance transducer, above all due to nonuniform thickness of the glass tube dielectric.

Table 1. Measurements by Using a TESLA Bridge.

h [mmHg]	0	7	21	26	36	45	49	57	70	87	99	117	126
C [pF]	26	27	28.5	29	30	31	32	33	34	37	39	40.5	41
h [mmHg]	136	150	160	166	184	191	197	204	221	247	274	302	317
C [pF]	43	45	46 5	48.5	51	54	56	57	58	62	67	70	72
h [mmHg]	331	352	371	379	402	431	446	470	491	497	503		
C [pF]	76	79	84	85	90	97	98	101	104	106	107		

Measurements have been also taken for a glass tube of the outside diameter D_s = 9 mm and the inside diameter of D_u = 8 mm (Fig. 10). An aluminum foil was wrapped around the tube, and the tube again filled with mercury. The results obtained with a PHILIPS bridge are given in Table 4, and the relationship plotted in Fig. 11.

The next measurements were for the capacitance transducer of Fig. 9, but by using a coaxial cable for the local TV

Table 2. Measurements by Using a TESLA Bridge.

h[mmHg]	26	31	40	47	58	68	77	86	97	110	117	128
C[pF]	42	42.5	43	43.5	46	47	48	49	52	53	54	55.5
h[mmHg]	133	137	143	148	157	167	180	188	197	204	220	228
C[pF]	56.2	57	58	60	62	64	65	67	69	71	75	76
h[mmHg]	236	242	260	265	272	279	288	296	309	318	330	346
C[pF]	77.4	79.3	81.5	83	84	86.5	87	88.2	89.7	91.5	93.2	95

Table 3. Measurements by Using a PHILIPS Bridge.

h[mmHg]	200	204	214	224	232	241	249	257	263	272	281	294
C[pF]	7.5	8	10	14	16	18	20	23	24	28	30	35
h[mmHg]	304	312	322	330	341	352	358	368	376	385	401	407
C[pF]	37	40	43	46	50	54	56	50	63	66	70.5	74.5
h[mmHg]	415	421	438	446	464	479	489					
C[pF]	78	80	86	90	95	98	100					

Table 4. Measurements for the Case of Fig. 10, by Using a
PHILIPS Bridge.

h[mmHg]	37	64	92	123	171	211	240	276	297	347	381	427
C[pF]	0	70	150	240	340	440	480	570	640	760	840	925

installation ($Z = 60$ Ω, $\ell = 41$ m, $C = 3500$ pF and $c = 85$
pF/m) as the connecting line. Measurements with a PHILIPS
bridge are shown in Table 5 and Fig. 12 and with a TESLA
bridge in Table 6 and Fig. 13, which demonstrate linear
relationships.

Measurements with a simple PVC conductor as the connecting line (2 x 0.75, $\ell = 10$ m, $C = 620$ pF, $c = 62$ pF/m) performed with a PHILIPS bridge are shown in Table 7 and Fig. 11
and with a TESLA bridge in Table 8 and Fig. 14, also proving
the linearity. It was already mentioned that the connecting
lines should have a low capacity and to be short. The use of
the coxial cable can be accepted as a good solution, however,

428

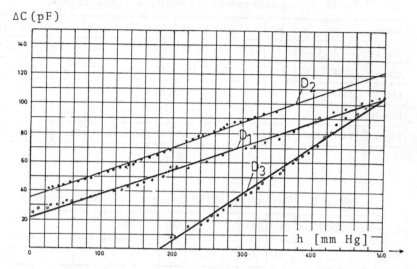

ΔC (pF)

Fig. 9. Capacitance to Mercury Column Relations: D_1, Change of Capacitance in Dependence of Mercury Column, Measured with the TESLA Bridge; D_2, Change of Capacitance in Dependence of Mercury Column, Measured with a TESLA Bridge; and D_3, Change of Capacitance in Dependence of Mercury Column, Measured with a PHILIPS Bridge.

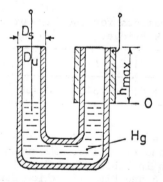

Fig. 10. Cylinder Type of Capacitance Transducer.

Table 5. Measurements For the Modified Case of Fig. 10, by Using a PHILIPS Bridge.

h [mmHg]	37	52	92	137	187	242	302	317	357	387	397	447	457
C [pF]	40	45	100	145	185	240	280	300	330	360	380	410	430

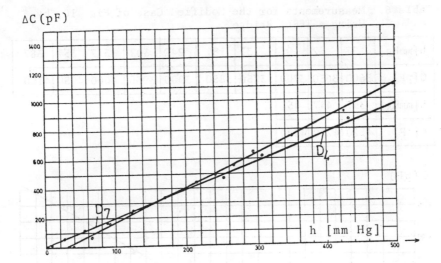

Fig. 11.   Capacitance to Mercury Column Relations: D_4, Capacitance Change in Dependence of Mercury Column Measured with PHILIPS, and D_7, Capacitance Change in Dependence of Mercury Column Measured with PHILIPS Bridge, in Case of a PVC Conductor.

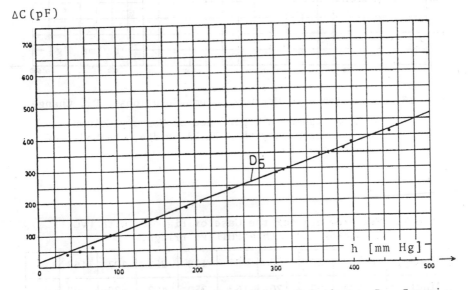

Fig. 12.   Capacitance to Mercury Column Relations: D_5, Capacitance Change in Dependence of Mercury Column, Measured with a PHILIPS Bridge, the Modified Case of Fig. 10.

Table 6.   Measurements for the Modified Case of Fig. 10, by
           Using a TESLA Bridge.

h[mmHg]	37	52	92	137	187	242	302	317	357	387
C[pF]	3600	3650	3700	3750	3850	3900	3950	4000	4050	4100
h[mmHg]	397	447	457							
C[pF]	4120	4200	4220							

ΔC (pF)

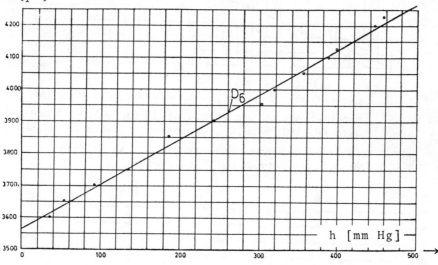

Fig. 13.   Capacitance to Mercury Column Relations: D_6, Change
           of Capacitance in Dependence of Mercury Column
           Change, Measured with a TESLA Bridge, the Modified
           Case of Fig. 10.

Table 7.   Measurements for the Case of Fig. 10, with PVC
           Conductor and with a PHILIPS Bridge.

h[mmHg]	0	7	23	55	87	125	253	307	467	
C[pF]	0	20	60	120	162	250	462	620	900	

431

Table 8. Measurements for the Case of Fig. 10, with a PVC
          Conductor, and by Using a TESLA Bridge.

h[mmHg]	0	7	23	55	87	125	253	307	467
C[pF]	700	740	750	810	850	950	1150	1250	1500

ΔC (pF)

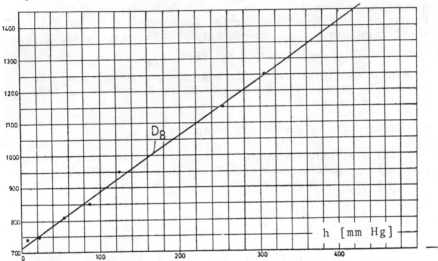

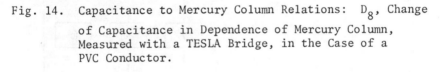

Fig. 14. Capacitance to Mercury Column Relations: D_8, Change
          of Capacitance in Dependence of Mercury Column,
          Measured with a TESLA Bridge, in the Case of a
          PVC Conductor.

the PVC conductor is unfavorable because of a high parasitic
capacitance.

     The unfavorable sensitivity of capacitance transducers
in case of liquids having the relative dielectric constants
ε > 1 can be removed by using an external cylindric electrode
formed by metallization of the glass tube, so that no fluid
is permitted to enter between the electrodes of the cylinder-
type capacitance transducers. The influence of environmental
conditions, such as the temperature, moisture and pressure,
can be neglected.

5. Feasibility of Remote Data Transmission.

     In order to realize the remote reading of measured values,
the capacitance transducer was connected to a pair of

432

transceivers type TR2200 (Kenwood, Trio Electronics, Inc., Tokyo, Japan). The capacitance transducer was connected to the transmitting circuit T_{XA}, and the instrument for measuring water levels to the receiving circuit R_{XB} of the transceiver equipment. The capacitance transducer represented part of the transmitter oscillator circuit, so that the changes in water level in the capacitance transducers from a minimum to a maximum level resulted in an oscillator frequency range from 2 to 6 kHz. The signal was the modulating signal of the transmitter carrier frequency generated at the transmitter T_{XA} antenna output. The signal, being thus modulated, was received by a receiver R_{XB}, where it was detected, amplified and fed to a digital-to-analog converter and finally displayed onto an indicating instrument in form of voltage changes.

6. Description of Electronic Equipment.

The electronic equipment is composed of two parts, the transmitting part denoted with A and shown in Fig. 15, and the receiving part denoted with B and shown in Fig. 16.

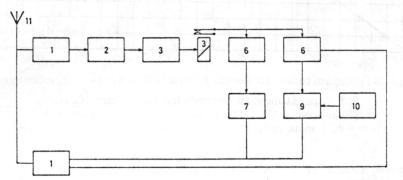

Fig. 15. Transmitting Scheme of the Measuring Point A.

The equipment at the measuring point A contains the following sub-assemblies (see Fig. 15):

- Transmitter T_{XA} of the Transceiver TR-2200 denoted as (1) at the bottom of Fig. 15;

- Receiver R_{XA} of the Transceiver TR-2200 denoted as (1) on the top of Fig. 15:

- A.F. amplifier denoted as (2) in Fig. 15, with the detailed circuit diagram given in Fig. 17;

20-14

433

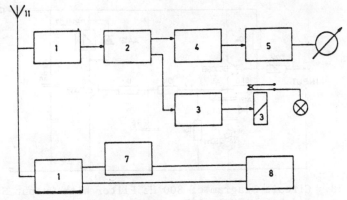

Fig. 16.   Receiving Scheme of the Measuring Point B.

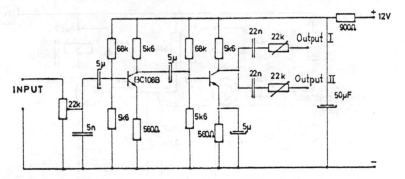

Fig. 17.   Circuit Diagram of A.F. Stage (Input with FM Detector
and Output for Remote Control and Measurement).

- Remote control circuit denoted as (3) in Fig. 15, with
  detailed circuit diagram indicated in Fig. 18, including the time delay circuit denoted in the diagram
  as (6) with detailed circuit diagram indicated in Fig.
  19;

- Oscillator circuit denoted as (7) in Fig. 15, giving
  a signal frequency of 750 Hz, as shown in Fig. 20;

- Two beat oscillator denoted as (9) in Fig. 15, with a
  detailed circuit diagram, as shown in Fig. 21;

- Capacitance transducer described in this paper, and
  denoted as (10) in Fig. 15; and

- Antenna denoted as (11) in Fig. 15, with detailed circuit diagram presented in Fig. 22.

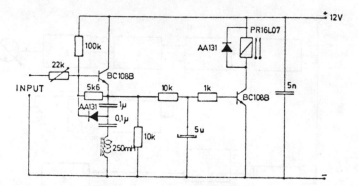

Fig. 18. Circuit Diagram of 800 Hz Filter With Output Stage and Relay PR 16 L07.

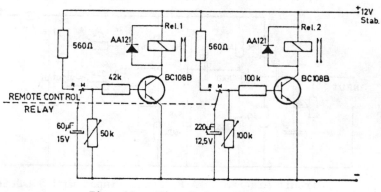

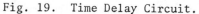

Fig. 19. Time Delay Circuit.

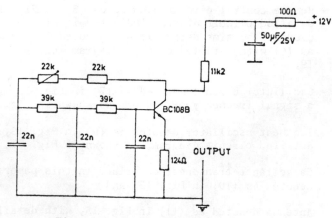

Fig. 20. Oscillator Circuit.

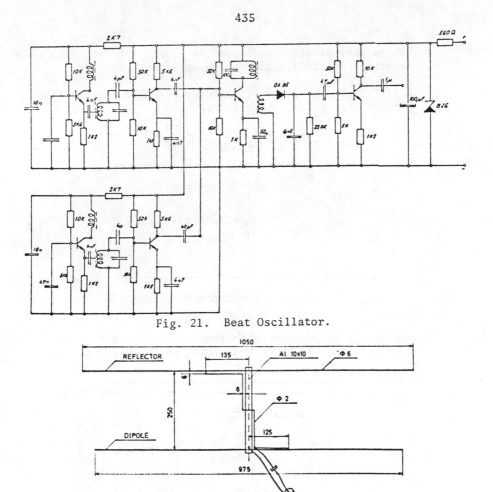

Fig. 21.   Beat Oscillator.

Fig. 22.   Detailed Circuit Diagram of the Antenna.

The equipment of the measuring point B contains the following sub-assemblies (see Fig. 16):

- Transmitter T_{XB} of the Transceiver TR 2200 denoted as (1) in the bottom of Fig. 16;

- Receiver R_{XB} of the Transceiver TR 2200 denoted as (1) on the top of Fig. 16;

- A.F. amplifier denoted as (2) in Fig. 16, with the detailed circuit diagram, as shown in Fig. 17;

- Remote control circuit denoted as (3) in Fig. 16, with detailed circuit diagram, as shown in Fig. 18;

- R.F. filter denoted as (4) in Fig. 16, with the detailed circuit diagram, as shown in Fig. 23;

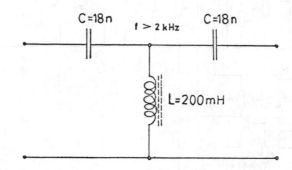

Fig. 23.   R.F. Filter Circuit Diagram.

- Digital-to-analog converter denoted as (5) in Fig. 16, with the detailed circuit diagram, as shown in Fig. 24;

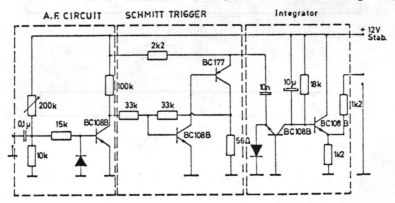

Fig. 24.   Detailed Circuit Diagram of the Digital-to-Analog Converter.

- Oscillator circuit denoted as (7) in Fig. 16, with the detailed circuit diagram, as shown in Fig. 20;

- Double push-button switch denoted as (8) in Fig. 16; and

- Antenna denoted as (11) in Fig. 16.

7. Description of Sub-assemblies According to their Numbers in Figs. 15 and 16.

(1) Transceiver, Type TR 2200, manufactured by Kenwood (Trio Electronics, Inc., Tokyo, Japan).

(2) A.F. RC-coupled amplifier with two transistor stages (Fig. 17). The amplifier has two isolated outputs, one envisaged for measurement and the other for remote control. (Note: it is possible to construct the assembly with more isolated outputs).

(3) A.F. filter, T-section with symmetric elements, with A.F. amplifier (Fig. 18).

(4) R.F. filter, T-section with symmetric elements, bandwidth f > 2 kHz (Fig. 23).

(5) Digital-to-analog converter containing A.F. amplifier, Schmitt trigger and integrator, performs the processing of variable frequency signal in that it converts the change of frequency into voltage changes suitable for indication on a voltmeter, of circuit diagram given in Fig. 24.

(6) Timing circuit, Fig. 18, operates on the principle of capacitor discharging into the transistor base and thus drives the transistor into conduction and energizes the relay. The sub-assembly contains two timing circuits, 5 second and 30 second circuits.

(7) Oscillator, designed as an RC oscillator (Fig. 20) for the rated frequency f = 750 Hz.

(8) Push-button switch.

(9) Two oscillators operating as beat oscillators giving a heterodyne frequency of 2 to 6 kHz. The oscillator circuit of one oscillator contains the capacitance transducer, the capacitance of which varies with the change of liquid level. This capacitance variation varies then the frequency of the oscillator.

(10) Capacitance transducer described under (2) of this paper.

(11) Antenna - type HB 9 CV, gain approx. 7 dB, with off-center coaxial line feed.

8. Operation.

When both transceivers are in operation, the indicating instrument at the measuring point B reads a certain voltage level. Now, the push-button switch (8) of Fig. 16 is instantly depressed and released. This action instantly switches on the transmitter T_{XB}, the carrier frequency of which, namely 144. 126 MHz, is modulated by the RC oscillator signal of 750 Hz, (7) of Fig. 16. The antenna transmits this signal from the measuring point A, and the receiver R_{XA} receives, detects and amplifies it in the amplifier, (2) of Fig. 15, as an A.F. signal of 750 Hz. This signal is then applied to the remote control circuit, (3) of Fig. 15, which via the relay circuit operates the timing circuit, (6) of Fig. 15, that after 5 seconds operates the measuring oscillators, (9) of Fig. 15. These oscillators incorporate the capacitance transducer, (10) of Fig. 15, and operate as beat oscillators giving a heterodyne frequency of 2 to 6 kHz (depending upon the capacitance of the capacitance transducer). The A.F. signal, obtained in this way, is fed into the transmitter T_{XA}, and finally via antenna, (11) of Fig. 15, a modulated signal is transmitted from the measuring point A. The receiver R_{XB} receives the carrier signal modulated with 2 to 6 kHz. After detection the signal is amplified in an A.F. amplifier, (2) of Fig. 16, and the signal of only 2 to 6 kHz is obtained. After passing through R.F. filter, (4) of Fig. 16, and through digital-to-analog converter, (5) of Fig. 16, the voltage change resulting out of frequency variation of the signal 2 to 6 kHz is displayed on an indicator (on the measuring point B), and this change is the result of variation of capacitance of the capacitance transducer (of the level of mercury, respectively, water level). After expiration of a 30 second measuring interval, the timing circuit, (6) of Fig. 16, switches to the off position.

9. Conclusions.

The method developed for recording hydrologic data is simple and reliable. Such an instrument can be also used for measuring levels of lakes and rivers. The instrument is economical in operation, of low power consumption, and its cost is about US $2,000. The instrument described can measure level variations as large as 10 m, and with a slight modification even larger. The instrument is protected against external damage, and is powered by an electric battery. Because the instrument is in operation only upon a measuring signal which lasts for about one minute, an automobile battery can be used to provide the energy required for its operation.

DISCUSSION

Yevjevich. The surprisingly good linearity of the developed capacitance instrument is its very impressive feature, because the linearity is usually a problem of such an instrument. The practical problems of interest in the application of this instrument in karst area are: (1) Does the instrument require special environmental conditions for its work? (2) For what length of time can the instrument work as an autonomous system without outside intervention? and (3) What are the chances for obtaining a permit for the use of certain radio frequencies for such purposes, in view of the fact that it is very difficult to obtain such a permit in the U.S.A.?

Mikulec. (4) Can the instrument be used also for the recording of water level variations higher than 10 meters, say 50-100 meters? and (5) What is the accuracy of the instrument?

Milatović. The answers to the above five questions are: (1) No special conditions are required for the work of the instrument since it works like any other transistor equipment; climatic changes have practically no effect upon its functioning; (2) If a standard automobile battery is used as the power for the radio equipment, with a normal usage, the instrument can be relied upon to function for at least half of a year, since the needed amount of electricity is small; (3) It is not easy to obtain a permit for the utilization of a radio frequency in Yugoslavia; however, since such an instrument is intended for use in unpopulated regions, and since the frequency needed for such work is in the area of 144MHz, it is possible to get such a permit; (4) The instrument can be used for recording higher water level variations, since it is the capacitance that is being used; it is only necessary to make longer glass pipes or to use either a serial set of U-tubes or an inductive probe; and (5) The accuracy of recordings depends on the accuracy of elements in the receiving/transmitting radio stations; the standard elements built in have a 10% tolerance. We achieve great accuracy (of 1-2%), because we use a frequency and its modulation for water level recording, and we have a quartz stabilization in the instrument, which has a frequency stability of about $1:10^6$. In addition, we consider the thickness of the glass pipes to be constant.